Study Guide for

Kinn's The Medical Assistant: An Applied Learning Approach

Twelfth Edition

Study Guide for

Kinn's The Medical Assistant: An Applied Learning Approach

Twelfth Edition

Deborah B. Proctor, EdD, RN
Professor and Medical Assistant Program Director
Butler County Community College
Butler, Pennsylvania

Alexandra Patricia Adams, MA, BA, RMA, CMA (AAMA)
Former Health Information Specialist Program Director
  & Administrative Medical Assisting Instructor
Ultrasound Diagnostic School (now Sanford-Brown College)
Professional Writer
Grand Prairie, Texas

3251 Riverport Lane
St. Louis, Missouri 63043

Study Guide for
Kinn's The Medical Assistant: An Applied Learning Approach   **ISBN: 978-1-4557-5687-2**

Copyright © 2014 by Saunders, an imprint of Elsevier Inc.

No part of this publication may be reproduced or transmitted in any form or by any means, electronic or
mechanical, including photocopying, recording, or any information storage and retrieval system, without
permission in writing from the publisher. Details on how to seek permission, further information about the
Publisher's permissions policies and our arrangements with organizations such as the Copyright Clearance
Center and the Copyright Licensing Agency, can be found at our website: www.elsevier.com/permissions.

This book and the individual contributions contained in it are protected under copyright by the Publisher (other
than as may be noted herein).

Notices

Knowledge and best practice in this field are constantly changing. As new research and experience broaden
our understanding, changes in research methods, professional practices, or medical treatment may become
necessary.

Practitioners and researchers must always rely on their own experience and knowledge in evaluating
and using any information, methods, compounds, or experiments described herein. In using such information or methods they should be mindful of their own safety and the safety of others, including parties for
whom they have a professional responsibility.

With respect to any drug or pharmaceutical products identified, readers are advised to check the most
current information provided (i) on procedures featured or (ii) by the manufacturer of each product to be
administered, to verify the recommended dose or formula, the method and duration of administration, and
contraindications. It is the responsibility of practitioners, relying on their own experience and knowledge of
their patients, to make diagnoses, to determine dosages and the best treatment for each individual patient,
and to take all appropriate safety precautions.

To the fullest extent of the law, neither the Publisher nor the authors, contributors, or editors, assume
any liability for any injury and/or damage to persons or property as a matter of products liability, negligence or otherwise, or from any use or operation of any methods, products, instructions, or ideas contained
in the material herein.

Previous editions copyrighted 2011, 2007, 2003, 1999, 1993, 1988, 1981, 1974, 1967, 1960, 1956

ISBN: 978-1-4557-5687-2

Vice President and Publisher: Andrew Allen
Executive Content Strategist: Jennifer Janson
Content Developmental Specialist: Laurie Vordtriede
Publishing Services Manager: Julie Eddy
Senior Project Manager: Richard Barber

Printed in the United States

Last digit is the print number: 9   8   7   6   5   4

Working together
to grow libraries in
developing countries

www.elsevier.com • www.bookaid.org

To the Student

This study guide was created to help you to achieve the objectives of each chapter in *Kinn's: The Medical Assistant: An Applied Learning Approach* and to establish a solid base of knowledge in medical assisting. Completing the exercises in each chapter in this guide will help reinforce the material studied in the textbook and learned in class.

STUDY HINTS FOR ALL STUDENTS

Ask Questions!

There are no stupid questions. If you do not know something or are not sure about it, you need to find out. Other people may be wondering the same thing, but may be too shy to ask. The answer could mean life or death to your patient. That is certainly more important than feeling embarrassed about asking a question.

CHAPTER OBJECTIVES

At the beginning of each chapter in the textbook are learning objectives that you should have mastered by the time you have finished studying that chapter. Write these objectives in your notebook, leaving a blank space after each. Fill in the answers as you find them while reading the chapter. Review to make sure your answers are correct and complete. Use these answers when you study for tests. You should also do this for separate course objectives that your instructor has listed in your class syllabus.

Vocabulary

At the beginning of each chapter in the textbook are vocabulary terms that you will encounter as you read the chapter. These terms are in bold type the first time they appear in the chapter.

Summary of Learning Objectives

Use the Summary of Learning Objectives at the end of each chapter in the textbook to help you review for exams.

Reading Hints

As you read each chapter in the textbook, look at the subject headings to learn what each section is about. Read first for the general meaning and then reread parts you did not understand. It may help to read those parts aloud. Carefully read the information given in each table and study each figure and its legend.

Concepts

While studying, put difficult concepts into your own words to determine whether you understand them. Check this understanding with another student or the instructor. Write these concepts in your notebook.

Class Notes

When taking lecture notes in class, leave a large margin on the left side of each notebook page and write only on right-hand pages, leaving all left-hand pages blank. Look over your lecture notes soon after each class, while your memory is fresh. Fill in missing words, complete sentences and ideas, and underline key phrases, definitions, and concepts. At the top of each page, write the topic of that page. In the left margin, write the key word for that part of your notes. On the opposite left-hand page, write a summary or outline that combines material from the textbook and the lecture. These can be your study notes for review.

Study Groups

Form a study group with some other students so that you can help one another. Practice speaking and reading aloud. Ask questions about material you find unclear. Work together to find answers.

References for Improving Study Skills

Good study skills are essential for achieving your goals in medical assisting. Time management, efficient use of study time, and a consistent approach to studying are all beneficial. Various methods can be used for reading a textbook and taking class notes. Some methods that have proven helpful can be found in *Saunders Health Professional's Planner*.

ADDITIONAL STUDY HINTS FOR ENGLISH AS A SECOND LANGUAGE (ESL) STUDENTS

Vocabulary

If you find a nontechnical word you do not know (e.g., drowsy), try to guess its meaning from the sentence (e.g., with electrolyte imbalance, the patient may feel fatigued and drowsy.). If you are not sure of the meaning or if it seems particularly important, look it up in the dictionary.

Vocabulary Notebook

Keep a small alphabetized notebook or address book in your pocket or purse. Write down new nontechnical words you read or hear, along with their meanings and pronunciations. Write each word under its initial letter so that you can find it easily, as in a dictionary. For words you do not know or for words that have a different meaning in medical assisting, write down how each word is used and how it is pronounced. Look up the meanings of these words in a dictionary or ask your instructor or first-language buddy (see the following section). Then write the different meanings or uses that you have found in your book, including the medical assisting meaning. Continue to add new words as you discover them.

First-Language Buddy

English as a second language (ESL) students should find a first-language buddy—another student who is a native speaker of English and who is willing to answer questions about word meanings, pronunciations, and culture. Maybe, in turn, your buddy would like to learn about your language and culture; this could be useful for his or her medical assisting career.

Contents

1 Becoming a Successful Student

VOCABULARY REVIEW

Match the following terms and definitions.

1. _____ The constant practice of considering all aspects of a situation when deciding what to believe or what to do

2. _____ Actions that identify the medical assistant as a member of a healthcare profession, including dependability, respectful patient care, initiative, positive attitude, and teamwork

3. _____ The way an individual looks at information and sees it as real

4. _____ The manner in which an individual perceives and processes information to learn new material

5. _____ The way an individual internalizes new information and makes it his or her own

6. _____ The process of considering new information and internalizing it to create new ways of examining information

7. _____ Sensitivity to the individual needs and reactions of patients

a. Learning style

b. Reflection

c. Professional behaviors

d. Processing

e. Empathy

f. Perceiving

g. Critical thinking

SKILLS AND CONCEPTS

Learning Style Inventory

Directions: Using the descriptions of various learning styles from Chapter 1, insert the correct Learning Style Stage Number into the diagram below by correlating the processing and perceiving style. In his book, Becoming a Master Student, Ellis discusses these different methods of information perception, processing, and learning.

Perceiving	Processing	
	Watching (Reflective)	**Doing (Active)**
Feeling (Concentrate)	Stage _____	Stage _____
Thinking (Abstract)	Stage _____	Stage _____

Time Management

Answer the following questions.

1. List five time-management skills.

    a. _____

    b. _____

    c. _____

    d. _____

    e. _____

Which of these do you think will require the most effort on your road to becoming a medical assistant? How can you better prepare yourself for the challenges ahead?

_____

_____

2. Describe five strategies for breaking the cycle of procrastination.

   a. _____

   b. _____

   c. _____

   d. _____

   e. _____

3. What barriers cause you to procrastinate? How can you prepare yourself to avoid procrastination?

   _____

   _____

   _____

   _____

Problem Solving and Conflict Management

True or False: Indicate which statements are true (T) and which are false (F).

1. _____ The best way to deal with conflict situations is through open, honest, assertive communication.

2. _____ The first step in conflict resolution is examination of the pros and cons.

3. _____ Conflicts should be resolved immediately.

4. _____ Sometimes you will not be able to solve problems, or a conflict may not be important enough for you to act to change the situation.

5. _____ It is best if you attempt to solve the conflict in a private place at a prescheduled time.

6. _____ You need to understand the problem and gather as much information about the situation as possible before you decide to act.

7. _____ As a future member of the healthcare team, you will frequently face problems and conflict.

Assertive Behaviors

True or False: Indicate which statements are true (T) and which are false (F).

1. _____ We are born either assertive or passive, and there is nothing we can do to change those behaviors.

2. _____ Assertive communication will get you what you want.

3. _____ A person who responds to conflict passively really is not bothered by the situation.

4. _____ Nonassertive individuals ultimately may respond with anger or an emotional outburst if pushed too far.

5. _____ Aggressive individuals ignore the needs of others.

Briefly answer the following questions.

6. Describe four different nonassertive behaviors.

   a. _____

   b. _____

   c. _____

   d. _____

2

7. Describe four different aggressive behaviors.

    a. _____

    b. _____

    c. _____

    d. _____

8. Explain the process of developing and delivering an assertive message.

_____

_____

_____

_____

STUDY SKILLS

1. Examine your own note-taking ability. Review the note-taking strategies described in Chapter 1, and record the ideas you plan to incorporate into your academic goals for this term.

_____

_____

_____

_____

CASE STUDIES

Read the case studies and answer the questions.

1. Dr. Weaver is running late seeing patients this afternoon. Sara Kline has been waiting in the examination room for Dr. Weaver for 30 minutes. She peeks her head out of the examination room doorway and demands to know what is taking so long. How should you, the medical assistant, approach this patient? How do you calm her down and explain the physician's situation without compromising other patients' confidentiality? What are some things you can do for the patient to make the wait not seem so long?

_____

_____

_____

2. Victoria Graham, a 68-year-old woman with diabetic retinopathy, arrives today for diabetes disease management education. How might the medical assistant approach Ms. Graham's learning style? What are some possible barriers and how can the medical assistant help Ms. Graham overcome them?

_____

_____

_____

_____

3. You have been working with another student to prepare for your next exam. The student asks to borrow your notes but has yet to return them so you can study for the exam. You are usually a nonassertive person, but you know that you have to get your notes back or you will not do well on the test. How can you formulate an assertive message? Summarize the steps to take and exactly what "I" message you will deliver.

_____

_____

_____

_____

WORKPLACE APPLICATION OPTIONS

1. You are the office manager for a busy family practice office. Over the past week, you have noticed that one of your employees has been 15 minutes late every day. Should you approach this employee? If so, how would you manage the situation? What are the main points you would want to stress to this employee? Are there any consequences? What follow-up, if any, should be done?

2. Physicians' offices are extremely busy and must deal with many daily demands. How should one prepare for proper time management? Why is it necessary to prioritize tasks? What are some ideas the medical assistant can use to get the most out of the day and stay organized?

3. Connie is the manager of a busy family practice office. The insurance clerk has complained that the receptionist takes too many smoking breaks and accepts too many personal calls while at work. What type of information should Connie obtain before approaching the receptionist? How should this situation be handled? Where? Who should be present?

4. After being on vacation for a week, Laura returns to the office to find her desk piled high with the following tasks. Laura decides to get organized and make a list of the items that need attention. Prioritize the tasks from "most important and urgent" to "needs to be done later today" and "may be done later this week." Explain your answers.
   a. Make a staff schedule for next week.
   b. Pull patients' charts for the laboratory results the office received this morning for the physician's review.
   c. Call and order immunization vaccines (the staff has informed you they are on the last vial).
   d. Call and confirm the patient appointments for tomorrow.
   e. Order general stock supplies (e.g., bandages, gauze, needles, and sharps containers).
   f. Review the insurance reimbursements the practice received for last month and address any claims that have not been paid.
   g. File charts.
   h. Edit the physician's schedule for a meeting scheduled next month.

INTERNET ACTIVITY OPTION

Conduct an Internet search on learning styles inventories. Multiple higher education institutions have different types of inventories available as well as more details on the importance of understanding how you learn. Share your findings with your classmates.

2 The Healthcare Industry

VOCABULARY REVIEW

Fill in the blanks with the correct vocabulary terms from this chapter.

1. A nurse sees several patients in a hospital emergency department and determines which patient is the most ill and should be seen by the physician first. The process the nurse is using is called _____.

2. An administrative assistant in a large clinic must write a letter to another state to determine whether a physician whom the clinic wants to hire has ever had his license revoked. This action is part of a process called _____.

3. A patient arrives at a physician's office and sees the physician. This event is called a(n) _____.

4. Accrediting agencies look for _____ or _____ to determine whether a healthcare facility is following required policies and regulations.

5. A physician who has been _____ has been charged with a crime but has not yet been tried in a court of law.

6. A person who is unable to pay for medical expenses is often called _____, and most hospitals will provide such patients with emergency care.

7. A group of healthcare practitioners involved in reviewing the charts of patients with a certain disease to determine the medical necessity of procedures might be serving in a(n) _____ organization.

8. When families look for an assisted living facility for a relative, they often consider the _____ that will add to the comfort and convenience of the patient.

9. Physicians who conduct a great amount of research are often _____ in medical journals and articles within their field of study.

10. A new hospital contacts the Joint Commission (formerly JCAHO) to begin the _____ process, which verifies that the facility meets or exceeds standards.

11. Dr. Robertson uses mostly herbs and natural supplements in his practice of medicine. Although he could be any type of physician, he probably practices _____.

12. Dr. Wray combines conventional medicine with manipulative techniques when treating patients. This type of medicine is called _____.

13. Dr. Stern treats patients by locating slight misalignments of the vertebrae and corrects them using manipulative techniques. She practices _____ medicine.

14. Dr. Margolis practices _____, which is a medical discipline in which treatments and medications are used to counteract the signs and symptoms of disease. Most of the physicians in the United States practice this type of medicine.

15. Susan works for Dr. Burns and has forwarded information about his medical license, medical training, and experience to Mercy Hospital. He is applying for _____ at the hospital.

5

Part I: Pioneers in Medicine

Fill in the blanks.

1. The surgical research technician who contributed to the success of the Blalock-Taussig procedure was

    _____.

2. _____ presented rules of health to the Jews around 1205 BC, making him the first advocate of preventive medicine and the first public health officer.

3. _____, known as the "father of medicine," was the most famous of the ancient Greek physicians, best remembered for an oath that physicians have taken for more than 2,000 years.

4. _____ was a Greek physician who migrated to Rome in AD 162 and became known as the "prince of physicians."

5. _____ was a Belgian anatomist who is known as the "father of modern anatomy."

6. In 1628, _____ announced his discovery that the heart acts as a muscular pump, forcing and propelling the blood throughout the body.

7. _____ was the first to observe bacteria and protozoa through a lens.

8. The famous English scientist _____ is known as the "founder of scientific surgery."

9. _____ observed that those who had contracted cowpox never contracted smallpox.

10. _____ directed that in his wards, the students were to wash and disinfect their hands before examining women in labor and delivering infants.

11. _____ saved the dairy industry of France from disaster in the nineteenth century by developing a process now called *pasteurization.*

12. _____ reasoned that microorganisms must be the cause of infection and should be kept out of wounds.

13. _____ was the first to use ether as an anesthetic agent.

14. Marie and Pierre _____ discovered radium in 1898, and they were awarded the 1902 Nobel Prize in Physics for their work on radioactivity.

15. _____, the founder of nursing, is known as the "lady with the lamp."

16. In 1881, _____ organized a committee in Washington that became the American Red Cross.

17. _____ became the American leader of the birth control movement.

18. _____ wrote about death and dying.

19. Salk and _____ almost eradicated polio, which was once a killer and crippler of thousands in the United States.

20. David _____, MD, considered by many to be one of the most brilliant minds today, is helping to piece together the puzzle of the human immunodeficiency virus (HIV).

21. During his terms as the surgeon general of the United States, _____ became a proponent of tobacco awareness, insisting that tobacco advertisements must be made less attractive to youth.

22. Considered an innovative leader in the field of hysterectomy alternatives and abnormal uterine bleeding,

   Dr. _____ also pioneered hysteroscopy.

23. Dr. _____ is best known for developing and commercializing the technique of in vitro fertilization (IVF).

24. Dr. _____ is noted for his series of innovative treatment protocols that have boosted cure rates at St. Jude to an unprecedented 90%.

25. Dr. _____ established a small medical clinic that has survived two hurricanes and a devastating fire, and she is nationally known for her business acumen and humane approach to preventive medicine.

Part II: National Healthcare Organizations

Spell out the following acronyms.

1. WHO

   _____

2. DHHS

   _____

3. USAMRIID

   _____

4. CDC

   _____

5. NIH

   _____

6. CLIA

   _____

7. OSHA

   _____

Part III: Healthcare Professionals

Use the appropriate terms to complete the sentences.

1. Dr. Hazlehurst bears responsibility for her practice 7 days a week. This practice is called a(n) _____.

2. A(n) _____ is formed when two or more physicians elect to associate in the practice of medicine without incorporating.

3. Dr. Sorrow and Dr. Wester sold their practice to a large artificial entity with legal and business status, and now they work for a(n) _____.

4. A(n) _____ is trained to locate subluxations of the spine and repair them, using x-ray examinations and adjustments.

5. _____ physicians, or DOs, complete requirements similar to those for MDs to graduate and practice medicine.

6. Duncan wants to become a(n) _____, who treats and prevents problems related to the teeth and gums and the tissue surrounding them.

7. The professional who is trained and licensed to examine the eyes, test visual acuity, and treat defects of vision by prescribing correctional lenses is called a(n) _____.

8. A(n) _____ is educated in the care of the feet, including surgical treatment.

9. _____ and medical laboratory technicians perform diagnostic testing on blood, body fluids, and other types of specimens to assist the physician in obtaining a diagnosis.

10. _____ provide direct patient care services under the supervision of licensed physicians and are trained to diagnose and treat patients as directed by the physician.

11. _____ are registered nurses who provide anesthetics to patients during procedures performed by surgeons, physicians, dentists, or other qualified healthcare professionals.

12. _____ assist patients in regaining their mobility and improving their strength and range of motion, which may have been impaired by an accident or injury or as a result of disease.

Part IV: Healthcare Facilities
Fill in the blanks.

1. Roger's hands were injured in an accident, and he must undergo rehabilitation. He is obtaining treatment at a(n) _____ health center so that he can prepare to return to work.

2. Susan's son, Brandon, had his tonsils removed at the _____ unit of their local hospital and went home later that evening.

3. _____ facilities have become very popular because they give the residents a sense of independence while still providing supervision and various amenities.

4. _____ centers provide patients an alternative to hospital emergency departments.

5. _____ diagnose and treat people who have sleep disorders.

Part V: Matching Patients with Physicians
Match the following patients with the physician who should treat them. The specialties are based on the divisions of medicine recognized by the American Board of Medical Specialties. Write the corresponding letter for the physician on the blank next to the patient's name.

1. _____ Mr. West has complained of problems with excessive gas and bloating after meals. He also has some pain in his lower abdominal area.

2. _____ Ms. Jindra has suffered from severe acne most of her adult life. She hopes to find a treatment that will give her more confidence in her appearance.

3. _____ The results of Ms. Robles's amniocentesis are abnormal, and her obstetrician suspects that she may be carrying a child who will be born with a birth defect.

4. _____ Ms. O'Neal is pregnant with her first child.

5. _____ Ms. Sklaar had gastric bypass surgery 2 years ago and now wants to undergo abdominoplasty to remove excess skin.

a. Dr. Stayer, pediatrician

b. Dr. Quincy, pathologist

c. Dr. Haskins, geneticist

d. Dr. Marrs, urologist

e. Dr. Cantrell, neurologist

f. Dr. DuBois, ophthalmologist

g. Dr. Gleaton, anesthesiologist

h. Dr. Kirkham, otolaryngologist

i. Dr. Jones, general surgeon

6. _____ Mr. Taylor experiences pain in his left eye when he is exposed to bright sunlight. He is concerned, because his mother and grandmother both lost their eyesight in their later years.

7. _____ Jack Monroe is the lead singer for a popular rock band. He experienced laryngitis during a world tour and needs to see a physician quickly to help him get back on the road.

8. _____ Sarah is 1 year old and needs several immunizations.

9. _____ Jimmie suffers from asthma related to reactions that occur when he is around grass, shrubs, and some animals.

10. _____ Mrs. Downey had a stroke and needs surgery to remove a small clot that has lodged in her brain.

11. _____ Andrea is having a hysterectomy and will be given a general anesthetic. While in the hospital, she meets the physician who will administer the anesthetic during surgery.

12. _____ Mrs. Ballard had an ovarian cyst, which was removed after a visit to the emergency department. She received a bill later from the physician who evaluated the cyst for malignancies.

13. _____ Ms. Harris had several polyps in her gastrointestinal tract. She was referred for surgery by her family physician.

14. _____ Ms. Richardson has had migraine headaches for about 6 months. Her family physician thinks she should see a specialist.

15. _____ Bobbie broke his arm and was taken to the emergency department. X-ray films were taken, and a physician read them.

16. _____ Mr. Oldman periodically suffers from kidney stones and may need surgery.

17. _____ Rhonda was taken to the emergency department after a car accident.

18. _____ Mr. Anton contacted a physician for removal of a minor cyst on his back.

19. _____ The entire Blair family sees one physician.

20. _____ Mr. Saxton will have surgery tonight to treat a punctured lung.

j. Dr. Faught, internal medicine

k. Dr. Martin, family practitioner

l. Dr. Rowinski, neurologic surgeon

m. Dr. Antonetti, plastic surgeon

n. Dr. Jackson, colorectal surgeon

o. Dr. Tips, allergist/immunologist

p. Dr. Roberts, radiologist

q. Dr. Skylar, dermatology

r. Dr. Burns, emergency medicine

s. Dr. True, obstetrics/gynecology

t. Dr. Williams, thoracic surgeon

Part VI: Short Essay Questions
Answer the following questions using complete sentences.

1. Why was the education offered by Johns Hopkins University Medical School so effective in training physicians?

_____

_____

_____

2. Explain the differences between the two medical symbols discussed in the chapter and what each icon represents.

_____

_____

_____

3. Why is the history of medicine important to us today?

_____

_____

_____

4. Which ancient cultures contributed to the medical terminology we use today?

_____

_____

_____

5. Which medical pioneer do you think contributed the most to medicine?

_____

_____

_____

6. Explain the role of the hospitalist.

_____

_____

_____

Part VII: Allied Healthcare Occupations and Licensed Medical Professions

Match the following descriptions with the appropriate healthcare occupation.

1. _____ Provides services such as injury prevention, assessment, and rehabilitation

2. _____ Is qualified to implement exercise programs designed to reverse or minimize debilitation and enhance the functional capacity of medically stable patients

3. _____ Practices medicine under the direction and responsible supervision of a medical doctor or doctor of osteopathy

4. _____ Performs diagnostic examinations and therapeutic interventions of the heart or blood vessels, both invasive and noninvasive

5. _____ Assists licensed pharmacists by performing duties that do not require the expertise of a pharmacist

6. _____ Assists in developing and implementing the anesthesia care plan

7. _____ Helps to improve patient mobility, relieve pain, and prevent or limit permanent physical disabilities

8. _____ Helps patients use their leisure in ways that enhance health, functional abilities, independence, and quality of life

9. _____ Identifies patients who have hearing, balance, and related ear problems

10. _____ Integrates and applies the principles from the science of food, nutrition, biochemistry, food management, and behavior to achieve and maintain health

11. _____ Evaluates, treats, and manages patients of all ages with respiratory illnesses and other cardiopulmonary disorders

12. _____ Evaluates disorders of vision, eye movement, and eye alignment

a. Audiologist

b. Cardiovascular technologist

c. Therapeutic recreation specialist

d. Physical therapist

e. Pharmacy technician

f. Dietetic technician

g. Anesthesiology assistant

h. Specialist in blood bank technology

i. Diagnostic medical sonographer

j. Kinesiotherapist

k. Occupational therapist

l. Orthoptist

m. Physician assistant

13. _____ Performs routine and standardized tests in blood center and transfusion services

14. _____ Uses equipment that produces sound waves, resulting in images of internal structures

15. _____ Uses the nuclear properties of radioactive and stable nuclides to make diagnostic evaluations of the anatomic or physiologic conditions of the body

16. _____ Prepares the operating room by selecting and opening sterile supplies

17. _____ Uses purposeful activity and interventions to achieve functional outcomes to maximize the independence and maintenance of health

18. _____ Performs tests to detect and diagnose various diseases and works closely with pathologists

19. _____ Provides medical care to patients who have suffered an injury or illness outside the hospital setting

20. _____ Formulates strategic, functional, and user requirements related to the processing of health data

n. Surgical technologist

o. Respiratory therapist

p. Athletic trainer

q. Medical technologist

r. Emergency medical technician

s. Health information specialist

t. Nuclear medicine technologist

CASE STUDY

Read the case study and answer the questions that follow.

Rebecca is a new employee at the Blackburn Clinic. She recently graduated from an accredited medical assisting school and completed her externship in a family practice clinic. She enjoys the variety of patients who come to the office, and she respects the physicians for their dedication to the art and science of medicine. The physicians with whom Rebecca works are strong proponents of continuing education, and they want Rebecca to attend no fewer than two seminars each year.

Research the history of family practices and answer these questions.

1. What types of patients are seen in family practice clinics?

    _____

    _____

    _____

2. What educational background does the physician need to become a family practitioner?

    _____

    _____

    _____

3. What are some of the more common illnesses that present in a family clinic?

    _____

    _____

    _____

4. What are the goals of the American Association of Family Practitioners?

    _____

    _____

    _____

WORKPLACE APPLICATION OPTIONS

Complete one or more of these activities and, if appropriate, share results with the class.

1. Visit a local hospital and introduce yourself to five medical professionals. Make an appointment to interview them and find out their job duties and their professional backgrounds. Write a thank-you note to each person after the interview.

2. Interview an office manager at a family practice. Ask about the positive and negative aspects of working with a variety of patients each day.

3. Investigate the hospital systems in your community or region. Choose one system and share its components with the class, explaining the services that each entity offers.

INTERNET ACTIVITY OPTIONS

Choose one or more of these activities and, if appropriate, share results with the class.

1. Choose one of the early medical pioneers discussed in this chapter and research him or her using the Internet. After conducting the research, write a report and present the person to the class. Be creative with the presentation by using PowerPoint or some type of audiovisual equipment.

2. Research the history of a particular illness. Prepare a short report on that illness and present it to the class.

3. Choose one of the allied health professions or licensed professions and research its educational requirements. Choose a profession that might be a future goal. Prepare a report for the class or write a report and submit it to the instructor.

3 The Medical Assisting Profession

Fill in the blanks with the correct vocabulary terms from this chapter.

1. Sandra should consider both the _____ and the _____ as she considers the various positions offered to her on graduation from her medical assisting training.

2. Robert is anxious to learn _____, because he would like to draw blood and possibly work in a local hospital laboratory.

3. The Wray Clinic recently began to offer _____ _____ to the employees, which gives them a part of the profits the clinic earns over the year.

4. It is important for graduates of medical assisting programs to gain _____ as soon as possible after graduation and to maintain it throughout their medical assisting career.

5. It is clear to Paula that there are many _____ to working as a medical assistant that make the profession worthwhile in ways other than compensation.

6. Alberta is interested in administrative medical assisting, because she is unsure whether she would enjoy performing _____ procedures.

7. Some high schools offer classes that allow students to explore the _____ _____ _____.

8. Both the American Association of Medical Assistants and the American Medical Technologists offer _____ _____ _____ for medical assistants.

9. _____ helps a team of medical assistants cover for one another in the event of illness or absence.

10. Medical assistants are the most _____ allied health professionals.

11. Some for-profit organizations offer _____ _____ after an employee has worked there for a specific period.

12. Bethany is looking forward to her _____ in a family practice clinic next month.

SKILLS AND CONCEPTS

Part I: The Medical Assisting Profession

1. Name the two major areas of medical assisting practice.

   a. _____

   b. _____

2. List five administrative duties a medical assistant might perform.

a. _____

b. _____

c. _____

d. _____

e. _____

3. List five clinical duties a medical assistant might perform.

a. _____

b. _____

c. _____

d. _____

e. _____

4. Provide an example of cross-training.

_____

5. Explain why hiring a medical assistant without any formal training often is more expensive.

_____

_____

6. Explain in your own words the history of medical assisting as a profession.

_____

_____

Part II: Professional Appearance
Determine which of the following normally would be part of the medical assistant's professional appearance. Place a check mark in the box marked "yes" or "no" to indicate whether that item would be acceptable in today's medical facilities.

	Yes	No	
1.	❑	❑	Hoop earrings
2.	❑	❑	Clear nail polish
3.	❑	❑	White uniforms
4.	❑	❑	Red nail polish
5.	❑	❑	One ear piercing
6.	❑	❑	Scrub tops
7.	❑	❑	Facial piercings
8.	❑	❑	Tennis or running shoes
9.	❑	❑	Excessive jewelry
10.	❑	❑	Tongue rings
11.	❑	❑	Lab coats
12.	❑	❑	Heavy eye makeup
13.	❑	❑	Street clothes with a lab coat
14.	❑	❑	Jeans

14

Chapter 3 The Medical Assisting Profession

Part III: Externships and Practicums

Explain briefly the solution you would choose for the following situations that might occur during an externship or practicum. Discuss and compare answers during class.

1. Anna notices that her supervisor at the externship frequently arrives late and leaves work early. The physician asks Anna casually one day if the supervisor is helpful and cordial to her. What should Anna say about the supervisor?

_____

_____

_____

2. One of Dr. Hammersly's patients, Brock Anderson, is extremely attractive, and Suzanne, the extern at the clinic, would like to get to know him better. When working with Brock's chart, Suzanne notices his home telephone number. She considers writing it down and contacting Brock after her externship is completed. Would this be acceptable behavior?

_____

_____

_____

3. On a very stressful day, Georgia assists a drug representative in placing drug samples in the storage area. She has battled a headache for most of the day. One of the drugs left behind is a mild painkiller called Ultram. Georgia has taken Ultram before for her headaches and doesn't think the physician will mind if she takes one at work. Would this be appropriate?

_____

_____

_____

4. Natasha was one of the most industrious medical assistant students in her class, always working hard and going the extra mile. When she begins her externship, she notices that the other assistants in the office are allowing her to do a large part of the work while they gossip and explore the Internet during working hours. How should Natasha handle this when her supervisor asks her how the externship is going?

_____

_____

_____

5. Randy graduated from the same school Angela currently is attending for medical assisting training. The two meet during Angela's externship at the office where Randy works, and they quickly become friends. Randy would like to ask Angela, a single parent, to a company picnic the following weekend, after Angela finishes her externship. Would this be acceptable behavior?

_____

_____

_____

6. Dr. Morton confides in Catrina, an extern, that he plans to fire Ashley, the medical assistant who books appointments for the clinic. He offers Catrina the job, which pays slightly more than she expected to make just out of school. The office is located very close to Catrina's apartment. Later in the week, Ashley and Catrina go to lunch together, and Ashley mentions that she is about to buy a new car. Should Catrina steer her away from such a major purchase, knowing that she is about to be fired?

_____

_____

_____

7. Bailee, an extern, is shocked to see one of the other medical assistants, Kristen, take $20 from the petty cash drawer and put it in her purse. When the physician asks about the petty cash balance, Kristen mentions that she gave a Girl Scout troop a $20 donation. What should Bailee do?

_____

_____

_____

8. Dr. Schilling storms into the clinic and calls a meeting. Taylor, an extern who has been at the clinic for 1 week, attends the meeting with the two other medical assistants in the office. When the physician insists that one of the three of them took a vial of Demerol from the drug cabinet, the two medical assistants look at Taylor. If Taylor is not guilty, how should she handle this situation professionally?

_____

_____

_____

Part IV: Professional Organizations

Fill in the blanks with the correct word choice.

1. Gail uses the CMA credential after her name, which stands for _____ _____ _____.

2. Which organization offers the CMA examination? _____

3. Patty uses the RMA credential after her name, which stands for _____ _____ _____.

4. Which organization offers the RMA examination? _____

5. Two agencies that accredit medical assisting programs are the _____ and the _____.

6. Explain the purpose of CEUs.

_____

7. Do both the AAMA and the AMT require CEUs or offer them as an option for recertification? _____

8. Explain the mission of the AAMA.

_____

_____

_____

9. Explain the mission of the AMT.

_____

_____

_____

10. Do candidates for the American Registry for Medical Assisting sit for a certification exam? How are they registered?

_____

_____

_____

11. List three certifications offered by the National Center for Competency Testing that the medical assistant might qualify to take.

_____

_____

_____

12. Which certification is offered upon graduation from your school?

_____

_____

_____

Part V: Short Essay Questions
Answer the following questions using complete sentences.

1. List several personal attributes a student should display during his or her externship.

_____

_____

_____

2. Explain why continuing education is critical to the success of the medical assistant.

_____

_____

_____

3. What are some of the subjects that will be included in most medical assistant training programs?

_____

_____

_____

Read the case study and answer the questions that follow.

Maryanne entered a medical assisting training program in June, and by mid-July she was struggling to do homework, take care of her infant son, and work part-time. She loves her classes but feels overwhelmed by the amount of work school requires. At times she thinks about quitting school, but she also realizes that a job as a medical assistant will be more rewarding than her current part-time job. Maryanne wants a position that she can be proud to hold. One of her instructors suggested that she make plans for the situations that could prompt her to give up her schooling.

1. How can Maryanne make plans for situations that might go wrong throughout her time in school?

_____

_____

_____

2. What types of situations could present problems for her?

_____

_____

_____

3. How can Maryanne budget her time effectively so that she is able to meet all her responsibilities?

_____

_____

_____

WORKPLACE APPLICATION OPTIONS

Choose one or more of these activities and, if appropriate, share results with the class.

1. Write a reasonable dress code policy for a fictional medical office. Include regulations for both male and female employees. Be specific about jewelry (e.g., nose rings, piercings, and so on), fingernail length, clean shoes, and all other aspects of an acceptable dress code.

2. Survey several physicians' offices to determine if certification or registration leads to a higher starting salary, or if the office increases salary after certification or registration.

INTERNET ACTIVITY OPTIONS

Choose one or more of these activities and, if appropriate, share results with the class.

1. Research the requirements for taking both the CMA and RMA examinations. Request or download an application to become a member of the American Association of Medical Assistants and the American Medical Technologists. Obtain a money order for the application fee and send the fees with your application. Answer the following questions:

   a. What CMA examination date is closest to your graduation? _____

   b. What is the fee for the CMA examination? _____

   c. How much are the initial dues for joining the AAMA based on your state of residence? _____

d. How much are annual dues for the AAMA based on your state of residence? _____

e. What local chapter is closest to you? When and where are the meetings held?

_____

_____

f. What RMA examination date is closest to your graduation? _____

g. What is the fee for the RMA examination? _____

h. How much are the initial dues for joining the AMT? _____

i. How much are annual dues for the AMT? _____

j. What local chapter is closest to you? When and where are the meetings held?

_____

_____

2. Research the medical assistant's scope of practice in your state and write a report on this subject. Present the report to the class.

3. Research the requirements of other certifications that you might be interested in obtaining. Which would you like to work toward, if any? Secure applications for those additional certifications.

4 Professional Behavior in the Workplace

VOCABULARY REVIEW

Fill in the blanks with the correct vocabulary terms from this chapter.

1. Dr. Babinski struggles with _____, often putting off doing tasks that should be completed.

2. Anna has worked as a medical assistant for almost 30 years, and her professionalism and compassion are above _____.

3. Susan Bessler is a certified medical assistant (CMA) who has supervised externships for almost 10 years; she expects students to display _____ when performing their duties at her clinic.

4. _____ is one of the most important attributes that medical assistants should display as they go about their duties.

5. James has learned that he must use _____ when dealing with the patients in the clinic, being careful not to reveal any confidential information to an unauthorized third party.

6. Roberta _____ the notes from the last staff meeting to all employees.

7. A few of the _____ that the professional medical assistant should possess include loyalty, initiative, and courtesy.

8. Because Julia has been dishonest about her reasons for missing work, her _____ has been called into question.

9. Kristen has a pleasant _____ when working with patients.

10. Medical assistants receive pay that is usually _____ with their experience and training.

11. Jessica holds drawings for small gifts at her staff meetings, which helps to raise employee _____.

12. Gene evokes a professional _____ when talking with patients that encourages them to place their trust in him.

13. Medical assistants must take _____ when they are performing both externship and job duties.

14. _____ is a cause for immediate dismissal from employment.

15. The phrase "office politics" has a negative _____.

Part I: Short Answer Questions

Briefly answer the following questions.

1. List the eight characteristics of the professional medical assistant.

    a. _____

    b. _____

    c. _____

    d. _____

    e. _____

    f. _____

    g. _____

    h. _____

2. List five obstructions to professionalism.

    a. _____

    b. _____

    c. _____

    d. _____

    e. _____

3. Define teamwork in your own words.

    _____

    _____

    _____

    _____

Part II: Practicing Professional Behavior

Answer the following questions.

1. Karen has developed a friendship with Angela, who has a wonderful personality but does not always do her share in the family practice clinic where they work together. Dr. Rabinowitz tells Karen that Angela is going to be terminated on Friday, and she asks Karen to take over some of Angela's duties until a replacement is found. How can Karen demonstrate loyalty to her employer in this situation? How can she demonstrate loyalty to her friend Angela?

    _____

    _____

    _____

    _____

2. Martin Smith is a patient who always disrupts the clinic. He constantly complains about everything from the moment he enters until the moment he leaves. Karen is at the desk when he arrives to check out and pay his bill. When she tells him that he has a previous balance from a claim that his insurance did not pay, he argues that Karen filed the claim incorrectly. Karen is not in charge of filing insurance claims and did not handle any part of the claim in question. How can she be courteous to this patient?

_____

_____

_____

_____

3. Karen works in the office laboratory. She is often asked questions about insurance and billing that she must refer to other personnel. How should Karen efficiently request information or assistance for the patient from other office personnel?

_____

_____

_____

_____

4. Karen and her fiancé ended their relationship last week. How can she deal with personal stressors while she is in the workplace?

_____

_____

_____

_____

5. A patient needs to be scheduled for an outpatient endoscopic examination. When Karen gives the instruction sheet to the patient, she suspects from his reaction that the patient is unable to read. How can Karen professionally handle this situation without causing embarrassment to the patient?

_____

_____

_____

_____

6. Which of the characteristics of professionalism is your greatest strength? Explain why.

_____

_____

_____

_____

7. Which of the five obstructions to professionalism will be most difficult for you to overcome? Explain why.

_____

_____

_____

_____

8. Explain the difference between drug abuse and drug addiction.

_____

_____

_____

_____

9. List the four criteria of substance abuse.

a. _____

b. _____

c. _____

d. _____

10. List the seven criteria that determine abuse if three are met within a 12-month period.

a. _____

b. _____

c. _____

d. _____

e. _____

f. _____

g. _____

CASE STUDY

Read the case study and answer the questions that follow.

Aaron is a new medical assistant in Dr. Royce's family practice. He was an exceptional student, and he consistently performed well on his externship, receiving commendations from the externship office manager as well as a written recommendation from the physician. One month after he started his job, Bethany asked him to make a bank deposit for her, usually a duty that she performs daily. Bethany told him she was leaving the bank deposit in the bottom left drawer of his desk. When Aaron looked for the deposit at the end of the day, it was not anywhere in his desk; he looked in every drawer and even took the drawers out to make sure it had not fallen behind them. All the employees looked for the deposit, but nobody found it. No one was able to reach Bethany on the phone. The next morning when Aaron opened his left bottom desk drawer, the deposit bag was there, but it was empty. Bethany had already reported to the physician that the deposit had not been made. The physician calls Aaron to his office to discuss the situation.

1. What do you think happened?

_____

_____

_____

2. How can you deal with employees who are determined to cause problems for others in the clinic?

_____

_____

_____

3. How can situations such as this be proven effectively when one is unsure about exactly what happened?

_____

_____

_____

WORKPLACE APPLICATION OPTIONS

Complete one or more of these activities and, if appropriate, share your results with the class.

1. *Professionalism* is a word used often with regard to medical personnel. What does professionalism mean? Write a report on the meaning of professionalism, highlighting a person you believe is the epitome of professionalism in the medical field. This person could be an instructor, a physician, or some other healthcare worker whom you have come to know. Be specific about the ways professionalism is apparent in this individual's actions and speech.

2. Create a document for an office policy manual that defines and explains how the medical assistant working in the physician's office should display professionalism toward patients, co-workers, physicians, and visitors.

INTERNET ACTIVITY OPTIONS

Complete one or more of these activities and, if appropriate, share your results with the class.

1. Find four articles on medical professionalism. What seems to be the primary issues in attempting to maintain professionalism in medical facilities?

2. What are some ways medical professionalism is taught in medical schools? Do these methods apply to medical assistants?

3. Research substance abuse support centers in your community. Determine what services they provide and the cost of their programs. Look for centers that offer free assistance or offer their programs on a sliding income scale.

4. Research professionalism requirements for other health professions. Talk about the ways that those requirements are similar to or different from those of a medical assistant. Compare professionalism in the healthcare industry to that in other professions, such as law enforcement or education. Talk about why medical professionalism is so critical.

5 Interpersonal Skills and Human Behavior

VOCABULARY REVIEW

Fill in the blanks with the correct vocabulary terms from this chapter.

1. Jill commented that the new office policies are confusing and _____.

2. Giving a patient an injection against his or her will could be considered _____.

3. Shane's remark was insulting and _____.

4. Whitney _____ denied leaving the narcotics cabinet unlocked.

5. Our society has become quite _____, as evidenced by the number of lawsuits that are filed claiming medical professional liability.

6. Angry employees who are being terminated might turn _____ in a short time.

7. The notion that large individuals are lazy is an example of a(n) _____.

8. Sayed uses positive _____ while training a new employee.

9. Rahima demonstrates _____ when she attempts to get her way in every situation.

10. Paula has learned that she uses _____ _____ when she feels threatened by her supervisor.

11. Karen felt intense _____ when her grandmother died.

12. _____ helps Angela make sure she understands exactly what a patient meant.

13. Roberto eventually was terminated for using _____ with several of the patients in the clinic.

14. Bobbie attended a seminar last week and learned about _____, which included the study of the spatial separation that individuals naturally maintain.

15. Sue Ann definitely felt out of her _____ _____ when she was asked to be a guest speaker at a regional American Association of Medical Assistants meeting.

16. Mrs. Robinson is able to _____ her words quite distinctly.

17. Dr. Kirkham warned that no employee should speak to the _____ about any of his celebrity patients.

18. Rodman has a(n) _____ _____ at work, because he speaks so little English.

19. It is important to consider the patient's _____ of the staff, clinic, and physician.

20. Dr. Rockwell took Julia off phone duty because the high _____ of her voice was disconcerting to many patients.

SKILLS AND CONCEPTS

Part I: Patient-Centered Care
Answer the following questions.

1. Define patient-centered care.

   _____

   _____

   _____

2. How can the medical assistant contribute to positive patient-centered care in the physician's office?

   _____

   _____

   _____

Part II: Open-Ended and Closed-Ended Questions
Label the following questions or statements as either open ended (O) or closed ended (C).

1. _____ Are you taking blood pressure medication?

2. _____ Are you allergic to aspirin?

3. _____ Would you tell me about your past surgeries?

4. _____ Do you have asthma?

5. _____ What types of attempts have you made to stop smoking?

6. _____ Explain what you feel when your migraines begin.

7. _____ Do you have hospitalization insurance?

8. _____ Do you want a morning or afternoon appointment?

9. _____ How are you feeling today?

10. _____ What type of trouble do you have when swallowing pills?

Part III: Defense Mechanisms

Match the following defense mechanisms with the appropriate statements.

1. _____ "Everyone forgets to clock in from lunch once in a while. Why am I being singled out and written up?"

2. _____ "I refuse to believe that I'm HIV positive. I've only had sex with two people in the past 5 years."

3. _____ "I would do a better job at work, but I can't do everything in 1 day like I'm expected to."

4. _____ "I know that the office manager is angry with me because I've been late, and I should talk to her, but I just can't deal with that stress right now."

5. _____ "Why are you attacking me about not filling out the narcotics log? You certainly aren't the perfect medical assistant!"

6. _____ "I know my blood sugar is high, and I have tried to avoid sugar, but at least I'm doing my exercises twice a week."

7. _____ "Dr. Roberts only yells at me because he's stressed about his patient load."

8. _____ "It doesn't matter what I do to please my family. They hate me anyway, and there's nothing I can do about it."

9. _____ "I have enough on my mind and don't need my co-workers complaining that I'm not doing my share of the work!"

10. _____ "I can't bear to go to Memorial Park for our office picnic, because that's where my ex-husband told me he wanted a divorce."

11. _____ "Sure she looks good, if you like people from the '60s!"

a. Verbal aggression

b. Projection

c. Sarcasm

d. Compensation

e. Physical avoidance

f. Regression

g. Apathy

h. Rationalization

i. Displacement

j. Repression

k. Denial

Part IV: Barriers to Communication

Determine which of the five barriers to communication applies in each example given.

1. Cylinda has lived in the South all her life, and when Bruce came to work at the office, his brusque attitude made her feel defensive. She was so offended by his manner of speaking that she began to avoid him in the hallways and during breaks. He constantly spoke of how much more he'd been paid in New York and stressed the efficiency of the clinic where he formerly worked. Cylinda considers him a typical Northerner, and her dislike of him is based largely on the fact that he is different from her and most of the people she knows.

   _____

2. Aretha dreads the days that Rahima Bathkar comes to the office. She is a pleasant patient, but Aretha cannot understand her well and feels as if she is not providing Rahima with the care she deserves. She is always worried that she is missing some information the physician needs to know to diagnose and treat the patient properly. Aretha takes extra time with Rahima, but she is concerned because there is no one to interpret for Rahima when she cannot find the right word in her broken English.

   _____

3. Allan and Rebecca Poe are an elderly couple who visit the clinic twice a month for Rebecca's diabetes. Rebecca is blind in one eye and cannot read easily. Allan has vision problems as well, so the staff must read to them any documents they are required to sign to ensure that they understand the information.

   _____

Chapter **5** **Interpersonal Skills and Human Behavior**

4. Tommy Lightman approached the office manager because he was concerned about the manner in which Sarah spoke to him in the office. He expressed that Sarah was quite short with him last Tuesday and seemed very distracted as she talked with him in the examination room before the physician came in to treat him. He also said that the physician seemed to spend less time with him that day than usual. Tommy was concerned that he was not wanted in the clinic and wanted to have his records sent to another physician. The office manager checks the appointment book and realizes that Tommy was in the office last Tuesday at 11 o'clock, which was the exact time that another patient was being transported to the hospital because of heart failure.

_____

5. Teresa has a difficult time dealing with Orlando Gutierrez. He comes for appointments twice a month and is trying desperately to lose weight. He currently weighs 435 pounds. He is a pleasant person, but Teresa has been raised to believe that those who are overweight are lazy individuals. She tries to avoid caring for him when he visits the clinic.

_____

Part V: Dealing with Barriers to Communication

Reread the scenarios in the previous section and explain how a medical assistant using good communications skills could professionally handle each situation.

1. How can Cylinda develop a positive working relationship with Bruce?

_____

_____

_____

2. What can Aretha do to improve communication with Rahima?

_____

_____

_____

3. How can the medical assistant make Rebecca Poe feel more comfortable with her disability in the physician's office?

_____

_____

_____

4. What can Sarah and the office manager do to change Tommy's perception about the incident that happened during his last office visit?

_____

_____

_____

5. What does Teresa need to do personally to deal with patients she doesn't care for who visit the clinic?

_____

_____

_____

Part VI: Communication During Difficult Times

Read the following descriptions and suggest effective ways to communicate with the patient. Identify whether the patient is probably experiencing anger, shock, grief, or a combination of these emotions.

1. Joanna Taylor has just been brought to the physician's office after learning that her 16-year-old son was killed in a car accident. She is not responding to questions.

   _____

   _____

   _____

2. Lafonda Williams has come to the physician's office because of injuries she sustained when her estranged husband assaulted her.

   _____

   _____

   _____

3. Jackson Holland is seeing the physician today for antidepressants because of work-related stress, as well as difficulty dealing with the death of his elderly mother.

   _____

   _____

   _____

4. James Ackard comes to the physician's office for treatment of a work-related injury.

   _____

   _____

   _____

Part VII: Death and Dying

List the stages of grief in proper order.

1. _____

2. _____

3. _____

4. _____

5. _____

Part VIII: Resolving Conflict

1. List three ways to resolve conflict.

   a. _____

   b. _____

   c. _____

2. How would the medical assistant professionally resolve a conflict with a co-worker?

_____

_____

_____

3. How would the medical assistant professionally resolve a conflict with a supervisor?

_____

_____

_____

Part IX: Boundaries

1. Define self-boundaries.

_____

_____

_____

2. List the four steps of setting boundaries at work.

a. _____

b. _____

c. _____

d. _____

Part X: Communicating with People of Other Cultures

1. If a non–English-speaking patient comes to the office without an interpreter, what should the medical assistant do?

_____

_____

_____

2. How can the medical assistant put a patient at ease who seems nervous about an office visit or a procedure?

_____

_____

_____

3. Why should the medical assistant avoid the phrase "I know how you feel"?

_____

_____

_____

Part XI: Maslow's Hierarchy of Needs

Draw and label the Transactional Communication Model as shown in Figure 5-4 in the text.

Part XII: The Process of Communication

Draw and label Maslow's hierarchy of needs as shown in Figure 5-7 in the text.

CASE STUDY

Read the case study and answer the questions that follow.

Janet has tried for months to reach Mr. Robinson, a cancer patient who comes to the clinic every 3 weeks. He does not have any family in the area, and he feels that no one is interested in him or the problems he faces. He is estranged from both of his daughters, whom he has told to stay out of his life. They have not seen or spoken to him in more than 10 years. Each visit, Mr. Robinson complains about how worthless his family is and how they have all deserted him in his time of need. However, Janet knows from reviewing the chart that Mr. Robinson was insistent that his daughters stay out of his life.

1. How involved should Janet get in this patient's life?

_____

_____

_____

2. How can she deal with Mr. Robinson's attitude during his office visits?

_____

_____

_____

3. Does Janet or the physician have the right to contact the daughters and discuss Mr. Robinson's condition with them?

_____

_____

_____

Chapter **5** **Interpersonal Skills and Human Behavior**

WORKPLACE APPLICATION OPTIONS

Complete one or more of these activities and, if appropriate, share your results with the class.

1. Solicit 10 volunteers to come to the classroom and role-play patients and co-workers. Develop several personalities by writing a synopsis of the chief complaints and general personality traits. Allow each student to experience each "patient" or "co-worker" and react to them using professional interpersonal behavior and good human relations skills. Discuss the activity in class and talk about what this role-play activity can teach medical assisting students.

2. Interview a mental health professional, professional counselor, psychiatrist, or psychologist about dealing with patients who use defense mechanisms and passive-aggressive behavior. Ask for suggestions in dealing with these patients in a positive, constructive way. Share the information with the class.

INTERNET ACTIVITY OPTIONS

Complete one or more of these activities and, if appropriate, share your results with the class.

1. Use the Internet to answer the following questions.

   a. How many different career fields do human relations and interpersonal skills affect?

   _____

   _____

   _____

   b. What is organizational behavior?

   _____

   _____

   _____

   c. How are human relations and interpersonal skills practiced in classrooms?

   _____

   _____

   _____

2. Write a classroom policy that stresses positive interpersonal skills and human relations. Share this policy with the class.

3. Research defense mechanisms and passive-aggressive communication on the Internet. Choose one behavior and prepare a report describing the behavior, providing examples of the behavior, and suggesting ways to communicate with a person using the behavior. Share the information with the class.

6 Medicine and Ethics

Fill in the blanks with the correct vocabulary terms from this chapter.

1. Melissa believes that one of her roles as a medical assistant is to be a patient _____, supporting both the patient and family members during illnesses.

2. Ben has conflicting views about _____ and is unsure as to whether he would want the option to die with dignity if he had an incurable, debilitating disease.

3. Jill understands that the _____ of her actions while she is at work could affect whether a patient complies with the physician's instructions.

4. _____ allows the medical assistant to consider his or her personal feelings about various ethical issues before being faced with those decisions while working with actual patients.

5. _____ or handicapped patients need special understanding and patience from those who are employed in medical facilities.

6. Bianca is an infertile patient who is participating in _____ _____ to research a new drug that may help her to conceive a child.

7. The members of the Council on Ethical and Judicial Affairs issue _____ about medical situations, similar to the way that the Supreme Court justices consider matters that are brought before the court.

8. _____ is a devotion to the truth.

9. Kristy considers being friendly toward the patients in the clinic as her _____ and a vital part of her job performance.

10. When a person has breached an ethical standard, _____ may be necessary to atone for the action.

SKILLS AND CONCEPTS

Part I: Making Ethical Decisions
List the five steps of ethical decision making.

1. _____

2. _____

3. _____

4. _____

5. _____

For the following scenarios, determine the type of ethical problem presented, the agent or agents, the course of action, and the outcome. Although these situations may present more than one ethical problem, choose only one possibility for each exercise.

1. Two sisters have arrived at a medical facility to discuss with the attending physician the course of action they should take regarding their dying father. Mr. Roberts, the patient, is no longer responsive. Cassandra wants to continue all possible medical treatment to keep her father alive. Janet insists that her father would not want his life prolonged by artificial means. Mr. Roberts did not give either sister a power of attorney, and he did not leave a written record of his wishes on this issue.

   a. Type of ethical problem

   _____

   b. Agent or agents

   _____

   c. Course of action (Suggest one.)

   _____

   d. Outcome (Suggest one.)

   _____

   e. How can the medical assistant refrain from inflicting his or her own opinions on patients?

   _____

   _____

   _____

2. Dr. Patrick is the chief of staff at a regional medical center. His specialty is oncology, and the hospital is considering the construction of a cancer center as part of a multimillion-dollar project. One of Dr. Patrick's partners, Dr. Adams, is vehemently opposed to the project because of the cost to the local taxpayers who support the hospital. Dr. Adams has threatened to leave the practice unless Dr. Patrick votes against the project. Dr. Patrick wants the center to be built, but he also realizes that if Dr. Adams leaves, the practice will suffer a drastic loss of income.

   a. Type of ethical problem

   _____

   b. Agent or agents

   _____

   c. Course of action (Suggest one.)

   _____

   d. Outcome (Suggest one.)

   _____

   e. How would you handle an ethical decision that has an equal number of pros and cons?

   _____

   _____

   _____

Part II: Types of Ethical Problems
Identify the type of ethical problem that each diagram represents.

1.

2.

3.

4.

Part III: Opinions on Medicoethical Issues
Write your personal opinion regarding the following medicoethical issues. After writing your opinion, consider differing opinions by writing a brief opposing argument.

1. Abortion

_____

_____

_____

2. Abortion: opposing opinion

_____

_____

_____

3. Stem cell research

_____

_____

_____

4. Stem cell research: opposing opinion

_____

_____

_____

5. Human cloning

_____

_____

_____

6. Human cloning: opposing opinion

_____

_____

_____

7. Genetic counseling

_____

_____

_____

8. Genetic counseling: opposing opinion

_____

_____

_____

9. Physician-assisted suicide

_____

_____

_____

10. Physician-assisted suicide: opposing opinion

_____

_____

_____

Part IV: Cases to Discuss

Explain your opinion regarding the following cases. Then, talk about the issues in class, contributing your opinions to the discussion.

1. Should a woman who has been raped and become pregnant seek an abortion?

_____

_____

_____

2. What harm can come to a patient's family if the medical professionals are incorrect about their assessment of abuse?

_____

_____

_____

3. If the chief executive officer (CEO) of American Airlines, the winner of last year's Academy Award for best actor, and a drug-abusing mother of three all are equally ill and need a liver transplant, which should receive the organ? On what would you base the decision?

_____

_____

_____

4. A man's sperm is used to fertilize his wife's eggs, which are frozen for later use. However, the man dies before the eggs can be implanted. Should the man's wife be able to use those eggs after her marriage to a second man?

_____

_____

_____

5. A medical assistant is recruited to work with a physician who is researching paralysis. Once the project is under way, the assistant discovers that the physician is using embryos that have been questionably obtained in the experimentation. What should the medical assistant do?

_____

_____

_____

6. What is a fair length of time to give a surrogate mother to petition to void a surrogacy contract?

_____

_____

_____

7. What could happen if parents were to "design" a baby, but it arrived flawed in some way or did not meet their expectations?

_____

_____

_____

8. If a parent mentioned in passing that he or she would want the right to commit suicide in the event of a terminal illness, would you support that decision if the situation did in fact arise?

_____

_____

_____

9. A physician recommends that a patient be taken off life support. The patient lives with his homosexual partner and has not had contact with his parents in more than 10 years. Both the partner and the parents discuss the situation with the physician. The partner does not want to remove life support, stating that the patient would want to have every opportunity to live. The parents insist that they know what is best for their son and demand that he be taken off life support. Who should prevail?

_____

_____

_____

10. How would a medical assistant handle the family of a patient who asks for advice about withdrawing life-prolonging treatment? To whom should the medical assistant defer the question?

_____

_____

_____

11. A mentally ill single woman who is institutionalized becomes pregnant and refuses to give up her maternal rights so that the child can be adopted. Even if she were to reconsider, what complications might result if the child is born deaf and has a severe liver disorder? Should the child be fed and cared for by the hospital staff?

_____

_____

_____

12. Should an 87-year-old patient with cardiovascular disease and stomach cancer undergo expensive breast reconstruction surgery?

_____

_____

_____

13. A woman dies with a living will that states she wants to donate her organs. Her mother does not want her daughter's organs donated. What should health professionals do in this situation?

_____

_____

_____

14. A very emotional patient, the mother of a child who was raped and killed, has been given the opportunity to attend the execution of the murderer. During a visit to her family physician, she expresses concern about being able to cope with the memory of her daughter during the execution and asks you whether you would attend in the same situation. How do you handle this situation?

_____

_____

_____

15. A family physician who is extremely religious prefers not to treat patients who are homosexual. A gay patient who is infected with HIV comes to his office. The physician refers the patient to an infectious disease physician. Is this considered ethical?

_____

_____

_____

Part V: Ethics and the Medical Assistant

1. Describe in your own words the behavior of an ethical medical assistant.

_____

_____

_____

_____

Part VI: Rights and Duties

1. Identify the following as a right, a duty, or neither.

   a. Healthcare services for all Americans

   Right   Duty   Neither

   b. Owning a gun when licensed

   Right   Duty   Neither

   c. Providing care to an elderly parent

   Right   Duty   Neither

   d. Nondiscrimination

   Right   Duty   Neither

   e. Life

   Right   Duty   Neither

2. Are there times when a right or duty in the preceding list is invalid or could be argued to be so? Explain your answer.

_____

_____

_____

Part VII: Confidentiality

1. List several physical places within the physician's office where confidentiality could be breached.

_____

_____

_____

2. What are the usual consequences of a breach of patient confidentiality?

_____

_____

_____

3. Explain why confidentiality is critical in the medical environment.

_____

_____

_____

41

Read the case studies and answer the questions that follow.

1. Robert is a patient who has tested positive for the human immunodeficiency virus (HIV). His employer invites the local blood bank to come to the workplace every 6 months and conduct a blood drive. Robert has declined to donate in the past because of his HIV status, but he often feels pressured by co-workers to give blood. None of them is aware that he is HIV positive. How do blood banks handle this situation today? Does Robert have alternatives that will resolve the situation? Explain your answer.

   _____

   _____

   _____

2. Cameron works for Dr. Christian, and she works hard to earn the trust of the patients. Mrs. Rainer confides to Cameron that she has been smoking, against Dr. Christian's advice, and she asks Cameron not to tell the physician. How should Cameron handle this situation? What should she tell the patient?

   _____

   _____

   _____

WORKPLACE APPLICATION OPTION

Complete this activity and, if appropriate, share your results with the class.

Stepping into the medical environment, where confidentiality is so important, may be a difficult adjustment for some new medical assistants. In any medical facility, you must think before speaking. At times, discussing patients and their conditions will not be appropriate. How can you change your way of thinking and be constantly aware of the constraints that patient confidentiality places on the discussion of patient information?

INTERNET ACTIVITY OPTIONS

Choose one or more of these activities and, if appropriate, share your results with the class.

1. Peruse the website for the Health Insurance Portability and Accountability Act (HIPAA) and download the quick fact sheets. Study this information to gain a basic knowledge of HIPAA guidelines before studying the law in more detail in Chapter 16.

2. Discuss ethics in the classroom. How do medical assisting students perform ethically while completing their education? Research this issue on the Internet and talk about it in class.

3. Read the preamble and the nine principles of medical ethics posted on the American Medical Association's website. Discuss each principle. What changes would you make to these principles? Are they applicable to the situations that arise in the medical world today?

4. Research the requirements for reporting positive HIV tests in your state. Share your findings with the class.

7 Medicine and Law

VOCABULARY REVIEW

Fill in the blanks with the correct vocabulary terms from this chapter.

1. Dr. Parker insists that a medical assistant be present during all of his patient examinations in order to avoid any _____ of wrongdoing or abuse.

2. Many physician offices require patients to sign a(n) _____ agreement, which means disagreements may be settled by a qualified third party.

3. If a person contributes to a patient's poor condition, he or she may be charged with _____.

4. Dr. Samantha Beddingfield was called to court to discuss her knowledge of malpractice cases as a(n) _____.

5. When a patient offers his or her arm to have blood drawn, he or she has _____ consent.

6. A doctor of _____ studies the law.

7. Dr. Cartwright failed to follow the care of a hospital patient to whom he was assigned and may be guilty of _____ or _____.

8. Civil cases must be proved by a(n) _____ of the _____.

9. Criminal cases must be proved by _____ _____.

10. Roger Askew is bringing a case against a physician in the death of his wife during surgery, making him the _____ in the case.

11. Something put into one's own words is _____.

12. A court must have _____ over a case before it can hear the arguments and make a judgment.

13. If Alisha writes down comments that are untrue and inflammatory about another person, she might be accused of _____.

14. City court is often called _____ court.

15. City regulations are often called city _____.

16. If either side in a lawsuit is unhappy with the results, in most cases the decision can be _____.

17. Vince suffered the loss of use of his arm after surgery, loss of wages by being rendered unable to work, and loss of his ability to earn a living. These losses are called _____ in court.

18. The constitutional guarantee that legal proceedings will be fair is called _____.

19. Judge Roberts has 12 cases on the _____ for the day.

43

20. The person who stands accused of a crime in court is called the _____.

21. The person who stands accused in a civil trial is called the _____.

22. Alyssa may be held _____ for damaging her boyfriend's car.

23. An intentional attempt to injure another person is called _____.

24. The unlawful use of force or violence against another person is called _____.

25. A(n) _____ is a major crime, such as rape or murder.

26. Consent that is detailed and usually in writing is called _____ consent.

27. Judge Conlin uses previous cases as models to determine his decisions on current cases. The previous cases are called _____.

28. Barbara Harris was served a(n) _____, which required her to appear in court.

29. The document requiring that records be produced in court is called a(n) _____ _____.

30. The final decision of the judge or jury is called the _____.

SKILLS AND CONCEPTS

Part I: Classifications of Law

1. What are the three basic categories of criminal law discussed in this chapter?

    a. _____

    b. _____

    c. _____

2. What are the three basic categories of civil law discussed in this chapter?

    a. _____

    b. _____

    c. _____

3. A law that is minor in nature and usually a breach of municipal regulations is called a(n) _____.

4. Civil law involves cases that are brought to court by _____.

5. Criminal law involves a crime against the _____ or _____.

6. Medical professional liability falls under what category of civil law? _____

Part II: Anatomy of a Medical Professional Liability Lawsuit

1. List the four elements of a valid, legal contract.

    a. _____

    b. _____

    c. _____

    d. _____

44

2. List the three steps in the creation of the physician-patient relationship.

   a. _____

   b. _____

   c. _____

3. What must a letter of withdrawal of care state?

   a. _____

   b. _____

   c. _____

4. How should a letter of withdrawal be mailed? _____

5. Does the letter of withdrawal have to explain to the patient the reason the physician chose to withdraw from care of the patient? Explain your answer.

   _____

   _____

   _____

6. Explain what is meant by having jurisdiction over a case.

   _____

   _____

   _____

7. What is the ultimate appellate court in the United States?

   _____

8. Explain the difference between a deposition and an interrogatory.

   _____

   _____

   _____

9. List three of the five ways to determine whether a subpoena is valid.

   a. _____

   b. _____

   c. _____

10. Briefly explain how a person called to testify in court should dress.

   _____

   _____

   _____

11. What is a defendant in a civil trial often called? _____

12. Define negligence.

_____

_____

_____

13. List the three general classifications of medical professional negligence.

_____

_____

_____

14. What is contributory negligence?

_____

_____

_____

15. What is meant by the phrase "the medical assistant acts as an agent of the physician"?

_____

_____

_____

16. Explain why medical professional liability falls under the jurisdiction of tort law.

_____

_____

_____

Part IV: Short Answer Questions
Fill in the blanks with the correct answers.

1. The formal action of a legislative body is called a(n) _____.

2. The performance of an act that is wholly wrongful and unlawful is _____.

3. The agency that regulates safety in the workplace is _____.

4. A law enacted by the legislative branch of a government is called a(n) _____.

5. Failure to perform an act that should have been performed is _____.

6. A solemn declaration made by a witness under oath in response to interrogation by a lawyer is called _____.

7. The pretense of curing disease is called _____.

8. The improper performance of a legal act is _____.

9. Something that is easily understood or recognized by the mind is called a(n) _____.

10. An authoritative decree or direction usually set forth by a municipal regulation is called a(n) _____.

11. The law that promotes accuracy in medical laboratories is _____.

46

Part V: Inside the Courtroom

Circle T or F to indicate whether the statement is true or false.

1. T   F   Lying under oath constitutes perjury.

2. T   F   Arriving late to the courtroom is acceptable if the witness has a good excuse.

3. T   F   Attorneys usually discover new information when questioning their clients in the courtroom.

4. T   F   A sustained objection means that the judge disagrees with the objection and will allow the question to stand.

5. T   F   It is not necessary to use "ma'am" or "sir" in the courtroom when addressing the judge.

6. T   F   If a question is confusing to a witness, he or she should ask the attorney to restate or repeat the question.

7. T   F   Discovery is pretrial disclosure of pertinent facts or documents pertaining to a case.

8. T   F   Arbitration is a cost-saving alternative to trial.

Part VI: The Four Ds of Negligence and Damages

1. A patient was given the wrong medication. No adverse effects occurred. Which of the four Ds is missing? Why does this affect the possibility of a lawsuit?

   _____

   _____

   _____

2. A car accident occurs at an intersection outside a physician's office during normal business hours. Do the physician and staff have a duty to provide direct care for the injured? Why or why not?

   _____

   _____

   _____

3. A patient is treated for low back pain caused by a fall at the local mall. The patient sues the physician, because the pain is unresolved. Which of the four Ds would be the most difficult for the patient's attorney to prove? Why?

   _____

   _____

   _____

4. A medical assistant mislabeled a vial of blood that was sent to an outside laboratory. Because of this mistake, a child was given the wrong diagnosis and later died. The child's family sued the medical assistant, the physician, and the hospital that owned the practice. The child's family was awarded $4 million. What type of damages is this?

   _____

   _____

   _____

5. A female patient was awarded punitive damages after a physician sexually molested her during her annual pelvic examination. What are punitive damages designed to do? Do you think punitive damages should be limited to a specific amount of money?

   _____

   _____

   _____

Chapter **7** **Medicine and Law**

Read the case study and answer the questions that follow.

A 10-year-old girl was brought to a physician's office in mid-August with a complaint of a headache after gymnastics practice. The clinic was a freestanding, minor emergency center and not the child's regular physician's office. The girl and the adult who had brought her to the clinic, her aunt, both denied that she had been in any type of accident and stated that her only complaint was the headache and being tired and hot. The aunt mentioned that the girl also seemed a bit disoriented during the drive to the clinic. The girl didn't recall having been at gymnastics practice less than an hour earlier. The child told the physician that she had been a gymnast for 6 years and that she really liked her coach.

The outside temperature had reached 101° F that day. The physician examined the patient and suggested that she be taken home to rest and rehydrate. No prescriptions were written, and the girl left the clinic. Two hours later, she could not be roused from sleep; her aunt immediately took her to the emergency department (ED) at the closest hospital. The girl's mother met them at the hospital just in time to be told that the girl had slipped into a coma. The ED physician suspected that the girl had experienced heat stroke. The aunt was shocked and mentioned that she had taken the girl to a clinic earlier; she questioned why this diagnosis had not been considered at that time. The girl's mother immediately called the clinic and berated the physician for putting her child in a coma.

What went wrong in this case? Who is responsible for the child's condition? Is this a "good" malpractice case?

_____

_____

_____

_____

_____

_____

_____

_____

_____

WORKPLACE APPLICATION OPTIONS

Complete one or more of these activities and, if appropriate, share your results with the class.

1. Research the laws that apply to medical clinics in your state. If possible, interview an office manager about the laws that apply to local clinics and ask what challenges arise in trying to comply with them. Share what you learn with the class.

2. Visit a local small claims court. Watch the proceedings and pay particular attention to the extent to which the plaintiff has prepared his or her case. Take notes during the proceedings and prior to the verdict, write down your prediction as to which party will prevail. Share your experience with your class.

INTERNET ACTIVITY OPTIONS

Complete one or more of these activities and, if **appropriate**, share your results with the class.

1. Use the Internet to find the place in your area where a small claims case would be filed. Obtain the paperwork necessary to file a claim. Create a fictional case and complete the paperwork as if you plan to file it in court.

2. Research mediators in your area. Find the name and contact information for at least three. With your instructor's permission, contact a mediator and ask the individual to speak to the class.

3. Research medical malpractice attorneys in your area. Find the name and contact information for at least three. With your instructor's permission, invite the attorney to speak to the class about how medical assistants can help prevent medical malpractice claims.

8 Computer Concepts

Fill in the blanks with the correct vocabulary terms from this chapter.

1. Jacob uses a(n) _____ _____ to write data onto a blank compact disk and stores the CD as a backup for the clinic's blank forms.

2. To assist with patient diagnosis, Dr. Matthews uses software that is equipped with a type of _____ _____.

3. The smallest unit of information inside the computer is called a(n) _____.

4. Olivia installed new _____ _____ on the office computers that will allow patients to check in without the assistance of a receptionist.

5. Ethan has asked that all the computer users in the clinic clear the computer _____ periodically so that websites stored there will be erased and the system will run faster.

6. The office manager asked Samantha to print a(n) _____ _____ of the minutes of the meeting for each person attending.

7. Daniel likes to change the _____ in the different sections of the clinic's patients' newsletter to make it more readable and attractive.

8. A picture that represents a program or an object on the computer is called a(n) _____.

9. Information entered into and used by the computer is called _____.

10. Tyler is responsible for operating the clinic's _____, which manages shared network resources.

11. Information that is processed by the computer and transmitted to a monitor or printer is called _____.

12. Christian was able to easily connect a(n) _____ to his home computer, which allows information to be transmitted over telephone lines and enables him to connect to the Internet.

13. Any type of storage used to prevent the loss of files in the event of hard drive failure is called _____.

14. The _____ tracks all patient information, including addresses, phone numbers, and details about insurance coverage.

15. A personal _____ assistant is a handheld computer that can perform many functions.

16. The initial part of a URL listing is called a(n) _____ _____.

Part I: Matching Exercises

Match the following terms with their definitions.

1. _____ Approximately 1 billion bytes   a. Terabyte

2. _____ Approximately 1 trillion bytes   b. Bit

3. _____ 8 bits   c. Megabyte

4. _____ Binary digits   d. Byte

5. _____ Approximately 1,024 bytes   e. Kilobyte

6. _____ Approximately 1 million bytes   f. Gigabyte

Part II: Input, Output, and Storage Devices

Label each of the following as an input, output, or storage device.

1. Mouse	Input	Output	Storage
2. Keyboard	Input	Output	Storage
3. Printer	Input	Output	Storage
4. Scanner	Input	Output	Storage
5. Speakers	Input	Output	Storage
6. CD-ROM	Input	Output	Storage
7. Zip drive	Input	Output	Storage
8. Touch screen	Input	Output	Storage
9. Floppy disk	Input	Output	Storage
10. Flash drive	Input	Output	Storage

Part III: Parts of the Computer

Provide the name of the computer part described in the sentences that follow.

1. Central unit of the computer that contains the logic circuitry and carries out the instructions of the computer's programs

   _____

2. Main circuit board of the computer

   _____

3. Devices inserted into a computer that give it added capabilities

   _____

4. Device used to display computer-generated information

   _____

5. Magnetic disk inside the computer that can hold several hundred gigabytes of information and is used to store the application software that runs on the computer

   _____

6. Device used to take information from one CD-ROM and write it to another CD-ROM

_____

7. Device over which data can be transmitted via telephone lines or other media, such as coaxial cable

_____

8. Allows music or MIDI files to be heard from the computer

_____

9. Software installed on a computer to allow a hardware device to function

_____

Part IV: The Computer as a Co-Worker
List seven ways computers assist workers in medical offices.

1. _____

2. _____

3. _____

4. _____

5. _____

6. _____

7. _____

Part V: Basic Computer Functions
Describe how the following functions are performed on the computer.

1. Open a document

_____

_____

2. Save a document

_____

_____

3. Rename a document

_____

_____

4. Cut and paste text

_____

_____

5. Copy text

_____

_____

6. Exit a program

_____

_____

7. Turn the computer on

_____

_____

8. Turn the computer off

_____

_____

Part VI: Short Answer Questions

1. What three elements differentiate microprocessors?

   a. _____

   b. _____

   c. _____

2. Explain peripheral devices and give one example of a peripheral device.

   _____

   _____

3. What is the function of a browser?

   _____

   _____

4. Define computer networking.

   _____

   _____

5. Why is computer security so important in today's medical office?

   _____

   _____

Part VII: File Formats and Printer Types

Match the following terms with their definitions.

1. _____ Inexpensive printer that provides a moderate-quality hard copy

2. _____ File format that supports color and often is used for scanned images

3. _____ Bitmapped graphics compiled by a graphics image set in rows or columns of dots

4. _____ Printer output similar to that of a photocopier; capable of complex graphics

5. _____ File format in which characters are represented by their ASCII codes

6. _____ File type commonly used for photographs

7. _____ File type that combines ASCII codes with special commands that distinguish variations

8. _____ File usually created by a word processor for various documents, including letters and forms

9. _____ Printer that uses a heating element that is energized during the printing process

10. _____ Type of printer that serves as a scanner, fax, and copier

a. .doc

b. .gif

c. Laser

d. .jpeg

e. .bmp

f. Dot matrix

g. .txt

h. Ink jet

i. .rtf

j. Multifunctional

CASE STUDY

Read the case study and answer the questions that follow.

Brooke Comis works for Dr. Tomms as a clinical medical assistant. She is a former office computer specialist who worked in the computer field for 12 years before she entered medical assisting school. She changed career fields because of the work prospects in technology and acted on her dream to enter the medical field. Unfortunately, she is the only person in the office who is knowledgeable about computers, the Internet, and networking. Whenever a computer is not functioning correctly or a problem occurs with the network, Dr. Tomms asks Brooke to fix it. When he decided to buy new computers, he expected Brooke to assemble all of them and set up a new network. Brooke gets more and more irate each time she is asked to perform these duties, because she is not compensated other than her normal hourly pay. She knows that if Dr. Tomms paid someone to do this work, it would cost him more than her monthly salary. Brooke is not certain how to handle this situation. What should she do first? How should she approach the physician? Should she refuse to perform computer work? What could happen if she refuses?

WORKPLACE APPLICATION OPTIONS

Complete one or more of these activities and, if appropriate, share your results with the class.

1. Assume that you have been selected to order a new computer system for the physician. The clinic's personnel include three physicians, six administrative personnel, and four clinical assistants, plus you, the office manager. Describe the minimum equipment needed. Consider printers, Internet access, scanners, and wireless needs. Investigate computers using the Internet and prepare a folder with photos or specifications that detail the equipment you have selected.

2. Completely disconnect a computer, including all cords and peripheral devices. Reconnect the computer, labeling the cords on each end as to where it should be placed (e.g., "printer"). Turn the computer on and use each device to make certain that it has been connected the right way. Students may want to complete this activity on a home computer, or the instructor may set up a computer in the classroom to disconnect and reconnect.

3. A group of physicians has decided to update the office computer system. Using the diagram of the medical office in Figure 11-1, determine placement of computers throughout the office as well as the logical location of printers, assuming that the office is using a wireless system.

INTERNET ACTIVITY OPTIONS

Complete one or more of these activities and, if appropriate, share your results with the class.

1. Use the Internet to locate a company that sells computers in your geographic area. Explore the site. Find a computer that you might consider purchasing, then answer the following questions.

   a. How much RAM and ROM does the system have? _____

   b. What is the clock speed? _____

   c. What is the baud rate of the modem? _____

   d. What software, if any, comes with the system? _____

   e. What is the total cost before taxes are applied? _____

2. Discuss Internet searches and how to determine reliable Internet sources.

3. Search for 10 websites that are related to medical assisting. Read the URL addresses. Determine if each would be considered a reliable, credible source of information based on the information obtained by reading the URL address.

4. Look for 10 search engines on the Internet. Enter the phrase "medical office computer systems" in each system and review the results. List five websites that contain information that would be useful in choosing computer systems for a medical facility.

Telephone Techniques

VOCABULARY REVIEW

Fill in the blanks with the correct vocabulary terms from this chapter.

1. Taylor Medical USA sells durable medical equipment and supplies to the public, so the company is considered to be a(n) _____.

2. Julie is careful of her _____, because she wants her voice to be clear and effective when she is speaking on the telephone.

3. Cassie's voice has a nice _____, which is a change in pitch or loudness when speaking.

4. Dr. LeGrand wishes to _____ her relationships with patients of different cultures so that she can understand their needs.

5. The office manager cautions the medical assistants to avoid _____, because most patients do not understand complicated medical terms.

6. The highness or lowness of sound is called its _____.

7. Laura _____ will be at work on time and will stay until the last patient leaves.

8. When speaking on the phone or in public, Dr. Conn knows that he should avoid _____ speech to keep the listeners interested and enthusiastic about what he has to say.

9. The medical assistants at Wray Medical and Surgical Clinic are proficient at _____.

10. Being placed on hold for an extended time becomes quite _____.

11. The utterance of articulate, clear sounds is _____.

12. It is pleasant to hear a person speak with _____.

13. Dr. Beard ordered the laboratory tests _____ so that the results would be reported to him immediately.

14. Mackenzie has learned to be _____ when she speaks with patients on the phone so that she maintains a good relationship with them.

15. Dr. Lightfoot prefers that the receptionist _____ all of his calls so that he can concentrate on the patients in the office during their examinations.

Part I: Answering Incoming Calls and Taking Phone Messages

Read the following incoming calls. Then use the telephone message forms to take an accurate message for each caller. The calls in quotations are taken from voicemail. Determine who should receive the message, three questions to ask the patient when the call is returned, and what actions need to be taken for proper follow-through. Although you are not required to list questions that are clinical in nature, you may include clinical questions if you like.

Staff Members at Dr. Julie Beard's Office

Physician	Dr. Julie Beard
Office manager	Julia Carpenter
Clinical medical assistant	Trina Martinez
Clinical medical assistant	Dean Howell
Scheduling assistant	Stephanie Dickson
Receptionist	Ginny Holloway
Insurance biller and medical records	Gloria Richardson

1. "Hello, this is Peter Young. I saw Dr. Beard on Monday about a rash on my forearms. This thing isn't getting any better. The cream she prescribed for me isn't helping the itching, and it's very uncomfortable. Is there anything else we can do to help it? My number is 972-555-9873." The message was received at 8:30 a.m. on Thursday, February 3.

   a. Who should receive this message?

   _____

   b. What questions should you ask the patient when returning this call?

   • _____

   • _____

   • _____

   c. What action should you take after speaking with the patient?

   _____

   _____

   _____

2. Gerald Morris calls Dr. Beard's office to ask whether his insurance has paid for his last office visit. He is an established patient and has worked as a city police officer for more than 10 years. After asking to place Mr. Morris on hold, you pull up his account on the computer. No insurance payment has been credited to his account, and a note indicates that his insurance was not in effect at the time of his office visit. Mr. Morris asks you to check with the insurance company and call him back, because he is concerned about resolving this issue. His phone number is 972-555-8824. This message was taken at 3:45 p.m. on September 4.

   a. Who should receive this message?

   _____

   b. What questions should you ask the patient when returning this call?

   • _____

   • _____

   • _____

c. What action should you take after speaking to the patient?

_____

_____

_____

3. "Hello, this is Savannah Yarborough. I visited with your receptionist earlier today, and she indicated that one of the medical assistants has resigned and you will have a position available in a few weeks. I am very interested in interviewing and presenting myself as a candidate for the job. I am a certified medical assistant with 6 years' experience. Please give me a call at your convenience. My telephone number is 817-555-9902. I look forward to speaking with you and perhaps scheduling an interview." This message was taken at 1:30 p.m. on May 1.

a. Who should receive this message?

_____

b. What questions should you ask when returning this call?

   • _____

   • _____

   • _____

c. What action should you take after speaking to Ms. Yarborough?

_____

_____

_____

4. Mr. Juan Ross called today at 10:15 a.m. to get his prescription for Ambien refilled. His pharmacy is Wolfe Drug, and the drugstore phone number is 214-555-4523. He is allergic to penicillin. Mr. Ross's phone number is 214-555-2377. Mr. Ross's message was received on July 23.

a. Who should receive this message?

_____

b. What questions should you ask the patient when returning this call?

   • _____

   • _____

   • _____

c. What action should you take after speaking to the patient?

_____

_____

_____

5. Mr. Benjamin Adams called to speak to the office manager so that he could express his dissatisfaction with the times he was offered for an appointment. His job is strict about attendance, and he cannot leave work until 4 p.m. He has requested appointment times after 4 p.m., but the scheduling assistant tells him that he cannot have an appointment any later than 4 p.m. Mr. Adams is concerned that he will not be able to be at the clinic at that exact time, and he is frustrated that the clinic is not more responsive to his needs. He called at 2:15 p.m. on March 14. His phone number at work is 972-555-6343, and his cell phone number is 214-555-8080.

a. Who should receive this message?

_____

b. What questions should you ask the patient when returning this call?

- _____
- _____
- _____

c. What action should you take after speaking to the patient?

_____
_____
_____

6. "This is Ms. Garrett from Blue Cross/Blue Shield, and it's 10 a.m. on June 5. I am calling to discuss employee benefits for the coming year with the office manager. BCBS provides insurance coverage for your clinic employees. Would you please have the office manager return my call when she has a few moments to talk? My number is 800-555-0024, extension 415. Thank you!"

a. Who should receive this message?

_____

b. What questions should you ask when returning this call?

- _____
- _____
- _____

c. What action should you take after speaking to Ms. Garrett?

_____
_____
_____

7. "This is Sarah at Cline Meador Lab with a stat lab report. It's 9:35 a.m. on November 16. The patient's name is Laura Williamson, and her white blood cell count is 18,000. Please notify Dr. Beard immediately. The lab phone number is 800-555-3333, and my extension is 255. If she has any questions, please have her give me a call. Thanks."

a. Who should receive this message?

_____

b. What questions should you ask or what information should you verify when returning this call?

- _____
- _____
- _____

c. What action should you take after speaking to Sarah?

_____
_____
_____

8. Judy Jordan has migraine headaches and occasionally takes hydrocodone to relieve the pain. Dr. Beard leaves the office for the weekend at noon on Friday, and office policy dictates that she is not to be paged except in emergencies. Patients with routine or lesser health issues are to be instructed either to make an appointment to come in and see the physician or to go to the emergency department. Ms. Jordan calls at 4:45 pm on Friday afternoon, March 9, after Dr. Beard has left the office. She requests that the staff authorize a refill for her pain medicine and insists on speaking to the office manager, who is in a meeting. Ms. Jordan's phone number is 214-555-9822.

   a. Who should receive this message?

   _____

   b. What questions should you ask or what information should you verify when returning this call?

   • _____

   • _____

   • _____

   c. What action should you take in this situation?

   _____

   _____

   _____

9. Gary Burritt is moving out of state, so he calls the office because he needs a copy of his medical records. Dr. Beard prefers to send medical records directly to the receiving physician. Mr. Burritt's phone number is 512-555-6679. Today's date is December 20, and this message was received at 11:45 a.m.

   a. Who should receive this message?

   _____

   b. What questions should you ask or what information should you verify when returning this call?

   • _____

   • _____

   • _____

   c. What action should you take in this situation?

   _____

   _____

   _____

10. Allan Jenkins is calling from the cleaning service to let the office manager know what supplies he needs. He leaves a message stating that the office needs window cleaner, paper towels, liquid cleanser, and floor cleaner. He says that the office manager does not have to call him back, but the service will be cleaning again on Friday evening and will need the supplies at that time. This message was received on Wednesday, April 7, at 8:10 a.m. The caller leaves his phone number, 903-555-2378, in case the office manager has questions.

   a. Who should receive this message?

   _____

   b. What action should you take in this situation?

   _____

   _____

   _____

11. "Hello. My name is Christina Cawtel, and I was referred to your office by Dr. Preston for evaluation of an ovarian cyst. Today is Wednesday, October 4, and it is 8 a.m. I would like to make an appointment for early next week if possible. My phone number is 817-555-9325. Oh, and by the way, I need to know if you are a provider for Aetna, because my company just changed to their managed care plan. I probably need to have a mammogram, too, and I want to see if you will order it before I come in for the appointment. Thanks."

a. Who should receive this message?

_____

b. What questions should you ask or what information should you verify when returning this call?

- _____

- _____

- _____

c. What action should you take in this situation?

_____

_____

_____

12. "My name is Janeen Shaw, and I am Dr. Beard's patient. It is just before 2 p.m., and I am trying to reach you as soon as you open your office after lunch. I am having a hard time breathing, and I have stomach pains. I am hurting all over my upper body, on my chest, my arms, my neck, just everywhere. I'm sweating, and I'm very nauseated. I'm 45, and I'm almost never ill. I wanted to find out if I can come in for an appointment today. Please call me back as soon as possible. My phone number is 601-555-3423. Thank you. Please call as soon as you can. I really feel awful."

a. Who should receive this message?

_____

b. What questions should you ask or what information should you verify when returning this call?

- _____

- _____

- _____

c. What action should you take in this situation?

_____

_____

_____

Part II: Handling Difficult Calls

Briefly explain how the following callers and types of calls should be handled.

1. Angry callers

_____

_____

_____

2. Sales calls

_____

_____

_____

3. Emergency calls

_____

_____

_____

4. Unauthorized inquiry calls

_____

_____

_____

5. Callers with complaints

_____

_____

_____

6. Callers who speak foreign languages or have heavy accents

_____

_____

_____

Part III: Using a Telephone Directory

Using your local telephone directory, find the following telephone numbers for your city or community.

1. Nonemergency number for the police department

_____

2. General information number for the nearest airport

_____

3. Local tax office

_____

4. American Red Cross office

_____

5. Acute care hospital

_____

6. Mental health and mental retardation center

_____

63

7. Meals on Wheels

_____

8. American Cancer Society

_____

Part IV: Answering the Telephone
Use the local telephone directory to find telephone numbers for the following medical specialty offices in your area. Call these offices to determine how they answer the telephone. Explain the purpose of your call to the staff member who answers the phone, and record the person's phone greeting in the space provided. Alternatively, write an original phone greeting for each of these medical specialty offices.

1. Ophthalmologist

_____

2. Oncologist

_____

3. General practitioner

_____

4. Chiropractor

_____

5. Cosmetic surgeon

_____

6. Dermatologist

_____

Part V: Short Answer Questions
Fill in the blank with the correct answer.

1. Selecting which calls will be forwarded to the physician immediately is a process called _____.

2. A study by Harvard University claims that the physician's _____ of voice has a direct link to medical professional liability claims.

3. The medical assistant should not eat, drink, or _____ while answering the office telephone.

4. The mouthpiece of the telephone handset should be held _____ inch(es) from the lips.

5. The medical assistant must maintain patient _____ at all times, even when on the telephone.

6. Telephone calls should be answered by the _____ ring.

7. Unsatisfactory progress reports from patients should be directed to the _____.

8. _____ calls help the physician communicate with family members in different parts of the country.

9. Medical offices should have a set of clearly written _____ that can be read to the caller who requests the information.

Part VI: Time Zones
Determine the correct times.

1. When it is 3 p.m. in Dallas, Texas, it is _____ in Los Angeles, California.

2. When it is 2 p.m. in Washington State, it is _____ in New York City.

3. When it is 5 p.m. in Las Cruces, New Mexico, it is _____ in Flint, Michigan.

4. When it is 4 p.m. in Augusta, Maine, it is _____ in Columbia, South Carolina.

5. When it is 11 a.m. in Biloxi, Mississippi, it is _____ in Chicago, Illinois.

Part VII: Telephone Technique

1. List five questions that might be asked of a patient who calls with an emergency situation.

    a. _____

    b. _____

    c. _____

    d. _____

    e. _____

2. The phrase that often calms an angry patient is _____ _____ _____

    _____.

3. Explain the procedure for transferring a phone call.

    _____

    _____

    _____

4. What should the medical assistant do if a caller refuses to identify himself or herself?

    _____

    _____

    _____

5. List the seven components of a proper telephone message.

    a. _____

    b. _____

    c. _____

    d. _____

    e. _____

    f. _____

    g. _____

Read the case study and answer the questions that follow.

Denise has been the receptionist for a moderately large clinic for the past 3 months. She replaced Dorothy, who retired. Denise has been overwhelmed by the number of calls to the clinic, and the office manager has spoken to her twice about missing calls. Denise insists that she is constantly on the phone answering and transferring calls. She is beginning to lose faith in herself, but as she considers why she is failing at her job, she realizes that two new physicians have joined the practice since Dorothy left, and numerous calls come to the clinic for those two physicians. Denise wants to suggest to the office manager that perhaps the time has come for a second receptionist, but she is unsure how to broach the subject. How can Denise begin her conversation with the office manager? What should she not do or say?

_____

_____

_____

_____

WORKPLACE APPLICATION OPTIONS

Complete one or more of these activities and, if appropriate, share your results with the class.

1. Contact a clinic office manager and ask whether he or she would allow you to shadow the office receptionist for a day. Take note of the types of calls that come into the clinic and how they are handled. Discuss the results of the visit with the class.

2. Invite a receptionist to the class to discuss telephone techniques for the medical office.

3. Call several physician offices and make notes regarding the first impression that the office creates through its telephone techniques. Share the information with the class.

4. Talk about appropriate voicemails that might be left when calling patients or business associates. Discuss how much the caller should say on a voicemail, and discuss what should be included in the message.

5. Talk about how calls from deaf patients, or other patients with disabilities, might be handled.

INTERNET ACTIVITY OPTIONS

Complete one or more of these activities and, if appropriate, share your results with the class.

1. Investigate telephone techniques and skills on the Internet and bring three tips to class. Share them with your classmates.

2. After researching information on the Internet, write a report that explains why the telephone is so important in making a good first impression.

3. Research the way telephones actually work. Prepare a brief report for the class.

4. Research the way Internet connections are made through phone systems. Prepare a brief report for the class.

10 Scheduling Appointments

VOCABULARY REVIEW

Fill in the blank with the correct vocabulary term from this chapter.

1. Angela arranged for a short time _____ between Dr. Patrick's speaking engagement and his first afternoon appointment so that he would have time for lunch.

2. Gayle gained _____ in computers by taking Saturday classes on the newest software.

3. A(n) _____ noise came from the autoclave when it was turned on this morning, so Pamela called service personnel to repair the machine.

4. Olivia realized that she needed to take a(n) _____ medical terminology course before she could register for anatomy and physiology.

5. All the medical assistants in the facility know that a(n) _____ _____ must be noted in the medical record, as well as the appointment book.

6. Before using an appointment book, establish the _____ by marking all times the physician is unavailable, so that patients will not be scheduled during those times.

7. A patient from a neighboring clinic caused a(n) _____ in the hallway as he left, because he disagreed with a billing statement.

8. _____ _____ are those who have been seen as patients in the clinic more than once.

9. The _____ among the staff at Dr. Wykowski's office has become strained since the office manager was terminated.

10. Cooperation and willingness to help other staff members is a(n) _____ part of the success of a practice.

11. The payment of benefits to the physician for services rendered is called _____.

12. A(n) _____ is a predeveloped page layout used to make new pages with a similar design, pattern, or style.

Part I: Appointment Reminder Cards

Practice completing appointment reminder cards on the forms provided.

1. Gayle Jackson has an appointment for August 23, 20XX, at 3 p.m. with Dr. Lupez.

2. Debra Odom has an appointment for May 1, 20XX, at 9 a.m. with Dr. Hughes.

3. Katrina Shaw has an appointment for June 13, 20XX, at 11:45 a.m. with Dr. Hughes.

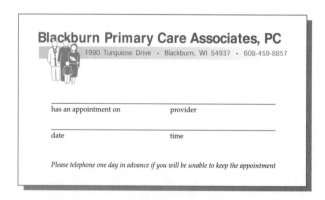

4. Joni Perry has an appointment for September 12, 20XX, at 2:40 p.m. with Dr. Lawler.

5. Savannah York has an appointment for December 15, 20XX, at 4:30 p.m. with Dr. Lupez.

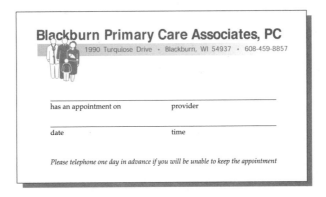

Part II: Guides for Scheduling

1. What three items must be considered when scheduling appointments?

   a. _____

   b. _____

   c. _____

2. Why is patient need an important consideration when planning the services the clinic will offer?

   _____

   _____

3. How can the medical assistant handle a physician who habitually spends more than the allotted time with patients?

   _____

   _____

4. List one advantage and one disadvantage to using an appointment book for scheduling.

   Advantage _____

   Disadvantage _____

5. List one advantage and one disadvantage to using a computer for scheduling.

Advantage _____

Disadvantage _____

6. Explain why the time length of appointments is important.

_____

_____

7. Define a template and explain its use with regard to appointment scheduling.

_____

_____

8. What is a repeating appointment?

_____

_____

9. What is the difference between an emergency appointment and an urgent appointment?

_____

_____

10. Explain why an emergency call should never be placed on hold.

_____

_____

Part III: Advance Preparation and Establishing a Matrix

Prepare Appointment Page 1 (see Work Product 10-1 on p. 47 of the Procedures Checklist) according to the following directions.

1. The date is Monday, October 13, 20XX.

2. Dr. Lawler and Dr. Hughes have hospital rounds from 8 to 9 a.m.

3. Dr. Lupez sees patients from 8 a.m. to noon and then has a medical conference.

4. Lunch is from noon until 2 p.m.

5. Dr. Lawler has a 4 p.m. meeting at the hospital.

6. Dr. Hughes and Dr. Lawler both prefer a break from 3:15 to 3:30 p.m. to catch up on telephone calls and other duties.

Part IV: Scheduling Appointments

Prepare Appointment Page 2 (see Work Product 10-2 on p. 49 of the Procedures Checklist) according to the following directions. Appointments can be scheduled for subsequent days in these exercises.

1. The date is Tuesday, October 14, 20XX.

2. Lunch is from noon until 2 p.m.

3. Dr. Lawler will be out Tuesday afternoon.

4. Dr. Hughes is out of town speaking at a conference.

5. Tracey and Keith Jones would like an appointment with Dr. Lawler right before lunch. Both are new patient physical examinations, and they would like to come to the office at the same time so that they can also discuss family planning.

6. John Edgar, Lydia Perry, and June Trayner are established patients who need follow-up appointments with Dr. Lupez.

7. Wayne Harris needs a new patient appointment with Dr. Lawler as early as possible.

8. Lucy Fraser needs an appointment with Dr. Lawler or Dr. Hughes and has to make the appointment after 3:30 p.m., because she picks up her children from school.

9. Asa Nordholm, Carrie Jones, and Seicho Ando need follow-up appointments with Dr. Lawler.

10. Talia Perez called and is having trouble with her new blood pressure medication. The soonest she can get off work and come to the clinic is 2:15 p.m.

11. Paula Nolen needs an allergy shot in the morning.

12. Amy Wainwright needs a well-woman examination and can come to the clinic any time before 3 p.m.

13. Pam Billingsley wants to come to the clinic in the late afternoon for a return check about her migraine headaches.

14. Adam Angsley needs an appointment with Dr. Lawler in the afternoon.

Prepare Appointment Page 3 (see Work Product 10-3 on p. 51 of the Procedures Checklist) according to the following directions. Appointments can be scheduled for subsequent days in these exercises.

1. The date is Wednesday, October 15, 20XX.

2. All of the physicians are in the office today.

3. Lunch is from noon until 2 p.m.

4. Dr. Lawler has three rechecks today, with Ella Jones, Fred Linstra, and Mary Higgins.

5. Winston Hill is an established patient coming in for an annual physical with Dr. Lawler. His neighbor can drive him to the clinic for a 2 p.m. appointment.

6. Elnar Rosen, an established patient, needs a physical with Dr. Hughes at around 10:15 a.m.

7. A staff meeting is scheduled for 9 a.m.

8. A representative from Allied Medical Supply is demonstrating a self-scheduling computer program at 4:30 p.m. for all staff members.

9. Bob Jones needs a morning appointment with Dr. Lupez.

10. Talia Perez is extremely nauseated and needs to return to the clinic today.

11. Robin Tower is a new patient who wants to see Dr. Lawler or Dr. Hughes.

12. Audrey Rhodes is a new patient who wants to see Dr. Lawler.

13. Victor Garner is a follow-up patient whom Dr. Lupez saw last week in the hospital. He is new to the clinic.

14. Charlie Robinson missed his appointment today at 11 a.m. with Dr. Hughes.

15. Peter Blake calls to see if he can be seen by one of the physicians at 11:15 a.m.

Prepare Appointment Page 4 (see Work Product 10-4 on p. 53 of the Procedures Checklist) according to the following directions. Appointments can be scheduled for subsequent days in these exercises.

1. The date is Thursday, October 16, 20XX.

2. Dr. Hughes is not in the office because his daughter is having a baby.

3. Lunch is from noon until 2 p.m.

4. All patients must be seen in the morning because the clinic is closed on Thursday afternoons.

5. Cassie LeGrand is coming to the clinic as a new patient to see Dr. Lupez.

6. Cassandra LeBrock is coming to the clinic as an established patient to see Dr. Lupez.

7. Raymond Smith wants to make an appointment at 1:45 p.m. with Dr. Lawler.

8. Benjamin Charles requests an appointment with Dr. Lupez at 3:45 p.m.

Prepare Appointment Page 5 (see Work Product 10-5 on p. 55 of the Procedures Checklist) according to the following directions.

1. The date is Friday, October 17, 20XX.

2. Dr. Lupez is the only provider in the office today.

3. Lunch is from noon until 2 p.m.

4. Cassie LeGrand returns today for laboratory work and a surgical consult with Dr. Lupez.

5. Bruce Wells is scheduled for a follow-up appointment at 10:15 a.m.

6. Ronald Trayhan calls to make an appointment with Dr. Lupez for 2:30 p.m.

7. Dr. Hughes calls to ask Dr. Lupez to see one of his young patients, Barbara Scott, at 3 p.m. for a high fever.

8. Stanley Allred calls for an appointment to see Dr. Lupez at 3 p.m.

Part V: Types of Scheduling

Briefly describe each type of scheduling, and list one advantage and one disadvantage of each.

1. Scheduled appointments

_____

_____

2. Open office hours

_____

_____

3. Flexible office hours

_____

_____

4. Wave scheduling

_____

_____

5. Modified wave scheduling

_____

_____

6. Double booking

_____

_____

7. Grouping procedures

_____

_____

8. Advance booking

_____

_____

Part VI: Special Circumstances

1. How can the medical assistant deal with patients who are consistently late for appointments?

_____

_____

2. How does the medical assistant handle a patient who arrives at the clinic to see the physician but does not have an appointment?

_____

_____

Part VII: Verifying Appointments

Write a brief script that could be used to verify patient appointments and that does not violate patient privacy.

_____

_____

_____

_____

Part VIII: Scheduling Inpatient and Outpatient Admissions and Procedures
Complete the referral forms in Work Products 10-6 to 10-9 on pages 57-64 of the Procedures Checklist for the following patients. Create fictional demographic information.

1. Cassie LeGrand is to report to Mercy Hospital for excision of a nasal polyp on Tuesday, October 24, 20XX. Dr. Lupez is her attending physician. Surgery is scheduled for Tuesday at 2 p.m. She will need blood work that morning. The procedure is considered outpatient, and Cassie will go home later that day if she does well. ICD code: 471.0 (Work Product 10-6).

2. Bob Jones arrives at Presbyterian Hospital to have a magnetic resonance imaging (MRI) scan on his right knee on Friday, November 2, 20XX. He needs an early morning appointment. ICD code: 715.8 (Work Product 10-7).

3. Lucille Saxton is to be admitted to the hospital for surgery for a bowel obstruction. Her surgery date is June 14, 20XX, and she must be admitted a day in advance for laboratory work and a chest x-ray examination. ICD code: 560.9 (Work Product 10-8).

4. Pam Burton needs to be admitted for several tests because of recurrent irritable bowel syndrome. She will be in the hospital for at least 3 days and should check in on July 23, 20XX, in the afternoon so that she will have taken nothing by mouth (NPO) before the blood tests are performed and x-ray films are taken the following morning. ICD Code: 564.1 (Work Product 10-9).

Read the case study and answer the questions that follow.

Janie Haynes consistently arrives at the clinic 15 to 45 minutes late. She always has a "good" excuse, but she could make her appointments on time if she had better time management skills. The office manager has mentioned to Paula, the receptionist, that Janie is to be scheduled at 4:45 p.m., and if she is late, the physician will not see her. Paula books Janie's next three appointments at that time, and Janie actually arrives early. However, on the fourth appointment, Janie arrives at 5:50 p.m., and Paula knows it is her responsibility to tell Janie she cannot see the physician. How does Paula handle this task? Is more than one option available?

_____

_____

_____

_____

_____

WORKPLACE APPLICATION OPTIONS

Complete one or more of these activities and, if appropriate, share your results with the class.

1. Call the receptionist five clinics. Tell the receptionist that you are studying scheduling in medical assisting school and are interested in the scheduling method that clinic uses. Tally the results each classmate obtains, then graph or chart the results for the class on one document. Discuss the frequency of the various methods of scheduling.

2. Invite a medical assistant who performs scheduling duties to speak to the class. Determine at least two questions to ask the scheduler in advance. Ask the scheduler to share the most difficult issues he or she faces while performing scheduling duties in the physician's office.

INTERNET ACTIVITY OPTIONS

Complete one or more of these activities and, if appropriate, share your results with the class.

1. Research scheduling software on the Internet and select a software package that would be functional for a physician's office. Gather information about the features and benefits and present the information to the class.

2. Research information about the different types of scheduling and how effective they are in physicians' offices. Determine the type of scheduling best suited to a family practice clinic. Present the ideas to the class.

3. Research self-scheduling software and determine the advantages and disadvantages of allowing patients to schedule appointments on the Internet. Present the information to the class or write an informative report about your findings.

4. Research electronic medical record software that includes a scheduling component. Look for user reviews on the various software types and determine which three seem to be the most user friendly. Share the information with the class.

Patient Reception and Processing

VOCABULARY REVIEW

Fill in the blanks with the correct vocabulary terms from this chapter.

1. Dr. Raleigh installed a(n) _____ system so that he could speak to the medical assistants in both the front and the back offices from the examination rooms.

2. Medical assistants must be aware of the _____ patients have of the office staff and take steps to ensure it is a positive one.

3. Susan filed the laboratory reports in _____ order.

4. _____ information includes the patient's address, insurance information, and e-mail address.

5. Any _____ offered to a patient should be within the physician's orders, so make sure a beverage with sugar is not offered to a diabetic.

6. Angela uses _____ devices to help her remember the duties to complete before leaving the office.

7. Employees prefer to work in an office with a(n) _____ environment.

8. Dr. Lawson has a(n) _____ desire to serve his patients and promote wellness.

9. A secondary use of health information that cannot be reasonably prevented is called a(n) _____ _____.

10. Medical assistants may find it helpful to write a patient's name using _____ spelling to remember its pronunciation.

SKILLS AND CONCEPTS

Part I: The Office Mission Statement

Create a mission statement for a fictional family practice.

_____

_____

_____

_____

_____

Part II: The Reception Area

1. Why is the first impression of the physician's office so important to patients?

_____

_____

_____

_____

2. List five items that might be found in the patient reception area.

   a. _____

   b. _____

   c. _____

   d. _____

   e. _____

3. If a computer is provided in the reception area, what cautionary measure should be taken to ensure patient privacy?

_____

_____

_____

_____

4. Describe the ideal receptionist for a physician's office.

_____

_____

_____

_____

Part III: Registration Procedures

List six items of demographic information found on a patient information sheet.

1. _____

2. _____

3. _____

4. _____

5. _____

6. _____

Part IV: Consideration for the Patient's Time

1. Why might a crowded waiting room be a sign of inefficiency rather than the physician's popularity?

   _____

   _____

   _____

2. Delays longer than _____ minutes should be explained to patients, and they should be allowed to reschedule if they want to do so.

3. No more than _____ or _____ patients should be waiting in the reception area at any given time.

4. What feelings do patients often experience when waiting in the physician's office?

   _____

   _____

   _____

Part V: Patient Confidentiality

1. How can the medical assistant help prevent a breach of patient confidentiality by the placement of charts in wall holders?

   _____

   _____

   _____

   _____

2. How can the medical assistant help prevent a breach of patient confidentiality while using sign-in sheets?

   _____

   _____

   _____

   _____

3. Provide two examples of incidental disclosure.

   a. _____

   b. _____

4. Why would some offices limit the number of people who can accompany a patient into the exam room?

   _____

   _____

   _____

5. Should the medical assistant ever discipline a disruptive child in the medical office? Why or why not?

   _____

   _____

   _____

   _____

6. How do glass partitions help keep patient information confidential? Are they useful in today's medical offices? Why or why not?

_____

_____

_____

_____

Part VI: Patient Checkout

Write a verbal response to the following patients in the checkout process.

1. Suzanne Anton is ready to leave the clinic, and she is informed that she owes a co-pay of $25 plus a past due balance of $10 that her insurance did not pay. She questions the $10 balance.

_____

_____

_____

2. Randy Stephens is leaving the clinic but is angry about his visit with the physician, who insists that he lose 40 pounds. He reluctantly pays his co-pay. He needs to schedule a follow-up appointment for 1 month, during which time the physician wants him to have lost 5 pounds by following a strict diet.

_____

_____

_____

3. Alfreda Williams has come to the clinic for a checkup. The physician is treating her for colon cancer, and she usually is cheerful, despite her prognosis. Today she seems distressed and hesitates before paying her bill of $65.

_____

_____

_____

Part VII: The End of the Day

1. Paige is preparing for the next workday. What are some tasks that will help her prepare for tomorrow's patients?

_____

_____

_____

2. List several routine tasks for closing an office.

_____

_____

_____

3. How can the medical assistant gain confidence in asking for payments and co-payments?

_____

_____

_____

Part VIII: Evaluating Reception Areas

Visit several reception areas in physicians' offices, hospitals, or clinics or consider your personal physician's office or one you have recently visited. Take note of the appearance and amenities in these facilities. Rate each reception area on a scale of 1 to 10. Total the figures to determine the "best" reception area.

	Locations				
	#1	#2	#3	#4	#5
Cleanliness					
Color scheme					
Seating					
Lighting					
Comfort					
Amenities					
Noise level					
Total					

1. Which location stood out as having an inviting reception area?

_____

_____

_____

2. What common problems, if any, were noted in more than one reception area?

_____

_____

_____

3. What amenities were noted in the reception areas?

_____

_____

_____

4. What improvements could be made to the lower-scoring reception areas?

_____

_____

_____

Read the case study and answer the question that follows.

Jill is the receptionist for Dr. Boles and Dr. Bailey, who are psychiatrists. Each week Sara Ables comes to her appointments but brings her two small children, Joey and Julie, ages 8 and 6 years, respectively. When Sara goes back for her appointment, the children are almost uncontrollable in the reception area. Although there are never more than two patients waiting, the kids are a serious disruption in the clinic. When Jill mentioned the problem to Dr. Boles, he said that Sara really needed the sessions and that Jill should try to work with Sara on this issue. What can Jill do to remedy the situation?

_____

_____

_____

_____

WORKPLACE APPLICATIONS OPTION

Complete this activity and, if appropriate, share your results with the class.

Design a registration form for a fictional clinic that includes all the information necessary for a new patient. Be creative with logos and fonts. Make the form attractive and easy to understand. Discuss what information is critical to know when processing a new patient.

INTERNET ACTIVITY OPTIONS

Complete one or more of these activities and, if appropriate, share your results with the class.

1. Search for innovations in patient reception on the Internet, including computer software containing features that allow patients to check themselves in for appointments. Present information on one of the systems to the class.

2. Find examples of office mission statements online. Compare them and write a brief report about the contents of the various statements.

3. Research the Americans with Disabilities Act. Determine what accommodations must be made in reception areas to comply with this law. Present the information to the class.

4. Look online for new patient paperwork used in actual physician offices. Download and examine three examples and discuss the functionality of the forms. Look for repetitive information. What changes could be made to the forms to improve them?

12 Office Environment and Daily Operations

VOCABULARY REVIEW

Fill in the blanks with the correct vocabulary terms from this chapter.

1. Julia noticed some _____ in the inventory when comparing last month's totals with the current month's totals.

2. Rhonda prefers that all _____ _____ be initialed by the person who checks in the package.

3. Dr. Hughes is _____ when dealing with conflicts within the office by talking with staff members and looking for ways to compromise.

4. Kayla enjoys developing a(n) _____ for office expenditures each fiscal year.

5. Items on _____ frustrate the office manager because of the follow-up required to make sure the item eventually arrives at the clinic.

6. When Douglas neglected to pay the supply bill by the due date, he _____ late charges and increased the total due by 2%.

7. Elaine, the office manager, reviewed the _____ _____ requirements before the coders left for a seminar in Dallas.

8. By the time Anna finished buying office supplies, she had _____ her money from Dr. Tarago and had to use $25 of her own money to cover the bill.

9. Dr. Tarago received a(n) _____ for speaking at the regional medical society meeting.

10. Physicians are constantly concerned about their _____ when budgeting and planning salary increases.

11. Julia knew that there were _____ circumstances involved with the patient statements being sent late during August.

12. September begins the _____ _____ for the clinic.

13. Dr. Hughes finally agreed to the _____ of his medical transcription.

14. Dr. Tarago gave Kayla a(n) _____ before she left to attend the medical assistants convention.

Part I: Opening the Office

1. List six duties that should be completed before patients start to arrive.

   a. _____

   b. _____

   c. _____

   d. _____

   e. _____

   f. _____

2. What parts of the medical record should be checked to see whether additional forms need to be added before a patient arrives for an office visit?

   _____

   _____

   _____

3. Explain the precautions that should be taken with prescription pads.

   _____

   _____

   _____

4. Why is patient traffic flow an important consideration in the office environment?

   _____

   _____

   _____

Part II: The Office Environment

1. List 10 expenses the physician's office incurs on a month-to-month basis.

   a. _____

   b. _____

   c. _____

   d. _____

   e. _____

   f. _____

   g. _____

   h. _____

   i. _____

   j. _____

2. List six tasks the medical assistant can do between patients or during slower periods.

   a. _____

   b. _____

   c. _____

   d. _____

   e. _____

   f. _____

3. List three things related to the office environment that the medical assistant can do to help the physician save money.

   a. _____

   b. _____

   c. _____

4. Explain why the number of individuals with keys and alarm codes should be limited in the medical office.

   _____

   _____

   _____

Part III: Medical Waste and Regular Waste

Note whether each of the following items should be classified as medical waste or regular waste.

1. Gauze used to stop bleeding after venipuncture

   _____

2. Tissues used in the reception room to clean eyeglasses

   _____

3. Blood tubes containing blood that has already been tested

   _____

4. Used syringes

   _____

5. Paper towels used to clean a mirror in a restroom used by patients

   _____

Part IV: The Office Policy and Procedures Manual

1. Why is the office policy and procedures manual important?

   _____

   _____

   _____

2. List five sections that might be found in an office policy and procedures manual.

a. _____

b. _____

c. _____

d. _____

e. _____

Part V: Equipment Inventory

Complete an inventory of either administrative or clinical equipment at the school using the form in Work Product 12-1. Give the form to the instructor when finished.

Part VI: Supply Inventory

Complete an inventory of either administrative or clinical supplies at the school using the form in Work Product 12-2. Give the form to the instructor when finished.

Part VII: Purchase Orders

Complete two purchase orders using an office supply catalog, newspaper ad, or the Internet. Complete one purchase order for supplies (things that are used up on a routine basis); complete the other for equipment (things that are reusable and usually of value).

Name _____

Date _____

PURCHASE ORDER   No. 1554

Bill to:

Blackburn Primary Care Associates PC
1990 Turquoise Drive
Blackburn, WI 54937

Ship to:

Blackburn Primary Care Associates, PC
1990 Turquoise Drive
Blackburn, WI 54937

Vendor: _____
_____
_____

Terms: _____

ORDER #	DESCRIPTION	QTY.	COLOR	SIZE	UNIT PRICE	TOTAL PRICE
					SUBTOTAL	
					TAX	
					SHIPPING	
					TOTAL	

PURCHASE ORDER

No. 1554

Bill to:

Blackburn Primary Care Associates PC
1990 Turquoise Drive
Blackburn, WI 54937

Ship to:

Blackburn Primary Care Associates, PC
1990 Turquoise Drive
Blackburn, WI 54937

Vendor: _____
_____
_____

Terms: _____

ORDER #	DESCRIPTION	QTY.	COLOR	SIZE	UNIT PRICE	TOTAL PRICE
					SUBTOTAL	
					TAX	
					SHIPPING	
					TOTAL	

Part VIII: Maintenance Logs

Use the form in Work Product 12-3 to compile a log of the administrative equipment in your classroom. Follow the example given on the first line. Give the form to the instructor when you are finished.

Part IX: Travel Expense Reports

Complete a travel expense report using the form in Work Product 12-4. Use the following information on the report.

Last month, the office manager sent Kayla to a workshop about upcoming coding changes. The workshop cost was $450 and was held in Washington, D.C. Her per diem included meal amounts of breakfast $10, lunch $18, and dinner $27. Figure the total for each expense category, the total expenses for the trip, and the amount to be reimbursed to the employee, if any.

Advance

$200 cash

Expenses/Receipts

Two hotel nights at the Regency Inn (May 2 and 3, 2012). Cost: $110 per night. Tax rate: 8.25%
Cab from airport to hotel (May 2, 2012): $22 plus 18% tip.
Cab from hotel to airport (May 4, 2012): $22 plus 18% tip.
Breakfast: Free each day at the hotel buffet

Lunch: Figure all tips at 18%
    May 2—$12.56
    May 3—$16.24
    May 4—$10.54

Dinner: Figure all tips at 18%
    May 2—$18.35
    May 3—$22.34

Phone: Calls to office from hotel room
    May 2—$2.13
    May 3—$3.43

A manual with examples of forms for the medical office was purchased at the seminar for $38. The seminar cost was paid several months in advance.

Part X: Emergency Preparedness

Using the Internet, find at least five agencies in your region that provide emergency preparedness. Present a brief report to the class on each agency and the services it provides.

CASE STUDY

Read the case study and answer the questions that follow.

Dianna had worked at the family clinic for 6 years in the front office. When a new medical assistant, Kiran, was hired to work the phones and schedule appointments, Dianna noticed that she was not following the office policy and caused several problems with the schedule. Some patients were very late in seeing the physician; this was unusual for the office, so complaints were made. Dianna volunteered to work with Kiran to help her schedule according to policy. She noticed that Kiran accessed the Internet and her e-mail frequently, but that did not seem to detract from setting appointments. Kiran promised to perform according to office policy, but after 3 weeks, the problems continued.

1. What should happen in this situation?

   _____

   _____

   _____

2. Why is the scheduler such an important position in the facility?

   _____

   _____

   _____

   _____

   _____

3. How can problems with scheduling affect office overhead?

   _____

   _____

   _____

WORKPLACE APPLICATION OPTIONS

Complete one or more of these activities and, if appropriate, share your results with the class.

1. Set up an interview with an office manager and discuss the cost of running a medical practice from month to month. Discuss the biggest expenses that the physician pays each month. Report what you discover to the class.

2. Discuss emergency preparedness for the medical office and determine with a team of classmates the logical contents of an emergency preparedness plan for a physician's office. Outline a plan and present it to the class.

INTERNET ACTIVITY OPTIONS

Complete one or more of these activities and, if appropriate, share your results with the class.

1. Find three medical suppliers on the Internet and compare their prices for each of the following items. Use local suppliers if information is available online about their products.

Item	Suppliers	Price #1	Price #2	Price #3
1 case of 4 × 4 gauze pads				
1 gallon of isopropyl alcohol				
1 case of table paper				

2. Research medical office layout designs on the Internet and design an office. Include a color scheme and floor plan. Present the design to the class using a computer presentation, poster, or handouts.

3. Research three local medical facilities on the Internet, looking for information such as company reports, financial information, company profiles, news, and current affairs. Write a report on one of the facilities to share with the class.

4. Research information on fire extinguishers, including their operation and the types for different uses. Prepare a report on the findings.

13 Written Communications and Mail Processing

Fill in the blanks with the correct vocabulary terms from this chapter.

1. Roberta has a(n) _____ tone in her voice when she speaks to the office staff, and this has caused friction between her and the employees.

2. Most of the mail the Blackburn Clinic sends is classified as _____ mail, which means it is sent within the boundaries of the United States.

3. Savannah asked Noble to _____ a memo among all of the employees.

4. Dr. Lupez suggested that the clinic sell or donate all of the _____ computer equipment once the new system arrived and was installed.

5. Jaci sometimes gets confused about subject and predicate _____ when she is writing.

6. Mrs. Abernathy reminded the students to make the margins _____ to the left when writing memorandums.

7. Dr. Lawler asked Roberta to order new stationery and specifically requested that the _____ be of a high quality.

8. All of the staff members enjoyed having Alicia as an intern because of her _____ personality with the patients.

9. The physicians considered rearranging the drug sample shelves _____ according to type of drug.

10. Dr. Hughes's _____ remark was out of character, and Suzanne was certain that he was simply stressed over a patient.

11. Ellen forgot to measure the _____ of a package before taking it to the post office to mail.

12. Jacqueline has a talent for writing _____ documents that are easy to understand.

13. Angela was _____ the newsletter yesterday afternoon.

Part I: Correspondence and Envelopes

Label the parts of the letter in the figure below, and write in the number of lines required between each section.

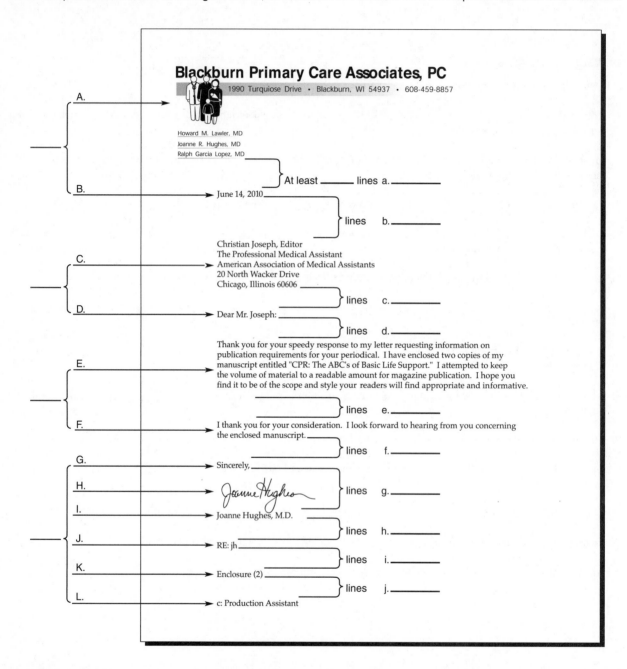

Complete Work Product 13-1 by writing the following addresses correctly according to OCR guidelines on the envelopes provided.

1. doctor john smith m.d. 301 west hughes street chicago illinois 54321

2. cindy johnson, physical therapist 1467 east green street suite 409b bayfield georgia 12345

3. jose kelley memorial lane number 321 west columbia florida 97654

Part II: Short Answers

1. What is a watermark?

   _____

   _____

   _____

2. Why is a portfolio useful in the medical office?

   _____

   _____

   _____

3. Explain how a ream of paper is determined.

   _____

   _____

   _____

4. List several pieces of equipment used for written communications.

   _____

   _____

   _____

5. List some of the supplies used for written correspondence.

   _____

   _____

   _____

6. What is standard letter-size paper?

   _____

   _____

   _____

7. List the four parts of a letter.

   a. _____

   b. _____

   c. _____

   d. _____

8. Name three items that should be on a continuation page.

   a. _____

   b. _____

   c. _____

9. What is the difference between registered and certified mail?

_____

_____

_____

10. Name and briefly define the parts of speech.

a. _____

b. _____

c. _____

d. _____

e. _____

f. _____

g. _____

h. _____

11. List the four types of letter styles and the differences between each one.

a. _____

_____

b. _____

_____

c. _____

_____

d. _____

_____

12. List three things to do before answering a business letter.

a. _____

b. _____

c. _____

Part III: Letters and Memos

Using the letterhead form in Work Products 13-2 and 13-4, the memo form in Work Products 13-3 and 13-5, and the fax form in Work Product 13-6, complete the following activities. Write the documents using one of the four letter styles discussed in the chapter. If allowed by the instructor, use templates for added creativity and customization.

1. Initiating Correspondence—Complete Work Product 13-2.

   Write a letter from Dr. Hughes to the president of the American Medical Association suggesting a topic for the next national convention. In the letter, indicate Dr. Hughes's interest in presenting the topic.

2. Initiating a Memo—Complete Work Product 13-3.

   Write a memo to all employees, making a change in office policy. The new policy should state that the new budget for continuing education per employee will change from $300 annually to $500 annually. Be sure to set an effective date.

94

3. Responding to Correspondence—Complete Work Product 13-4.

   Respond to an invitation to speak at a local Rotary Club meeting on the subject "Health, Wellness, and Eating Well."

4. Responding to a Memo—Complete Work Product 13-5.

   Respond to a memo from a supervisor who wants an update on the progress made toward arranging the drug sample area into categories as directed by the physician. Make sure to include an estimated date of completion for the project.

5. Initiating a Fax—Complete Work Product 13-6.

   Design a cover sheet for a fax message using the form in Work Product 13-6 or a template. On the cover sheet, indicate that test results for a patient are attached. Be certain to address the issue of patient confidentiality.

Part IV: Proofreaders' Marks

Notate the following document with proper proofreaders' marks so that the final version is grammatically correct. Turn in a typed, corrected copy to the instructor. Discuss the marks in class and determine if more than one correction would make the document grammatically correct.

The medical assistent plays a important role in an emergency. All medical assistant must have currant training in cardio-pulmonery resescatation (CPR) & first aide, and they must be to able perform the procedures for which they were trained in capacities both Be willing to help whatever help is needed. Realize that stress compods medical emergency and can complicat other medical problem's. Be awere of the personnel need to step away for a few momants and collect you're thoughts, or just take a few momants to breath in and out slowly Often only a few minues away from the Situation provide a new serge of energy to take back to the job hand. The smallest acts vital are in an emergeancy; even the simple task of taking down names and injeries helps emergency workersprocess pateints faster and get they the care them need. Make it a habet to be a volunter and put to use the valueble medical skills you have learned in class, during the ixternship, and on the job

_____

_____

_____

_____

_____

_____

_____

_____

_____

_____

_____

_____

_____

_____

_____

Read the case study and answer the questions that follow.

Barbara recently graduated as a medical assistant and obtained employment at a local physician's office. She and the office manager have seemed to be at odds since Barbara redesigned several forms that had been in use at the clinic but had been copied over and over again and looked quite unprofessional. Barbara did not ask permission to redo the forms; she was attempting to help and to make a good impression. Since that incident, the office manager has given Barbara two written reprimands for minor issues.

1. What should Barbara do?

   _____

   _____

   _____

2. How could she have prevented this situation from the beginning?

   _____

   _____

   _____

3. Is the office manager at fault?

   _____

   _____

   _____

WORKPLACE APPLICATION OPTION

Complete this activity and, if appropriate, share your results with the class.

Collect several documents from various healthcare facilities. Compare the quality of the documents. Do they make a good first impression? Are they clearly copies that have been made over and over again? Grade the documents and revise those that are graded below a B so that they present a positive, professional image of the facility.

INTERNET ACTIVITY OPTIONS

Complete one or more of these activities and, if appropriate, share your results with the class.

1. Compare the services offered by companies such as FedEx, UPS, DHL, and the USPS. Determine the lowest cost for sending an overnight letter or package.

2. Research reference books that would be valuable to the medical assistant's library. Find and compare costs and make a list of several books that would be useful in the physician's office.

3. Go to the Microsoft Office home page and look for templates. Download several of the business templates and customize them for the Blackburn Primary Care Associates.

4. Research and write protocols for using e-mail in the physician's office.

5. Look up fax disclosure statements and compare the wording. Examine Microsoft Word templates of fax cover sheets and compare the disclosure statements as well as the format and design of the templates. Design a fax cover sheet for a typical physician's office.

6. Search for current postage rates for the following:
   a. First-class letter
   b. 2-pound package
   c. Large mailing envelope, over 12 × 12 inches in size
   d. Certified letter
   e. 8 × 10 envelope sent as Registered Mail, return receipt requested

7. Look for instructions on using the Microsoft Mail Merge feature in Word. Explore the information while in the program and determine the usability of the feature in a physician's office. What tasks might be made easier using this feature?

The Paper Medical Record

VOCABULARY REVIEW

Fill in the blank with the correct vocabulary term from this chapter.

1. Veronica prefers a(n) _____ filing system, in which combinations of letters and numbers are used to identify a file.

2. Julia prefers a(n) _____ filing system, in which the letters of the alphabet are used to identify a file.

3. Paula Ann feels that only a(n) _____ filing system provides patient confidentiality.

4. Dr. Banford uses a(n) _____ file to help him remember that a certain action must be taken on a certain date.

5. Teresa wants to _____ the current software library with programs for making brochures and designing websites.

6. The clinic physician records _____ information when questioning patients about their illnesses.

7. The clinic physician records _____ information when examining the patient.

8. When Mira files documents into medical records, she lays one report on top of another, with the most recent on top; this filing method is called _____.

9. The office manager is particular about the _____ under which documents are filed, because she wants to be able to access information quickly.

10. Dr. Lawler scheduled an appointment with his accountant to discuss the _____ of the office financial records.

11. Georgina avoids _____ by taking care of issues and documents as they are presented to her rather than setting them aside for later.

12. Naomi has a(n) _____ interest in the success of the new hospital, because she owns shares in its stock.

13. The medical assistant must never remove entries in a patient's record by _____.

14. Dr. Lupez's _____ _____ was irritable bowel syndrome, not colon cancer.

15. Jose read the memo about the new medical records _____ schedule with interest, because his job includes filing.

SKILLS AND CONCEPTS

Part I: Filing Medical Records

Place the following names in the correct order for filing in the right column.

1. Cassidy Kay Hale
2. Candace Cassidy LeGrand
3. Taylor Ann Jackson
4. Anton Douglas Conn
5. Mitchel Michael Gibson
6. Lorienda Gaye Robison
7. LaNelle Elva Crumley
8. Allison Gaile Yarbrough
9. Sarah Kay Haile
10. Marie Gracelia Stuart
11. Karry Madge Chapmann
12. Randi Ann Perez
13. Cecelia Gayle Raglan
14. Sarah Sue Ragland
15. Riley Americus Belk
16. Starr Ellen Beall
17. Mitchell Thomas Gibson
18. George Scott Turner
19. Winston Roger Murchison
20. Sara Suzelle Montgomery
21. Tamika Noelle Frazier
22. Alisa Jordan Williams
23. Alisha Dawn Chapman
24. Bentley James Adams
25. Montana Skye Kizer
26. Dakota Marie LaRose
27. Robbie Sue Metzger
28. Thomas Charles Bruin
29. Percevial "Butch" Adams
30. Carlos Perez Santos

1. _____
2. _____
3. _____
4. _____
5. _____
6. _____
7. _____
8. _____
9. _____
10. _____
11. _____
12. _____
13. _____
14. _____
15. _____
16. _____
17. _____
18. _____
19. _____
20. _____
21. _____
22. _____
23. _____
24. _____
25. _____
26. _____
27. _____
28. _____
29. _____
30. _____

100

Chapter **14** The Paper Medical Record

Copyright © 2014 Elsevier, Inc. All rights reserved.

Part II: Subjective and Objective Information

Note whether the following information is usually subjective or objective.

Patient's address _____

Yellowed eyes _____

Patient's e-mail address _____

Insurance information _____

Elevated blood pressure _____

Bloated stomach _____

Complaint of headache _____

Weight of 143 pounds _____

Bruises on upper arms _____

Patient's phone number _____

Part III: Short Answers

1. List four reasons medical records are kept.

    a. _____

    b. _____

    c. _____

    d. _____

2. Explain the concept of the ownership of medical records.

    _____

    _____

    _____

3. Why might color-coded files be more efficient than an alphabetic filing system?

    _____

    _____

    _____

4. What are the two major types of patient records found in a medical office?

    a. _____

    b. _____

5. What type of form should be completed if a patient no longer wants to allow his or her medical records to be released to a person or an organization?

    _____

    _____

    _____

Part IV: Releasing Medical Records

Complete an Authorization to Release Medical Records form using your name as the patient.

```
┌──────────────────────────────────────────────────────────────────┐
│                    RECORDS RELEASE AUTHORIZATION                   │
│                                                                    │
│   TO _____ │
│                            Doctor or Hospital                      │
│                                                                    │
│      _____ │
│                                Address                             │
│   I HEREBY AUTHORIZE AND REQUEST YOU TO RELEASE TO:                │
│                                                                    │
│                                                                    │
│                                                                    │
│   ALL RECORDS IN YOUR POSSESION CONCERNING _____ │
│                                                                    │
│   _____ ILLNESS AND/OR  │
│                                                                    │
│   TREATMENT DURING THE PERIOD FROM _____ TO _____.  │
│                                                                    │
│   NAME _____ TEL. _____  │
│                                                                    │
│   ADDRESS_____  │
│                                                                    │
│   SIGNATURE _____ DATE _____  │
│                   (If relative, state relationship)                │
│   WITNESS_____ DATE _____   │
│                                                                    │
│         25-8104 © 1973 BIBBERO SYSTEMS, INC., PETALUMA,, CA.       │
└──────────────────────────────────────────────────────────────────┘
```

Part V: Charting, Changing, and Correcting Medical Records

Correct the following medical record entries as noted, as it would be done on a medical chart. Then rewrite the entry correctly on the line provided.

1. The correct date of this appointment was October 12, 20XX. Chart the correction.

   10-21-20XX   Patient did not arrive for scheduled appointment. *P. Smith, RMA*

   _____

2. The patient stated that the chest pain began 2 weeks ago. Chart the correction.

   1-31-20XX   Patient complained of chest pain for the last 2 months. No pain noted in arms. No nausea. Desires an electrocardiogram (ECG) and blood work to check for heart problems. *R. Smithee, CMA (AAMA)*

   _____

   _____

   _____

3. The correct date for the last refill was 3-20-20XX. Chart the correction and follow-up actions.

   4-22-20XX   Patient requested that Rx for Vicodin be refilled. Last refill was 4-20-20XX. Dr. Lawton refused refill and requested patient schedule follow-up appointment. *S. Ragland, RMA*

   _____

   _____

   _____

4. What additional follow-up might be needed in this situation?

   _____

   _____

   _____

5. Mr. Eric Robertson canceled his surgical follow-up appointment today for the third time. Chart this information.

   _____

   _____

   _____

6. Angela Adams called to report that she was not feeling any better since her office visit on Monday. She wants the doctor to call in a refill for her antibiotics. The chart says that she was to return to the clinic on Thursday if she was not feeling better. Today is Monday, and she says she cannot come to the clinic this week. The physician wants to see her before prescribing any other medications. Chart this information.

   _____

   _____

   _____

7. Mary Elizabeth Smith called the physician's office to report redness around an injection site. She was in the office 3 hours ago and received an injection of penicillin. She says she also is itching quite a bit around the site and is having trouble breathing. The doctor has left the office for the day. Office policy states that if the physician is out of the office and a patient presents or calls with an emergency, he or she is to be referred to the emergency department. Chart the action that the medical assistant should take.

   _____

   _____

   _____

8. Suzanne Melville presents to the office complaining of pain in her lower back, extending down her leg, both on the right side of her body. She states that she has a history of kidney stones and this pain feels similar to the previous incidents. She requests pain medicine and asks if she should go to the hospital for an ultrasound. When the physician comes in to see Suzanne, she tells him that the pain is not similar to the previous pain that she had with kidney stones. The medical assistant misunderstood the patient regarding the pain, and the correct information needs to be charted.

   _____

   _____

   _____

Chapter **14** The Paper Medical Record

9. Erica Dunlap comes to the clinic as a new patient and brings copies of her medical records from her previous physician. She has a history of hypertension, migraine headaches, and now complains of pelvic pain. She arrives for a pelvic exam and wants to discuss a hysterectomy with the doctor. The previous physician was listed in the medical record as Dr. George Smithee, but on a later appointment, Ms. Dunlap mentions that the doctor's name was Jorge Smyth, not Smithee.

_____

_____

_____

10. Bob Filmore calls to alert the office that he needs a refill of his thyroid medication, and he speaks to Susan, one of the medical assistants. He states that the medication is Armour Thyroid 60 mg daily. When the authorization fax comes in from the pharmacy, it indicates that Bob had been taking 120 mg—two of the 60-mg tablets each day. Susan calls Bob and clarifies that he is taking the correct dosage, calls in the refill after the physician authorizes it, then charts all of the information in his medical record.

_____

_____

_____

11. Alisha brings her son, Collin, to the clinic with a fever. Collin is a twin, and his brother's medical record is filed right next to his. The medical assistant, Anne, pulls Collin's brother's record by mistake and uses it to chart all of the information regarding the office visit. When Alisha calls the next day to report that Collin is not better, Anne pulls Collin's file and realizes that she and the physician wrote in the wrong chart the day before. She pulls both charts to make the necessary corrections.

_____

_____

_____

Part VI: Filing Procedures

List and explain the five basic filing steps.

1. _____

_____

_____

2. _____

_____

_____

3. _____

_____

_____

4. _____

_____

_____

5. _____

_____

_____

Read the information that follows and answer the questions.

The Blackburn Clinic is considering the purchase of new filing equipment. The clinic currently uses an open-shelf method, with the patient's names in alphabetic order, but would like to change to an alphanumeric system.

1. What must the staff at the clinic consider before making this change?

   _____

   _____

   _____

2. How would the office implement this change so that it causes the least disruption to the patients and staff?

   _____

   _____

   _____

WORKPLACE APPLICATION OPTION

Complete this activity and, if appropriate, share your results with the class.

Visit three medical offices and determine the type of filing system each uses. Ask the receptionist about the pros and cons of each system. Share this information with the class.

INTERNET ACTIVITY OPTIONS

Complete this activity and, if appropriate, share your results with the class.

1. Research paper-based filing systems on the Internet and determine which system you would choose for a medical office. Cite three reasons for your choice.

2. Look for special paper-based, color-coding systems on the Internet. How might these be used in a physician's office?

3. Look for filing tips on the Internet. Which of these tips might help you file faster and more efficiently in the medical office?

15 The Electronic Medical Record

VOCABULARY REVIEW

Fill in the blanks with the correct vocabulary terms from this chapter.

1. Jennifer explained that a(n) _____ of electronic health information usually included documents from two or more different health facilities.

2. The electronic record that originates from one facility is called the electronic _____ record.

3. The electronic record that originates from more than one facility is called the electronic _____ record.

4. Behavior that is generally or widely accepted is called _____.

5. A system that is capable of interacting with another system is said to be _____.

6. A(n) _____-based medical record is used in combination with a paper-based record to optimize patient care.

7. Medical _____ refers to the study of medical computing.

8. The values of which determine characteristics or behavior are its _____.

9. Circumstances that would make it unreasonable for the covered entity to comply with administrative simplification is called reasonable _____.

10. Reasonable _____ is the business care and prudence expected from a person seeking to satisfy a legal requirement.

11. A conscious, intentional failure or reckless indifference to an obligation is called _____.

12. Meriting condemnation, responsibility, or blame for an act is called _____.

13. A process of electronic data entry of medical practitioner or provider instructions is called _____.

14. A special account on a computer that is used for system administration is called the _____ account.

Part I: Electronic Medical Records

1. List three of the five requirements listed in President George W. Bush's order establishing the goal of having electronic medical records (EMRs) for most Americans by 2014.

   a. _____

   _____

   b. _____

   _____

   c. _____

   _____

2. List five advantages of the EMR system.

   a. _____

   _____

   b. _____

   _____

   c. _____

   _____

   d. _____

   _____

   e. _____

   _____

3. List five disadvantages of the EMR system.

   a. _____

   _____

   b. _____

   _____

   c. _____

   _____

   d. _____

   _____

   e. _____

   _____

Part II: American Recovery and Reinvestment Act and HITECH Act

1. By what other name is the American Recovery and Reinvestment Act known?

   _____

2. What does HITECH stand for?

   _____

3. Define meaningful use.

   _____

4. To comply with meaningful use statutes, providers must show that they are using EMR technology in two measurable

   ways, including _____ and _____.

5. Define and explain e-prescribing.

   _____

   _____

   _____

6. Explain the contents of Subtitle D of the HITECH Act.

   _____

   _____

   _____

7. Define the following terms:

   a. Reasonable cause

   _____

   _____

   _____

   b. Reasonable diligence

   _____

   _____

   _____

   c. Willful neglect

   _____

   _____

   _____

Part III: EMR Capabilities

1. What is the approximate cost of implementing an EMR system for a physician's office with five physicians?

   _____

2. Briefly describe three capabilities of an EMR system. Why do you think each capability will enhance patient care?

   a. _____

   _____

   b. _____

   _____

   c. _____

   _____

Part IV: The Patient and the EMR

Discuss how you would talk with a patient who has expressed legitimate fears about having health information in electronic form. Explain what you would say to the patient and how you would reassure the individual.

_____

_____

_____

_____

_____

_____

_____

_____

Part V: Nonverbal Communication and the EMR

List several things to remember when in the exam room with the patient and the electronic device that houses the EMR system. Specifically, what should you, as the medical assistant, do to put the patient at ease?

_____

_____

_____

_____

_____

_____

_____

_____

Part VI: Nationwide Health Information Network (NHIN)

1. Briefly explain the purpose of the Nationwide Health Information Network.

   _____

   _____

   _____

   _____

2. List two goals of the Nationwide Health Information Network.

   a. _____

   _____

   b. _____

   _____

3. What are some of the governmental agencies you think will be a part of the effort to meet the goals of the Executive Order of 2006?

   _____

   _____

   _____

   _____

   _____

   _____

   _____

Part VII: Backup Systems for the EMR

List three backup systems for an EMR system in a physician's office.

   a. _____

   _____

   b. _____

   _____

   c. _____

   _____

CASE STUDY

Read the information that follows and answer the questions.

Dr. Adkins and Dr. Brooks want to expand their office to make sure they can take advantage of cutting-edge technology. Their goal is to use electronic equipment to perform as much of the work as possible so that all staff members can keep caring for the patients in the forefront of their minds. Dr. Adkins is fairly satisfied with the system the clinic has now. However, Dr. Brooks, a "technology geek," wants the newest, greatest, and best electronics in his clinic. The office manager gives Sloan the opportunity to research electronic medical records systems to determine which are considered the best of the best.

Research what is available in your local and regional areas, make a brief report about the availabilities, and present it to the class.

1. What new possibilities did you discover in your research?

   _____

   _____

   _____

   _____

2. Why do you think many physicians are slow to adopt new technology?

   _____

   _____

   _____

   _____

3. As a medical assistant, what type of technology would make your duties easier?

   _____

   _____

   _____

   _____

   _____

WORKPLACE APPLICATION OPTIONS

Complete this activity and, if appropriate, share your results with the class.

Determine whether a local physician's office that uses an EMR system would allow the class to visit, perhaps on an afternoon when patients are not in the clinic. Take a list of at least five questions about using an EMR system. Observe how the system works and watch to see if the employees seem to have more or less of a workload. Watch the interaction of the employees with each other and ask whether they think the system is more of a help or a hindrance as they go about their duties.

INTERNET ACTIVITY OPTIONS

Complete one or more of these activities and, if appropriate, share your results with the class.

1. Research the cost of an EMR system on the Internet. Find a low-, moderate-, and high-cost system. Compare the features of each and share your information with the class.

2. Find a company that sells EMR systems. Ask a salesperson to present information to your class. Ask whether he or she can demonstrate the capabilities of the system.

3. Search for blogs used by medical assistants and look for those who have EMR systems in their clinics. What types of problems do they discuss? Are they promoting any specific systems that seem to work well?

4. Research the possible amounts of payments that physicians might expect to receive when they comply with the requirements of the HITECH Act and meet the required objectives. Share your research with the class.

16 Health Information Management

VOCABULARY REVIEW

Fill in the blanks with the correct vocabulary terms from this chapter.

1. Dr. Charles received a memo from Smith-Park Hospital that reminded him to _____ several of the medical records.

2. Janie records any _____ _____ that happens to a patient while he or she is in the hospital.

3. Chris asked if there was a way to _____ outgoing e-mail messages so that they could not be altered before reaching their destination.

4. Anne knows that medical facilities must meet certain _____ to maintain accreditation.

5. After reviewing several hundred files, Alex was concerned about the _____ information in several patient records.

6. Betty reminded Joanne to be careful not to _____ numbers or letters when entering information into the computer.

7. The _____ _____ office in a healthcare facility is concerned with providing the best and most efficient care possible to the patients.

8. Dr. Hughes knew that penicillin was a(n) _____ for Kathleen Schultz, so he ordered a different antibiotic.

9. The new user manual has several _____, which must be corrected.

10. The medical assistant should never attempt to _____ the regulations that apply to medical records.

11. An injury caused by medical management rather than the underlying condition of the patient is called a(n) _____ event.

12. A(n) _____ _____ is a medical error that is corrected before it affects the patient.

SKILLS AND CONCEPTS

Part I: Short Answers

1. Define health information management in lay terms.

    _____

    _____

    _____

2. List five ways in which healthcare data are used.

    a. _____

    b. _____

    c. _____

d. _____

e. _____

3. Explain what is meant by the underuse of medical services.

_____

_____

_____

4. Explain what is meant by the overuse of medical services.

_____

_____

_____

5. List five of the statistics collected by the National Center for Health Statistics (NCHS).

a. _____

b. _____

c. _____

d. _____

e. _____

Part II: Characteristics of High-Quality Health Data

Determine which of the nine characteristics of high-quality health data is involved in the following scenarios. Use each quality only once, and choose the one that best represents the facts presented in the scenario.

1. Janeen is concerned because the computer system did not upload the entries made the previous day.

_____

2. Suzanne found a notation inside the medical record that a patient was allergic to sulfa drugs, but she noticed that the sticker on the outside of the record was marked NKA.

_____

3. Sabrina brought a chart to the physician's attention in which he had written to prescribe 200 mg of Imitrex to a patient. Sabrina had heard the physician tell the patient that he was prescribing 100 mg. The physician corrected the error before writing the prescription.

_____

4. Steven was unfamiliar with an abbreviation used in the medical record. He asked the office manager about the abbreviation, and she explained its use in the physician's office. In previous facilities, Steve had seen the same abbreviation used a different way.

_____

5. After an employee was terminated, Chris changed applicable passwords so that the individual could no longer access the system.

_____

6. Patricia researched the Health Insurance Portability and Accountability Act (HIPAA) website to make certain she understood a portion of the privacy law.

_____

7. The new patient database allows several staff members to access data at the same time.

_____

8. Joshua was reprimanded for not filing laboratory reports on a daily basis and for allowing the documents to stack up over several days.

_____

9. Dr. Adams realized that some information entered into the patient database was not being used for treatment purposes, so he sent a memo to the staff and confirmed that the information no longer needed to be collected.

_____

Part III: Acknowledging and Disclosing Medical Errors

Number the following events in the order they would be performed in the event of a medical error at the physician's office.

_____ Offer a sincere apology when talking to the patient.

_____ Call the patient and ask him or her to come to the office.

_____ Give the patient the opportunity to ask questions.

_____ Tell the physician about the error.

_____ Complete an incident report and document the error in the chart.

_____ Document the discussion of the error with the patient.

_____ Meet with the patient in a private area where there will be no interruptions.

_____ Allow the physician to explain the error to the patient.

Part IV: Medical Errors

1. Define an adverse event.

_____

_____

2. Define a sentinel event.

_____

_____

3. Define a near miss.

_____

_____

4. List five reasons a physician might be hesitant to disclose a medical error to the patient.

a. _____

b. _____

c. _____

d. _____

e. _____

5. Who should be told about an error first?

_____

115

Part V: Incident Reports

A medical assistant gives an injection of penicillin to a patient who reported an allergy to amoxicillin. The patient complains of itching and experiences shortness of breath and wheezing while sitting in the treatment room. The physician gives the patient epinephrine and observes him for 30 minutes, during which time the itching, shortness of breath, and wheezing fully resolve. Complete an incident report for this sentinel event.

Incident Report
Do Not File in Medical Records

Confidential and privileged health care quality improvement information prepared in anticipation of litigation

Name: _____ Employee ☐ Patient ☐ Visitor ☐

Attending physician: _____
MR # _____ SS # _____
D.O.B. __/__/__   Sex: M[ ] F[ ]
Admission date: __/__/__
Primary diagnosis: _____

Facility name: _____
_____
Site (if applicable) _____
City _____
Facility ID# _____
State _____
Phone # _____

SECTION I: General Information

General Identification (circle one):
- 001 Inpatient
- 002 Outpatient
- 003 Nonpatient
- 004 Equipment only

Location (circle one):
- 005 Bathroom/toilet
- 006 Beauty shop
- 007 Cafeteria/dining room
- 008 Corridor/hall
- 009 During transport
- 010 Emergency department
- 011 Exterior grounds
- 012 ICU/SCU/CCU
- 013 Labor/delivery/birthing
- 014 Nursery
- 015 Outpatient clinic
- 016 Patient room
- 017 Radiology
- 018 Recovery room
- 019 Recreation area
- 020 Rehab
- 021 Shower room
- 022 Surgical suite
- 023 Treatment/exam room

Treatment Rendered (circle one):
- 024 Emergency room
- 025 First aid
- 026 None
- 027 Transfer to other facility
- 027 X-ray

SECTION II: Nature of Incident (Circle all that apply):

- 001 Adverse outcome after surgery or anesthetic
- 002 Anaphylactic shock
- 003 Anoxic event
- 004 Apgar score of 5 or less
- 005 Aspiration
- 006 Assault or altercation/combative event
- 007 Blood or IV variance
- 008 Blood/body fluid exposure
- 009 Code/arrest
- 010 Damage/loss of organ
- 011 Death
- 012 Dental-related complication
- 013 Dissatisfaction/noncompliance*
- 014 Equipment operation*
- 015 Fall with injury*
- 016 Fall without injury*
- 017 Handling of and/or exposure to hazardous waste
- 018 Informed consent issue
- 019 Injury to other
- 020 Injury to self
- 021 Loss of limb
- 022 Loss of vision
- 023 Medication variance*
- 024 Needle puncture/sharp injury
- 025 Paralysis
- 026 Patient-to-patient altercation
- 027 Perinatal complication*
- 028 Poisoning
- 029 Suspected nonstaff-to-patient abuse
- 030 Suspected staff-to-patient abuse
- 031 Thermal burn
- 032 Treatment/procedure issue
- 033 Ulcer: nosocomial stage III/IV

* Complete appropriate area in Section III

SECTION III: Type of Incident

If death, circle all that apply:
- 001 After medical equipment failure
- 002 After power equipment failure or damage
- 003 During surgery or postanesthesia
- 004 Within 24 hours of admission to facility
- 005 Within 1 week of fall in facility
- 006 Within 24 hours of medication error

Blood/IV Variance Issues (circle all that apply):
- 007 Additive
- 008 Administration consent
- 009 Contraindications/allergies
- 010 Equipment malfunction
- 011 Infusion rate
- 012 Labeling issue
- 013 Reaction
- 014 Solution/blood type
- 015 Transcription
- 016 Patient identification
- 017 Allergic/adverse reaction
- 018 Infiltration
- 019 Phlebitis

Dissatisfaction/Noncompliance (circle all that apply):
- 020 AMA
- 021 Elopement
- 022 Irate or angry (either family or patient)
- 023 Left without service
- 024 Noncompliant patient
- 025 Refused prescribed treatment

Falls (circle all that apply):*
- 001 Assisted fall
- 002 Found on floor
- 003 From bed
- 004 From chair
- 005 From commode/toilet
- 006 From exam table
- 007 From stretcher
- 008 From wheelchair
- 009 Patient states—unwitnessed
- 010 Unassisted fall
- 011 While ambulating
- 012 Witnessed fall

* For any marks in this field, Section V must be completed

Medication Variance Issues (circle all that apply):
- 013 Contraindication/allergies
- 014 Delay in dispensing
- 015 Incorrect dose
- 016 Expired drug
- 017 Medication identification
- 018 Narcotic log variance
- 019 Not ordered
- 020 Ordered, not given
- 021 Patient identification
- 022 Reaction
- 023 Route
- 024 Rx incorrectly dispensed
- 025 Time of dose
- 026 Transcription

Part VI: Confidentiality Statement

Evaluate the following confidentiality statement for Diamonte Hospital. Revise the statement to make it appropriate for a medical practice setting. Use proofreader marks to indicate your proposed changes in the confidentiality statement. Rewrite the completed, revised statement on the letterhead form on the next page.

DIAMONTE HOSPITAL

Diamonte, Arizona 89104 • TEL. 602-484-9991

CONFIDENTIALITY STATEMENT

I, _____ , understand that in the course of my activities/business at or for Diamonte Hospital, I am required to have access to and am involved in the viewing, reviewing, and/or processing of patient care data and/or health information.

I understand that I am obligated by State Law, Federal Law, and Diamonte Hospital to maintain the confidentiality of these data and information at all times.

I understand that a violation of these confidentiality considerations may result in punitive legal action against me.

I certify by my signature below that this Confidentiality Statement has been explained to me, and I agree to the principles contained herein as a condition of my activity/business at or for Diamonte Hospital.

_____
Signature/date

_____
Witness/date

Blackburn Primary Care Associates
1990 Turquoise Drive
Blackburn, WI 54937
(555) 555-1234

Read the case study and answer the questions that follow.

Alberto discovered that three people accessed the medical records of a player on the local professional football team who had been brought to the physician's office for follow-up on injuries sustained in a car accident. He realizes that the information accessed involved the results of the player's blood alcohol level.

1. What should Alberto do?

   _____

   _____

   _____

2. What type of penalty, if any, is appropriate for those who accessed the information?

   _____

   _____

   _____

WORKPLACE APPLICATION OPTION

Complete this activity and, if appropriate, share your results with the class.

Determine how total quality management ideas can be worked into the mission statement for a physician's office. Write a mission statement that stresses quality management. How does quality management affect patients in a medical office?

INTERNET ACTIVITY OPTIONS

Complete one or more of these activities and, if appropriate, share your results with the class.

1. Explore the NCHS website. Investigate one of the issues in the Vital Statistics area. Use information found there to write a report about any area of interest and present it to the class.

2. Explore the Joint Commission (formerly JCAHO) website. Peruse the sections of the site that refer to standards, patient safety, and sentinel events. Choose a fact and write a brief report.

3. Research total quality management on the Internet and write a two-page report on how quality management can improve efficiency in a physician's office.

4. Research websites that patients might use to "self-diagnose." Which of the websites found would likely be considered the five best and most reliable? Discuss search results with the class and talk about how the profession might judge and classify "reliable" medical websites. Discuss whether physicians, nurses, and medical assistants might differ on their perceptions of reliable medical websites for patient reference.

5. Obtain a copy of an issue of the Federal Register that contains information on health-related issues. Discuss the issue presented. Determine whether the class as a whole agrees or disagrees with the government regulations put forth in the article or the regulations presented therein.

Privacy in the Physician's Office

VOCABULARY REVIEW

Fill in the blanks with the correct vocabulary terms from this chapter.

1. Dr. Lawton is considered a healthcare _____, because he provides services and treatments to patients.

2. The _____ against Dr. Rosales was one of his former patients, Risa Jackson, who believed that his staff had violated her privacy.

3. Byron knows that he is not allowed to _____ any information about a patient without a release from the patient for that information.

4. Sarah could _____ from what the patient said that he was nervous about his upcoming surgery.

5. STAT Medical Billing provides services to the Blackburn Clinic, so the company is considered a(n)

   _____ _____.

6. Julia has difficulty understanding the _____ in which many federal documents and regulations are written.

7. Janease knew that she could _____ two employees from guilt, because they were both at lunch when the incident happened.

8. The _____ on the privacy statement was hard for a layperson to understand, so Annette decided to rewrite the document.

9. Roberta was assigned to be the temporary _____ _____ at the clinic while Maritza was on maternity leave.

10. The Office of _____ _____ investigates breaches of laws that pertain to HHS.

11. The Office of _____ _____ enforces privacy standards.

12. Dr. Hughes had to prove _____ _____ in that he made every attempt to notify the patient before mailing test results to her home.

13. The _____ _____ _____ _____ in a patient's record is private and must not be shared without a release from the patient.

14. Health information that is transmitted in electronic form is called _____ _____

   _____.

15. The patient's information that pertains to his or her health is called _____ _____

   _____.

16. The moving of funds from one account to another without the use of paper documents is called _____ _____.

17. An explanation that accompanies checks and relays details of payment is called a(n)

_____.

SKILLS AND CONCEPTS

Part I: The Health Insurance Portability and Accountability Act

1. List six benefits provided by the Health Insurance Portability and Accountability Act (HIPAA) Privacy Rule to patients or providers.

   a. _____

   b. _____

   c. _____

   d. _____

   e. _____

   f. _____

2. Briefly explain the Title I provision of HIPAA.

   _____

   _____

3. Briefly explain the Title II provision of HIPAA.

   _____

   _____

4. List six rights HIPAA gives to patients.

   a. _____

   b. _____

   c. _____

   d. _____

   e. _____

   f. _____

5. List six items of information a Notice of Privacy Policies must include.

   a. _____

   b. _____

   c. _____

   d. _____

   e. _____

   f. _____

Part II: Patients' Rights under HIPAA

Determine which right under HIPAA applies to each of the following scenarios. Use each right only once.

1. Susan Enlow discovered that her date of birth was incorrect when she requested her medical records from the Blackburn Clinic. She was moving to another city and wanted to take the records with her to her new provider. Susan surmised that the error might have been the reason her insurance company rejected several claims. She contacted the Blackburn Clinic in writing and asked them to correct the error and then to determine whether any claims were outstanding that might need to be resubmitted to her insurance carrier.

   Right to _____

2. Keiran requested that the clinic send a copy of his most recent physical examination and laboratory results to Dr. Ballard, who was seeing him about a long-standing problem with his knees.

   Right to _____

3. Louie requested that all communication from the physician's office be sent to his office address, because he was in the midst of a tense divorce.

   Right to _____

4. The Blackburn Clinic gives a copy of its Notice of Privacy Policy to all patients and makes sure a signature is obtained or a note is attached to prove that the patient was offered the policy.

   Right to _____

5. A few days after seeing Dr. Reynolds, Rita received an e-mail from a company that offered multivitamins. Dr. Reynolds had suggested that she begin taking multivitamins and mentioned that a friend sold a vitamin drink that she might be interested in trying. Rita did not give permission for release of her e-mail address at the visit. She called the clinic and asked whether her e-mail address had been distributed to anyone outside the clinic.

   Right to _____

6. Suyen made a written request to the Blackburn Clinic that no information about her treatment for drug dependency be released to anyone without her specific written permission.

   Right to _____

Part III: Incidental Disclosures

Determine which of the following situations could be classified as an incidental disclosure.

Situation	Incidental Disclosure	
	Yes	No
1. Ms. Allen, a patient waiting in the radiology department of a large clinic, over-hears Dr. Smith mention that another patient has been diagnosed with testicular cancer, but she does not hear the patient's name during the discussion.		
2. Bob Mitchell, a patient at Mercy Hospital, overhears a physician telling his roommate that he needs surgery for carpal tunnel syndrome.		
3. As Zaria passes the nurses' station at a local hospital, she hears the nurses talking about the patient in room 2114. They mention that he has been diagnosed with terminal cancer. Zaria knows the patient's family and hears that they have not been given the diagnosis yet.		
4. Paula Stanley signs in at the front desk of the medical clinic and notices that her college professor signed in to see the physician 30 minutes ago.		

Part IV: Notice of Privacy Practices

Read the Notice of Privacy Practices in Figure 17-1 of the textbook. Based on the information in that policy, answer the following questions.

1. Can the patient obtain a copy of his or her medical record?

   ❏ Yes   ❏ No

2. Can the patient request that certain information in his or her medical record not be released to certain persons or organizations?

   ❏ Yes   ❏ No

3. Can the patient have a copy of the Notice of Privacy Practices?

   ❏ Yes   ❏ No

4. Can the clinic use the information in the patient's medical record to compile statistics about certain diseases treated by the practice without additional permission from the patient?

   ❏ Yes   ❏ No

5. Does the clinic have to honor all requests from the patient regarding the release of his or her protected health information?

   ❏ Yes   ❏ No

Part V: Privacy in the Physician's Office

1. How does an electronic fund transfer (EFT) increase patient privacy in the physician's office?

   _____

   _____

2. When did EFT requirements go into effect?

   _____

   _____

3. On what date must HIPAA-covered entities be compliant with EFT regulations?

   _____

   _____

4. What HIPAA regulation is the first to regulate business associates?

   _____

   _____

5. What must pharmacies, health plans, and other covered entities do before sending out marketing materials?

   _____

   _____

Read the case study and answer the questions that follow.

Morgan was given a copy of the Privacy Law and told to write the Notice of Privacy Practices for their clinic. After she began reading the law, she became somewhat discouraged because of the legalese and the slow pace at which she had to read to make sure she comprehended the message and requirements. She decided to attend a private training seminar on HIPAA compliance and found the instructor to be very knowledgeable.

1. How can such seminars be beneficial to the practice?

   _____

   _____

   _____

2. How can the medical assistant determine whether a seminar is worth attending?

   _____

   _____

   _____

3. Research seminars in your area and request information about them. Compare data with the information collected by the rest of the class.

WORKPLACE APPLICATION OPTION

Complete this activity and, if appropriate, share your results with the class.

Determine what certifications are available that relate to HIPAA. What are the requirements for obtaining these special certifications? Why might these be beneficial for the medical assistant? Is there a particular certification you are interested in obtaining?

INTERNET ACTIVITY OPTIONS

Complete one or more of these activities and, if appropriate, share your results with the class.

1. Research the HIPAA website and find information about complaints. Then write an office policy for patients that details how to make a complaint if the patient thinks his or her privacy has been violated.

2. Find the exact Public Law number that details the Health Insurance Portability and Accountability Act.

3. Conduct a search for the Office of the Inspector General, and look for the forms that are used to report violations of privacy or confidentiality. Download a copy of the form and discuss it with the class.

4. Find five additional links, other than the HIPAA website, that provide useful, reliable information on HIPAA compliance.

5. Determine misleading marketing ploys that sometimes are used to promote HIPAA training.

6. Research programs that provide a specialized certificate in HIPAA proficiency or privacy/security.

7. Find several Notices of Privacy Practices on the Internet. Print them and take them to class. Discuss the similarities and differences in the forms. Talk about the verbiage that should be used with the patient to explain the reason for the form, and discuss questions and concerns that the patient may have. Look up "Health Information Privacy" at www.hhs.gov for more information about Privacy Practices Notices.

18 Basics of Diagnostic Coding

VOCABULARY REVIEW

Fill in the blanks with the correct vocabulary terms from this chapter.

1. In medical coding, assessment and diagnostic statement are synonymous with _____.

2. _____ is any contact between a patient and a provider of service.

3. The _____ is the physician's determination of what is, or may be, wrong with the patient based on the findings from the H&P.

4. The abbreviation "CC" is a statement in the patient's own words that describes why he or she is seeking medical attention. The letters "CC" stand for _____.

5. _____ refers to the signs and symptoms of a disease.

6. The _____ lists conditions, injuries, and diseases in alphabetical order by main, modifying, and subterms.

7. Services that support patient diagnoses (e.g., laboratory or radiology services) are known as

   _____.

8. In the context of ICD-9-CM, the word *and* should always be interpreted as _____.

   a. and

   b. and/or

   c. or

9. _____ are broad sections of the ICD-9-CM coding manual grouped by disease or illness.

10. _____ is used when one or more code is necessary to identify a given condition.

11. Converting verbal or written descriptions into numeric and alphanumeric designations is called _____.

12. _____ refers to the abbreviations, punctuation, symbols, instructional notations, and related entities that help the medical assistant or coder select an accurate and specific code.

13. The determination of the nature of a disease, injury, or congenital defect is a(n) _____.

14. The _____ is the information about the diagnosis or diagnoses of the patient that has been extracted from the medical documentation.

15. The cause of the disorder; a claim may be classified according to _____.

16. _____ terms are always written in italics, and the word _____ is often enclosed in a box to draw particular attention to these instructions.

17. H&P or HPE is an acronym for _____.

18. _____ is the current system for classifying disease to facilitate the collection of uniform and comparable health information for statistical purposes and indexing medical records for data storage and retrieval.

19. _____ is the initial identification of the condition or complaint that the patient expresses in the outpatient medical setting.

20. The term _____ must always be followed and is found in the Alphabetic Index, Volumes 2 and 3—it is a direction given to a coder to look in another place.

21. _____ is a direction given to the coder to look elsewhere if the main term or subterm (or subterms) for that entry are not sufficient for coding the information.

22. _____ is a direction given to the coder to see a specific category (three-digit code). This must always be followed.

23. The SOAP notes system of charting includes the following four things:

    a. _____

    b. _____

    c. _____

    d. _____

24. The term _____ is at the etiology code when the underlying condition is sequenced first followed by the manifestation.

25. In the context of ICD-9-CM, the terms _____, _____, and _____ in a title dictate that both parts of the title must be present in the statement of the diagnosis order to assign the particular code.

SKILLS AND CONCEPTS

Part I: Getting to Know ICD-9 Coding

1. There are several pertinent reasons for the use of ICD-9-CM codes. Choose those from the following list that do NOT apply.

   a. Standardizing a system of diagnostic coding accepted and understood by all parties in the reimbursement cycle

   b. Creating a more convenient method of data storage and retrieval

   c. Assisting in the maximization of reimbursement

   d. Lengthening the claims-processing time

   e. Facilitating and measuring regulatory compliance by use of guidelines and other instructions

   f. Assisting in measuring the appropriateness and timeliness of medical care

2. Fill in the blanks in the following paragraph.

   The ICD-9-CM code is located in Volume 1, the Tabular Index, of the ICD-9-CM coding manual. The code consists of a(n) _____ category code that represents a specific disease, illness, condition, or injury, within a general disease category. For example, 250 is the disease classification, or category, for diabetes mellitus. Up to _____ additional digits must be used, which add further definition and specificity. These additional digits are the fourth digit, or _____, and the fifth digit, or _____, respectively.

3. The basic ICD-9-CM manual contains three volumes. Fill in the blanks regarding these three volumes.

_____ are used for diagnostic coding by hospitals, physicians, and all other providers of outpatient service(s). _____, also known as the Tabular Index, contains all of the diagnostic codes grouped into 17 chapters of disease and injury. _____ are broad sections of the ICD-9-CM coding manual grouped by disease or illness (e.g., Chapter 10 contains diagnostic codes for diseases of the genitourinary system).

_____ is called the Alphabetic Index and is used in the same way an alphabetic index in any textbook is used except that it refers the user back to the category codes in the Tabular Index, rather than page numbers.

_____ is used by hospitals to code procedures and services performed within the hospital in-patient environment. Most physician-providers do not use this volume.

4. Match the following terms.

   a. Section   Fourth digit

   b. Category   Also called a chapter

   c. Subcategory   Fifth digit

   d. Subclassification   Also called a classification

5. This digit is used to describe whether any disease process or manifestation exists that was caused by the disease. _____

6. This code is used on occasions when circumstances other than disease or injury are recorded as a diagnosis or problem. _____

7. This code is used to classify environmental or external causes of injury, poisoning, or other adverse effects on the body. _____

8. Match the following terms.

   a. Morphology of Neoplasms   Appendix A

   b. Glossary of Mental Disorders   Appendix B

   c. Classification of Drugs   Appendix C

   d. Classification of Industrial Accidents   Appendix D

   e. List of Three-Digit Categories   Appendix E

9. The abbreviation _____ is the equivalent of "unspecified" and means that the diagnostic statement does not provide more specificity or definition.

10. This abbreviation is to be used only when the coder lacks the information necessary to code the term to a more specific category. _____

11. Four basic forms of punctuation are used in the Tabular Index. Which of the following is NOT one of the forms of punctuation?

   a. Brackets

   b. Parentheses

   c. Question marks

   d. Braces

   e. Colon

12. Two other conventions used in both the Alphabetic Index and the Tabular Index are the use of _____ and _____ fonts.

13. _____ type is used for all codes and titles in the Tabular Index.

14. _____ type is used for exclusion notes and to identify any diagnosis that cannot be used as the primary diagnosis.

Instructional notations are notes included in the Tabular Index to provide additional guidance when selecting a specific diagnosis code. Here are the most common instructional notations, fill in the blanks with the appropriate terms.

1. A notation indicating that under a category or other subdivision separate terms can be found that will serve to further define, give examples of, or provide modifying adjectives, and sites or conditions. _____

2. Terms that are enclosed within a box and are printed in italics. These notations indicate that there are some code classifications that cannot be used with the code being selected. _____

3. Used to define terms and give coding instructions. They are often used to list the fifth-digit subclassification(s) for certain categories. _____

4. The _____ instruction follows a main term and indicates that a different term should be referenced.

5. This notation is a variation of the SEE instruction. _____

6. The _____ instruction is generally found following a main term in the Alphabetic Index and directs the coder to another area with additional index entries that may be useful.

7. This note directs the use of codes that are not normally intended to be used as a principal diagnosis or are not to be sequenced before the underlying disease. _____

8. This word should be interpreted to mean *and* or *or*. _____

9. This word in the Alphabetic Index is sequenced immediately following a main term. It provides additional definition or specificity to the code description. _____

Match the following terms.

a. Main terms   Always indented two additional spaces from the level of the preceding line

b. Modifying terms   Appear in bold

c. Subterms   Are found in the Alphabetic Index indented below main terms

d. Modifiers   Indented two spaces to the right under the main term

Fill in the blanks with the appropriate terms.

1. Three tables and one supplementary index are in the Alphabetic Index. The tables include the _____, _____, and _____.

2. The supplementary index is the Index to _____ (E codes).

3. The _____ Table lists the types of hypertension and the manifestations and causes of hypertension.

4. _____ is defined as a type of hypertension whose clinical course progresses rapidly to death.

5. _____ hypertension is a type that does not threaten a patient's health status significantly.

6. _____ hypertension is used only when there is no documentation in the clinical record that the hypertension is malignant or benign.

7. The _____ Table lists neoplasms by anatomic location.

8. A benign neoplasm is a _____.

Part II: Beginning the Encounter Process

1. Information pertinent to code selection is culled from a variety of medical documents. Which is NOT a part of the diagnostic statements.

   a. Encounter form

   b. Treatment notes

   c. Discharge summary

   d. Operative report

   e. Nurses notes

   f. Radiology report

   g. Pathology report

   h. Laboratory report

2. The _____ is generally a preprinted form and is also the most common form used by the medical assistant to obtain the charges and diagnosis when performing charge and payment data entry and insurance billing.

3. _____ are the second most common medical documents from which diagnostic information can be obtained.

4. The _____ begins with a statement in the patient's own words that describes why the person is seeking medical attention. This statement is called the _____ and is often abbreviated _____ in the History documentation in the medical record.

5. The _____ is used primarily for extracting procedure and diagnostic information for patients who were hospitalized, rather than seen in the physician's office.

6. The _____ will also be used for extracting procedure and diagnostic information for patients who underwent surgery as an outpatient or inpatient.

7. _____, _____, and _____ reports are used to support/establish the diagnostic statements. Any findings from these reports must be documented in the treatment notes in the medical record, in order to be used for diagnostic coding, charge entry, or insurance billing purposes.

8. A(n) _____ describes a disease, condition, or injury named after a person, such as Hodgkin's disease.

9. _____ are abbreviations of words that create a new word—for example, the _____ for gastroesophageal reflux disease is GERD. GERD and gastroesophageal reflux disease are both medical terms.

10. _____ are slightly different, abbreviations are "shorthand" for common medical terms.

11. _____ are words that are similar in meaning and can be used interchangeably.

12. A series of questions called a(n) _____ can assist the medical assistant in navigating the Alphabetic and Tabular Indexes while the steps for diagnostic coding are performed. The _____ for the main text is designed to guide the selection of the appropriate ICD-9-CM diagnostic code.

Part III: Coding Exercises

Code the following diagnoses to the highest level of specificity.

1. The Smith's newborn has a birthmark on his neck.

   _____

2. Mr. Epstein suffers from Bruck's disease.

   _____

3. Jenny developed bronchitis over spring break after inhaling gas fumes while sitting in a traffic jam.

   _____

4. Carolyn has experienced dumping syndrome periodically since her gastric bypass surgery.

   _____

5. Robert has experienced pain when he urinates for the past 3 weeks.

   _____

6. Julia has been nauseated for about a week but has not complained of vomiting.

   _____

7. Paul has trench foot, which is a condition of moist gangrene caused by freezing of wet skin.

   _____

8. Benjamin was given a health examination the night he entered prison to serve a life sentence.

   _____

9. Angela was classified as morbidly obese, so she qualified for gastric bypass surgery.

   _____

10. Joseph was diagnosed with academic underachievement disorder and sent for counseling.

    _____

11. Morgan Smith had an acute myocardial infarction, commonly referred to as a heart attack.

    _____

12. Jessica was placed in the neonatal ICU because she was diagnosed with transient tachypnea at birth.

    _____

13. Terri constantly struggles with her maxillary sinus, especially in the winter.

    _____

14. The physician told Roger that he had epididymitis but it was not a result of a venereal disease.

    _____

15. Judy has experienced neck pain for 1 week, but she does not know why the pain began.

_____

16. Kevin has suffered from low back pain for years.

_____

17. Brad was bitten by a brown recluse spider.

_____

18. The Abbotts' child died of sudden infant death syndrome.

_____

19. Mitral stenosis was Mrs. Richland's final diagnosis.

_____

20. Georgia went into anaphylactic shock after drinking milk.

_____

21. Joey was taken to a psychologist because he was having recurrent nightmares.

_____

22. Roger has benign essential hypertension.

_____

23. Susan was having trouble breathing, and her physician told her she had a nasopharyngeal polyp that needed to be removed.

_____

24. Kristy's son, Christian, suffers with croup syndrome and has been hospitalized three times because of the disorder.

_____

25. Ron saw Dr. Jarrett because of an anal fissure, which resulted from a nontraumatic tear of his anus.

_____

26. Griffin saw Dr. Redford for treatment of a common head cold.

_____

27. A tetanus toxoid vaccination was administered to a child who stepped on a rusty nail.

_____

28. Mrs. Garrett developed a decubitus ulcer on her buttocks while she was a patient in a nursing home.

_____

29. Paige has a migraine headache, and the physician did not mention intractable migraine in the medical record.

_____

30. Pat has Graves' disease, and the physician did not mention thyrotoxic crisis or storm on the medical record.

_____

31. Mary is in rehabilitation for episodic cocaine dependence.

_____

32. Jonathan has been diagnosed with attention deficit disorder, without mention of hyperactivity.

_____

33. Angelica has had chronic cystic mastitis for years.

_____

34. Mr. Robertson had a transient ischemic attack (TIA) at home and was rushed to the hospital.

_____

35. Ray noticed a ringing in his ears after working for 6 months on a construction site.

_____

36. Raul has been diagnosed with iron-deficient anemia because he is not getting enough iron in his diet.

_____

37. Camille has had recurrent earaches in the 2 years since her birth, and the physician diagnosed chronic purulent otitis media.

_____

38. Sally's newborn was diagnosed with pyloric stenosis and required surgery.

_____

39. Stephanie has a urinary tract infection, but the physician does not yet know what organism caused the illness.

_____

40. Don has insomnia, which the physician thinks is a result of drug abuse.

_____

41. Mabel Johnson has rheumatoid arthritis and takes daily medication to control the pain.

_____

42. Cynthia has a plantar wart but does not want to have it removed yet.

_____

43. Sebastian fractured his clavicle at the sternal end during a football game. The fracture was closed.

_____

44. Peggy contracted herpes simplex with herpetic vulvovaginitis.

_____

45. Eric noticed blood in his semen, and the physician diagnosed hematospermia.

_____

46. Kayla had a sore throat and fever and was diagnosed with infectious mononucleosis.

_____

47. Gerald has osteoarthritis in his shoulder region and is scheduled to begin physical therapy next week.

_____

48. Tray has had three headaches, not diagnosed as migraines, in the past week.

_____

49. Amanda was diagnosed with multiple sclerosis.

_____

50. Jeffrey has a personal history of alcoholism.

_____

51. Butch had four back surgeries and developed a continuous dependence on hydrocodone.

_____

52. Jake went to an ophthalmologist to have a splinter removed from his cornea.

_____

53. Tammy suffered from severe pain in the temporomandibular joint area.

_____

54. Josephine was struck by lightning during a thunderstorm.

_____

55. Barry's alcoholism has caused cirrhosis of the liver.

_____

56. The Wickers' newborn had a skin condition called cradle cap.

_____

57. Adam has been a paraplegic since a car wreck 2 years ago.

_____

58. Hudson suffered a ruptured abdominal aneurysm and had emergency surgery.

_____

59. Mr. Emmett had atherosclerosis of the extremities with gangrene just before his death.

_____

60. The woman with Munchausen syndrome by proxy had three children die before law enforcement grew suspicious.

_____

61. Ginger experienced dermatitis as a result of using a tanning bed.

_____

62. The Lewis couple's first child was born with Down syndrome.

_____

63. Lee Anna has experienced painful menstruation during her last three cycles.

_____

64. James had one testicle removed because of seminoma. The tumor was the primary site and incident of his cancer.

_____

65. Jacqueline has uncontrolled diabetes mellitus type 2 with ketoacidosis.

_____

66. Mrs. Julius died last week from congestive heart failure.

_____

67. Gary saw the physician to follow up on his previous diagnosis of cardiomegaly.

_____

68. Dr. Albertez thinks that Mr. Tidwell's Parkinson's disease was drug induced.

_____

69. Jerry developed Kaposi's sarcoma during the final stages of AIDS. The sarcoma was present in his lymph nodes.

_____

70. Sally developed a postoperative fever because of an infection (code infection only).

_____

71. Terri attempted suicide by ingesting a handful of lithium.

_____

72. Beaumont's divorce affected every aspect of his life.

_____

73. Mr. Maxwell's physician knew that his patient would have to be hospitalized once he diagnosed diverticulitis of the colon with hemorrhaging. Mr. Maxwell, at age 95, could not risk staying at home and allowing the bleeding to continue.

_____

74. Susan was stung by a jellyfish while swimming off the coast of Mexico.

_____

75. Alaydra has tunnel vision, which makes it difficult to drive safely.

_____

76. The escaped criminal was cornered by the police and shot because he raised his gun and pointed it at a police officer.

_____

77. Riley has acute myocarditis and was admitted to the hospital.

_____

78. Alisha underwent artificial insemination in an effort to have a child.

_____

79. Jackie's baby was breech and was delivered using forceps.

_____

80. Ordell has acute esophagitis and complained that he had been sick for 3 days.

_____

81. Robert dislocated his shoulder while playing baseball. This was a closed anterior dislocation of the humerus.

_____

82. Betty has allergic gastroenteritis.

_____

83. Mrs. Ralphy was diagnosed with systemic lupus erythematosus.

_____

84. Winston has synovitis of the knee.

_____

85. Mrs. Radson had a skin condition known as bullous pemphigoid, in which blisters formed in patches all over her skin.

_____

86. Osteomalacia made it impossible for Robbie to walk.

_____

87. Henry has oral leukoplakia, which may have been caused by smoking a pipe.

_____

88. Ricky was diagnosed with acute lymphocytic leukemia.

_____

89. The Smithsons' 4-year-old daughter has Hurler's syndrome, which was diagnosed a few months after she was born.

_____

90. Patricia has had uterine endometriosis for several years and may require a hysterectomy in the future.

_____

Chapter **18 Basics of Diagnostic Coding**

Dr. Rogers saw Mrs. Arrant in the office this morning. Mrs. Arrant has been diagnosed in the past with congestive heart failure, diabetes mellitus type 2, and chronic myelocytic leukemia. She comes to the clinic today complaining of chest pain and has a fever of 101.8°. Code all of these conditions. In which order would they be written on an encounter form?

WORKPLACE APPLICATION OPTION

Complete this activity and, if appropriate, share your results with the class.

Determine what certifications are available that relate to coding. What are the requirements for obtaining these special certifications? Why might these be beneficial for the medical assistant? Is there a particular certification you are interested in obtaining?

INTERNET ACTIVITY OPTIONS

Complete one or more of these activities and, if appropriate, share your results with the class.

1. Research the American Health Information Management Association (AHIMA) website, and explore opportunities for a career in coding.

2. Locate a job description for a medical billing and coding specialist, and determine the daily duties that coders perform in medical offices or large clinics.

3. Write a report on the importance of coding accurately. Share the information with the class.

4. Find five additional links other than the AHIMA website that provide useful information on billing and coding.

5. Research programs that provide a specialized certificate in billing or coding proficiency.

19 Basics of Procedural Coding

VOCABULARY REVIEW

Fill in the blanks with the correct vocabulary terms from this chapter.

1. The primary procedure or service code selected when performing insurance billing or statistical research is a category _____ code.

2. Jerri sometimes has difficulty with _____ codes, which designate procedures or services that are grouped together and paid for as one procedure or service.

3. Jules prepared a(n) _____, or summary, of the diagnostic statements on Mr. Ford's medical record.

4. _____ are found at the beginning of each of the six sections of the CPT-4 manual, and Rebecca refers to them often when coding procedures.

5. Category _____ codes are for new experimental procedures or emerging technology.

6. A procedure, service, or diagnosis named after a person is called a(n) _____.

7. Codes in which the components of a procedure are separated and reported separately are called _____ codes.

8. Code additions that explain circumstances that alter a provided service or provide additional clarification or detail are called _____.

9. The main divisions of the CPT-4 manual are called _____.

10. Abbreviations are also called _____.

CODING EXERCISES

Code the following procedures.

1. Dr. Smith visits Eula Fairbanks, a patient with dementia, in the nursing home for less than 30 minutes and performs an expanded problem-focused examination with MDM of low complexity.

   _____

2. Jessica Lundy, a newborn, was admitted to the pediatric critical care unit after her birth, where Dr. Williams provided her initial care.

   _____

3. Because Lucille Westerman had multiple health problems, she was admitted for observation after a fainting spell. Dr. Adams took a comprehensive history and performed a comprehensive examination, then made medical decisions of high complexity regarding her care.

   _____

4. Dr. Wray saw Tammy Luttrell in the office as a new patient. He took a detailed history and performed a detailed examination, then he made medical decisions of low complexity.

_____

5. Sylvia Julius saw Dr. Bridges for her allergies. The physician took a problem-focused history, performed a problem-focused examination, and made straightforward decisions regarding her care.

_____

6. Bonnie Sadler comes to the office to have blood work drawn for an obstetric panel. What is the code for the obstetric panel only?

_____

7. The office charges Bonnie Sadler, a college student, for drawing a blood specimen. What is the code for venipuncture?

_____

8. Terri Smithson had laparoscopic gastric bypass surgery using the Roux-en-Y procedure.

_____

9. Kim Errant had an outpatient kidney imaging with vascular flow to make certain that her kidneys were functioning normally.

_____

10. Georgie Ebersol had blood drawn for a total bilirubin. Code the blood test only.

_____

11. Roy Messing's urine was tested for total protein.

_____

12. Jerry Orchard was tested for his blood alcohol level.

_____

13. Andrea Adams has a bleeding disorder and has to undergo regular coagulation time tests. Her physician uses the Lee and White method.

_____

14. Dr. Airheart sent Roberto's specimen to the microbiology laboratory to check for *Cryptosporidium*.

_____

15. The body was sent to the county medical examiner's office for a forensic autopsy, which was performed by Dr. Stein.

_____

16. Jonathan Boyd was required to have a polio vaccine by his school. He received an oral dose.

_____

17. Julia Anderson has a lithium level drawn to make certain that her dosage was accurate and appropriate.

_____

18. Cynthia Hernandez was exposed to hepatitis, so her physician ordered an acute hepatitis panel.

_____

19. Sam Livingston, a baby in the neonatal unit, had total bilirubin tests drawn each morning.

_____

20. Susan's husband has blood drawn regularly to measure his quinidine levels.

_____

21. Bobby had to undergo treatment of a clavicular fracture, without manipulation, after his injury during a football game.

_____

22. Betty received anesthesia for the vaginal delivery of her child.

_____

23. Anesthesia was provided to Ron Smith, a brain-dead patient whose organs were being harvested for donation.

_____

24. Dr. Partridge participated in a complex, lengthy telephone call regarding a patient who was scheduled for multiple surgeries.

_____

25. When Terri Anderson was involved in a major car accident, the emergency department physician took a comprehensive history, performed a comprehensive examination, and then made highly complex decisions.

_____

26. Tim Taylor is a new patient with a small cyst on his back. Dr. Young took a problem-focused history, performed a problem-focused examination, and then made straightforward medical decisions.

_____

27. Jim Angelo, an established patient, saw the physician for a minor cut on the back of his hand. The physician spent approximately 10 minutes with Jim.

_____

28. Vera Carpenter was admitted to the hospital for diabetes mellitus, congestive heart failure, and an infection of unknown origin. Dr. Antonetti performed a consultation by doing a detailed history and examination, and MDM of low complexity that took about an hour, including the time spent writing orders in her medical record.

_____

29. Carla had a nasal polyp removed that was hindering her ability to breathe. The excision was a simple one and was performed in Dr. Wilson's office.

_____

30. Darla's son, Andy, was examined for pinworms.

_____

31. The police asked the laboratory technician to perform an arsenic test on a tube of blood.

_____

32. An incision was made into the newborn's pyloric sphincter to allow food to travel through his digestive system.

_____

Chapter **19** **Basics of Procedural Coding**

33. Ben, a 6-year-old, had his tonsils and adenoids removed after recurrent infections.

_____

34. Edward had one testicle removed because of a growing tumor attached to it. An inguinal approach was used, and during the surgery the physician explored the abdominal area to look for other growths.

_____

35. Alex's mother insisted that she have her ears pierced by a physician so that the procedure would be as clean as possible.

_____

36. Fonda was diagnosed with an abdominal ectopic pregnancy, which Dr. Tomlinson removed surgically.

_____

37. The medical assistant performed a simple urinalysis, using a dipstick and a microscope to examine the specimen.

_____

38. Wayne had blood drawn for a complete blood count (CBC) with an automated differential white blood cell (WBC) count.

_____

39. Paula had an inflammation somewhere inside her body, as evidenced by her sedimentation rate. The test was automated.

_____

40. Jimmie's physician ordered computed tomography of his abdomen with contrast material.

_____

41. Joan had a laparoscopic biopsy of her left ovary.

_____

42. Craig had to undergo a direct repair of a ruptured aneurysm of the carotid artery, which was performed by neck incision.

_____

43. Emma was given a urine pregnancy test in the clinic before receiving x-ray examinations to diagnose her back disorder, using a color comparison test kit.

_____

44. Jennifer's child was tested for serum albumin.

_____

45. Angela had a qualitative lactose test using a urine specimen.

_____

46. Sarah's probation officer required her to have a blood chemistry test for methadone.

_____

47. The two children that had been lost in the woods were tested for Rocky Mountain spotted fever.

_____

142

48. Marcus has a total T-cell count every month.

_____

49. After her needlestick injury, Felicia was tested for the hepatitis B surface antibody.

_____

50. Dr. Torrid thought that Katrina might have the Epstein-Barr virus, so he tested for the early antigen.

_____

51. Dr. Battson performed a chlamydia culture on the vaginal specimen.

_____

52. Juan was given a test for herpes simplex, type 2.

_____

53. Mr. Albertson was given a blood test for uric acid.

_____

54. Derrick had a Western blot test last week. The interpretation and report are due back to the physician by tomorrow.

_____

55. Roy had a urine test for total protein.

_____

56. The emergency physician ordered a lead test on the small child, thinking she had perhaps ingested some paint chips.

_____

57. Joy has monthly blood tests to evaluate her iron-binding capacity.

_____

58. Andi was tested for chromium yesterday and has a return appointment next week.

_____

59. All gastric bypass patients are required to have a basic metabolic panel before surgery is scheduled.

_____

60. June had an obstetric panel run on her second appointment with the physician.

_____

61. Royce had a chest x-ray, single frontal view, to check for pneumonia.

_____

62. Dr. True suspected that Joey had fractured his sternum, so he ordered an x-ray that would show two views of the bone.

_____

63. Jessalyn had a magnetic resonance imaging (MRI) of her spinal canal and its contents.

_____

64. Dr. Tompkins visited a new patient at her home and spent about 20 minutes diagnosing and treating her for the flu. A problem-focused history and examination with straightforward MDM was performed.

_____

65. Dr. Revy was on standby for about 20 minutes while the decision was made as to whether the patient would have a cesarean section.

_____

66. Judge Jordan has his blood checked for potassium levels monthly.

_____

67. Steven Pauly needs a chest x-ray examination, and the physician has requested four views.

_____

68. Linda Ellis had a complete hip x-ray examination with two views because her physician was considering hip replacement surgery.

_____

69. Judy had a theophylline level drawn during her last office visit.

_____

70. Joy had a closed treatment of a coccygeal fracture.

_____

71. Mrs. Dickson went to see Dr. Donner for a complete radiologic examination of the scapula.

_____

72. Bobbie returned to the physician's office to have a short-leg walking cast applied after wearing the larger cast for 4 weeks.

_____

73. Dr. Angell ordered a radiologic examination of Sylvia's mastoids, requesting two views.

_____

74. Sammy had a uric acid test during his last office visit.

_____

75. Peter asked his physician to repeat his creatine phosphokinase (CPK) total because it had been slightly high on his last visit.

_____

76. Bryce has a digoxin level drawn every 3 months.

_____

77. The pathologist prepared tissue for drug analysis.

_____

78. Julie was quite dehydrated for a week, so her physician ran an electrolyte panel.

_____

79. Frank asked the physician how a magnesium level related to his illness.

   _____

80. Joel's physician thought that he had an adrenal insufficiency, so he ordered an adrenocorticotropic hormone (ACTH) stimulation panel.

   _____

81. All three children who lived in the condemned home were subjected to a quantitative carbon monoxide test.

   _____

82. When Ariel turned 50, her physician recommended that she have an occult blood test annually, which she completed and returned to the office for testing.

   _____

83. Most diabetic patients periodically have a blood glucose test performed at the physician's office in addition to the test strip checks that they perform at home.

   _____

84. Selenium can be detected with a blood test.

   _____

85. Sarah's infant returned to the physician's office to have a phenylketonuria (PKU) test a few weeks after she was born.

   _____

86. Van Stephens had blood work done on Monday to check his triglycerides.

   _____

87. Karry has been to the physician for several days in a row to have ovulation tests, which are done by visual color comparison.

   _____

88. Samuel's vitamin K test results were slightly below normal.

   _____

89. Dr. Grant runs a spun microhematocrit on each of his pregnant patients at every prenatal visit.

   _____

90. Trent had a serum folic acid test run this morning at his physician's office.

   _____

Find all procedures that need to be coded for billing purposes in the following text.

Roberta Sleether is a new patient who saw Dr. Morganstern to complain of feeling tired all of the time. She stated that she was exhausted even after a full 8 hours of sleep at night. Roberta said that she did not have much of an appetite and that she had been eating mostly salads and chicken, with a bowl of fruit as snacks. She is not overweight and her blood pressure and other vital signs were normal. Dr. Morganstern decided to perform a CBC, an electrolyte panel, and a lipid panel. He also ordered a urinalysis, an iron-binding capacity, and a vitamin B_{12} test. The physician asked if she had noticed any blood in her urine or stool, and she denied blood in the urine but did mention she had several episodes of diarrhea. Dr. Morganstern added an occult blood test as well as a stool culture to check for pathogens. The physician placed Roberta on multivitamin therapy and told her to return in 1 week to discuss her laboratory test results. He spent approximately 30 minutes with Roberta, taking a detailed history and performing a detailed examination, making low-complexity medical decisions. Roberta scheduled her appointment for the following week and left the clinic.

WORKPLACE APPLICATION OPTIONS

Complete one or more of these activities and, if appropriate, share your results with the class.

1. Select a medical specialty, and research the procedure codes that would be commonly used within that practice.

2. Contact a practice and make an appointment to meet the person who performs coding tasks. Discuss the challenges and rewards of the job. Prepare a report for the class based on the interview with the coders.

3. Design an encounter form for a fictional medical practice. Choose the specialty, and make certain that the codes chosen for the form are applicable to the specialty practice.

INTERNET ACTIVITY OPTIONS

Complete one or more of these activities and, if appropriate, share your results with the class.

1. Research job postings on the Internet that relate to billing and coding.

2. Working in groups, prepare a report on the sections of the CPT-4 manual. Discuss the most common codes within each section.

3. Search for coding hints and tips online. Prepare a report for the class, and discuss the tips and how to use them to code more effectively.

20 Basics of Health Insurance

VOCABULARY REVIEW

Fill in the blanks with the correct vocabulary terms from this chapter.

1. _____ is the maximum amount of money many third-party payers allow for a specific procedure or service.

2. An alphanumeric number issued by the insurance company giving approval of a procedure or service is a(n) _____.

3. An individual entitled to receive benefits from an insurance policy or program or from a government entitlement program offering healthcare benefits is considered the _____.

4. The amount payable by an insurance company for a monetary loss to an individual insured by that company, under each coverage, is known as _____.

5. The _____ states that when an individual is covered under two insurance policies, the insurance plan of the policyholder whose birthday comes first in the calendar year (month and day, not year) becomes the primary insurance.

6. _____ is a payment method used by many managed care organizations in which a fixed amount of money is reimbursed to the provider for patients enrolled during a specific period of time, no matter what services were received or how many visits were made.

7. In the insurance business, companies that assume the risk of an insurance policy are considered the _____.

8. CHAMPUS is the acronym for _____.

9. The health benefits program run by the Department of Veterans Affairs (VA) that helps eligible beneficiaries pay the cost of specific healthcare services and supplies is the (give full name and acronym) _____ _____.

10. A(n) _____ provision frequently is found in medical insurance policies whereby the policyholder and the insurance company share the cost of covered losses in a specified ratio.

11. _____ reimburses the insured for expenses resulting from illness or injury according to a specific fee schedule as outlined in the insurance policy and on a fee-for-service basis.

12. A(n) _____ is the sum of money paid at the time of medical service; it is a form of coinsurance.

13. Typically met on a yearly or per-incident basis, this specific amount of money, a(n) _____, is what a patient must pay out of pocket before the insurance carrier begins paying.

14. _____ are the spouse, children, and sometimes domestic partner or other individuals designated by the insured who are covered under a healthcare plan.

15. _____ provides periodic payments to replace income when an insured person is unable to work as a result of illness, injury, or disease.

16. The _____ is the date on which an insurance policy or plan takes effect so that benefits are payable.

147

17. _____ is a term that indicates whether a patient's insurance coverage is in effect and the patient is eligible for payment of insurance benefits.

18. The term for limitations on an insurance contract for which benefits are not payable is _____.

19. A(n) _____ is a letter or statement from the insurance carrier that describes what was paid, denied, or reduced in payment. It also contains information about amounts applied to the deductible, the patient's coinsurance, and the allowed amounts.

20. A(n) _____ is a letter or statement from Medicare that describes what was paid, denied, or reduced in payment. It also contains information about amounts applied to the deductible, the patient's coinsurance, and the allowed amounts.

21. An established schedule of fees set for services performed by providers and paid by the patient is called _____.

22. A(n) _____ is an organization that contracts with the government to handle and mediate insurance claims from medical facilities, home health agencies, or providers of medical services or supplies.

23. Medicaid and Medicare are examples of _____ plans.

24. Insurance written under a policy that covers a number of people under a single mast er contract issued to their employer or to an association with which they are affiliated would be considered a(n) _____ policy.

25. The _____ is the person responsible for paying a medical bill.

26. _____ is protection in return for periodic premium payments that provides reimbursement of expenses resulting from illness or injury.

27. The Kassebaum-Kennedy Act—which was designed to improve portability and continuity of health insurance coverage; to combat waste, fraud, and abuse in health insurance and healthcare delivery; to promote the use of medical savings accounts; to improve access to long-term care services and coverage; to simplify the administration of health insurance; and to serve other purposes—is also called the (please provide the whole name and acronym) _____.

28. A(n) _____ is an organization that provides a wide range of comprehensive healthcare services for a specified group at a fixed periodic payment. These organizations can be sponsored by the government, medical schools, hospitals, employers, labor unions, consumer groups, insurance companies, and hospital-medical plans.

29. _____ pay for all or a share of the cost of covered services, regardless of which physician, hospital, or other licensed healthcare provider is used. Policyholders of these plans and their dependents choose when and where to get healthcare services.

30. A(n) _____ is designed specifically for the use of one person (and his or her dependents) and is not associated with the amenities of a group policy (e.g., lower premiums).

31. The individual or organization covered by an insurance policy according to the policy terms, usually the individual or group that pays the premiums, is called the _____.

32. An umbrella term for all healthcare plans that provide healthcare services in return for preset monthly payments and coordinated care through a defined network of primary care physicians and hospitals is _____.

33. Tax-deferred bank or savings accounts that are combined with a low-premium, high-deductible insurance policy and designed for individuals or families who choose to fund their own healthcare expenses and medical insurance are called _____.

SKILLS AND CONCEPTS

Match the following terms and definitions.

_____ Medicaid

_____ Medicare

_____ Medigap

a. A federally sponsored health insurance program for those over 65 years or individuals under 65 years but disabled

b. A term sometimes applied to private insurance products that supplement Medicare insurance benefits

c. A federally and state-sponsored health insurance program for the medically indigent

Fill in the blanks with the correct word choice.

1. A(n) _____ is a physician or other healthcare provider who enters into a contract with a specific insurance company or program and by doing so agrees to abide by certain rules and regulations set forth by that particular third-party payer.

2. The person who pays a premium to an insurance company and in whose name the policy is written in exchange for the insurance protection provided by a policy of insurance is the _____.

3. _____ is a process required by some insurance carriers in which the provider obtains permission to perform certain procedures or services or to refer a patient to a specialist.

4. The periodic (monthly, quarterly, or annual) payment of a specific sum of money to an insurance company for which the insurer, in return, agrees to provide certain benefits is called a(n) _____.

5. The _____ is a general practice or nonspecialist provider or physician responsible for the care of a patient for some health maintenance organizations; also called a *gatekeeper*.

6. An insurance term used when a primary care provider wants to send a patient to a specialist is _____.

7. An explanation of benefits that comes from Medicaid is called _____.

8. The fee schedule designed to provide national uniform payment of Medicare benefits after adjustment to reflect the differences in practice costs across geographic areas is called the _____.

9. A(n) _____ is a special provision or group of provisions that may be added to a policy to expand or limit the benefits otherwise payable. It may increase or decrease benefits, waive a condition or coverage, or in any other way amend the original contract.

10. A(n) _____ is funded by an organization with an employee base large enough to enable it to fund its own insurance program.

11. When a patient or insured individual refers himself or herself to a specialist without requesting the referral from the primary provider, this is known as _____.

12. _____ plans provide benefits in the form of certain surgical and medical services rendered, rather than cash. This type of plan is not restricted to a fee schedule.

13. An organization that processes claims and performs other business-related functions for a health plan is a(n) _____.

14. Entities that make payment on an obligation or debt but are not parties of the contract that created the debt are known as _____.

Chapter **20 Basics of Health Insurance**

15. A government-sponsored program under which authorized dependents of military personnel receive medical care; the program originally was called CHAMPUS but now is called _____.

16. A(n) _____ is a review of individual cases by a committee to make sure services are medically necessary and to study how providers use medical care resources.

17. _____ is insurance against liability imposed by employers to cover medical expenses and lost wages to employees who are injured on the job and to pay benefits to dependents of employees killed in the course of or arising out of their employment.

Read the following paragraph and then fill in the blanks.

The medical assistant's tasks related to health insurance processing are initiated when the patient encounters the provider, either by appointment, as a walk-in, or in the emergency department or hospital. To complete insurance billing and coding properly, the medical assistant must perform the following tasks.

1. Obtain information from the patient and insured, including _____, employment, and _____ data.

2. Verify the patient's _____ for insurance payment with the insurance carrier or carriers, as well as _____ available, exclusions, and whether _____ are needed to refer patients to specialists or to perform certain services or procedures, such as surgery or diagnostic tests.

3. Perform _____ and _____ coding and review the encounter form or charge ticket for completeness once the provider sees the patient.

4. Calculate insurance _____ and coinsurance amounts and provide the patient with a statement showing the _____ expense, the amount the patient owes.

5. Obtain _____ for referral of the patient to a specialist or for special services or procedures that require advance permission.

6. Complete an insurance claim form and submit it to the insurance company for _____ for services and procedures performed.

7. Post payments and adjustments on the patient ledger or account and examine the _____, _____, or _____ from the insurance company to identify what was paid, reduced, or denied and the deductible, coinsurance, and allowable amounts.

8. Make adjustments to the account of the allowable amount, which is either written off (adjusted) or passed on to the patient for _____.

9. Bill the patient for any _____ or, if there is a secondary insurance, complete the secondary insurance claim form and submit it to the insurance company with a copy of the EOB showing payment from the primary insurance company.

10. _____ on any rejected or unpaid claims ensure that any requests from the insurance carrier for more information about specific claims are addressed.

11. Adhere to the _____ requirements for each insurance carrier to prevent zero payments from the insurance company and inability to bill the patient.

Match the types of insurance benefits with their description.

_____ Hospitalization

_____ Surgical

_____ Basic medical

_____ Major medical

_____ Disability

_____ Dental care

_____ Vision care

_____ Medicare supplement

_____ Special risk insurance

_____ Liability insurance

_____ Life insurance

_____ Long-term care insurance

a. A benefits program that offers a variety of options (fee-for-service or managed care plans) that reimburse a portion of a patient's dental expenses and may exclude certain treatments

b. Provides reimbursement for all or a percentage of the cost of refraction, lenses, and frames

c. Helps defray medical costs not covered by Medicare

d. Protects a person in the event of a certain type of accident, such as an airplane crash

e. Provides payment of a specified amount upon the insured's death

f. Covers a continuum of broad-ranged maintenance and health services to chronically ill, disabled, or mentally retarded individuals

g. Pays all or part of a surgeon's or assistant surgeon's fees

h. A form of insurance that insures the beneficiary's earned income against the risk that a disability will make working uncomfortable, or impossible, with weekly or monthly cash benefits

i. Pays all or part of a physician's fee for nonsurgical services, including hospital, home, and office visits

j. Provides protection against especially large medical bills resulting from catastrophic or prolonged illnesses up to a maximum limit, usually after a deductible and coinsurance have been met

k. Pays the cost of all or part of the insured person's hospital room and board and specific hospital services per DRG guidelines

l. Often includes benefits for medical expenses due to traumatic injuries and lost wages payable to individuals who are injured in the insured person's home or in an automobile accident

Answer the following questions.

1. List three advantages of the managed care concept.

   a. _____

   b. _____

   c. _____

2. List three disadvantages to the managed care concept.

   a. _____

   b. _____

   c. _____

3. List 10 items of information the medical assistant should obtain from the patient before calling the insurance company for preauthorization or precertification.

_____

_____

_____

_____

_____

_____

_____

_____

_____

_____

4. List two types of people who would qualify for Medicare.

   a. _____

   b. _____

5. The _____ is the official daily publication for rules, proposed rules, and notices of federal agencies and organization, as well as Executive Orders and other presidential documents.

CASE STUDY

Survey all class members and determine the various types of insurance coverage that are represented by the students. Assign each student a different insurance company and have him or her call to verify benefits. Choose a medical procedure and have the students call and verify the amounts of coverage for that particular procedure. If students are uncomfortable exchanging health insurance information, allow them to verify and obtain amounts of coverage for their own insurance.

WORKPLACE APPLICATION OPTIONS

Complete one or more of these activities and, if appropriate, share your results with the class.

1. Working in small groups, obtain a quote for health insurance coverage for a small group. Use the Internet to research companies and choose three or four from which to obtain quotes.

2. Design a document that provides information as to what should be placed in each box of the health insurance claim form. Place the document into a report cover with sheet protectors, and turn it in for a special project grade.

3. Obtain encounter forms from several different physicians' offices. Use them to create mock patients, listing a diagnosis and several procedures. Complete an insurance claim form for each patient and an encounter form. As an option, work in groups and present the patients to the class.

21 The Health Insurance Claim Form

VOCABULARY REVIEW

Fill in the blanks with the correct term from this chapter.

1. _____ is the transfer of the patient's legal right to collect benefits for medical expenses to the provider of those services, authorizing the payment to be sent directly to the provider.

2. The process of examining claims for accuracy and completeness before submitting the claims is called a(n) _____, which can be performed manually or electronically with computer billing software.

3. Often referred to when tracking medical services used by patients or researching claims, a(n) _____ is the path left by a transaction when it has been completed.

4. _____ are insurance claim forms that have been completed correctly and can be processed and paid promptly if they meet the restrictions on covered services and blocks.

5. A centralized facility to which insurance claims are transmitted, a(n) _____ separates, checks, and redistributes claims electronically to various insurance carriers.

6. A method of electronic claims submission in which computer software allows a provider to submit an insurance claim directly to an insurance carrier for payment is called _____.

7. _____ claims are claims that contain errors or omissions that must be corrected so that the claims can be resubmitted to an insurance carrier to obtain reimbursement.

8. _____ claims are claims that are submitted to insurance processing facilities using a computerized medium, such as direct data entry, direct wire, dial-in telephone digital fax, or personal computer download or upload.

9. The transfer of data back and forth between two or more entities using an electronic medium is called _____.

10. A(n) _____ is a mark that is accepted as proof of approval of or responsibility for the content of an electronic document.

11. The number used by the Internal Revenue Service to identify a business or an individual functioning as a business entity for income tax reporting is known as a(n) _____.

12. A claim that is missing information and is returned to the provider for correction and resubmission is called a(n) _____, or sometimes an *invalid claim.*

13. _____ is the electronic scanning of printed blocks as images and the use of special software to recognize these images as ASCII text for uploading into a computer database.

14. The term for the acronym NPI is _____.

15. The term for the acronym PIN is _____.

16. The term for the acronym UPIN is _____.

17. Hard copies of insurance claims that have been completed and sent by surface mail are known as _____.

18. Any company, individual, or group that provides medical, diagnostic, or treatment services to a patient is considered a(n) _____.

19. A number assigned to a provider by a carrier for use in the submission of claims is called a(n) _____.

20. _____ claims are claims that have been returned unpaid to the provider for clarification of questions and that must be corrected before resubmission.

21. The number assigned by fiscal intermediaries to identify providers on claims for services is the _____.

22. The universal claim form was developed by the Health Care Financing Administration (HCFA) [now known as the Centers for Medicare and Medicaid Services (CMS)] and approved by the American Medical Association (AMA) for use in submitting all government-sponsored claims. It now is also known as the _____.

23. A medical assistant may submit insurance claims to a third-party payer or an insurance carrier in one of two ways:

_____.

Fill in the blanks with the correct word choice.

1. Name two advantages of using hard (paper) claims.

   a. _____

   b. _____

2. Name two disadvantages of using hard (paper) claims.

   a. _____

   b. _____

3. List two benefits of the ICR scanning system.

   a. _____

   b. _____

4. A number of rules must be followed when completing the paper CMS-1500 form so that the insurance carrier can scan the claim. Give 10 examples of these rules when completing a paper CMS-1500.

   a. _____

   b. _____

   c. _____

   d. _____

   e. _____

   f. _____

   g. _____

   h. _____

   i. _____

   j. _____

5. Now list the other six rules for completing the paper CMS-1500 form so that the insurance carrier can scan the claim.

a. _____

b. _____

c. _____

d. _____

e. _____

f. _____

6. The transaction and code set for the CMS-1500 electronic claims submission is called the _____.

7. Implementation Guides for each of the transaction and code sets requirements for electronic data submission can be obtained through the Center for Medicare and Medicaid Services (CMS). List three types of data that can be submitted electronically.

a. _____

b. _____

c. _____

8. List two ways electronic claims can be submitted.

a. _____

b. _____

9. Clearinghouses typically also provide additional services. List three of them.

a. _____

b. _____

c. _____

10. Give one major advantage of electronic submission of insurance claims.

_____

11. The first section of the patient registration form includes the patient information. List four items that are recorded in this section.

a. _____

b. _____

c. _____

d. _____

12. The patient registration form should be completed by the patient or the patient's guardian. List two things the medical assistant should do to confirm the information.

a. _____

b. _____

13. Detail the 16 steps for gathering patient information and the other information required to complete an insurance claim form.

a. _____

b. _____

c. _____

d. _____

e. _____

f. _____

g. _____

h. _____

i. _____

j. _____

k. _____

l. _____

m. _____

n. _____

o. _____

p. _____

14. Once the patient's and the insured's demographic and insurance information has been collected, the next step is to verify the patient's eligibility and benefits. By what method or methods is this usually done?

_____

_____

_____

15. If any diagnostic or therapeutic services or procedures are to be rendered by the provider that require preapproval, a(n) _____ must be done to obtain an authorization number.

16. A CMS-1500 claim form has _____ blocks or items. The blocks are divided _____ sections.

17. List the information contained in each section of a CMS-1500 claim form.

Section 1: _____

Section 2: _____

Section 3: _____

18. The type of insurance that the patient has is indicated in block _____.

19. Block 1a is used for what vital piece of information? _____

20. Block 2 should contain the patient's name. This is the person receiving treatment or supplies. In what order should the patient's name be entered? _____

21. Block 3 contains what two pieces of information? _____

156

22. Block 4 contains the _____. This is the person who holds the policy.

23. The patient's address and phone number are entered in which block? _____

24. Block 6 is Patient Relationship to Insured. Explain what the following titles mean in this block.

    a. Self: _____

    b. Spouse: _____

    c. Child: _____

    d. Other: _____

25. The insured's permanent address and telephone number are entered in block 7. How does the information in this block differ from that in block 5? _____

26. Block 8 is Patient's Status. To what specifically does this refer and why is this information important?

    _____

27. In Section 3, the Patient/Insured section, which blocks are completed for the primary insurance and which blocks are completed only if a secondary insurance claim is being submitted?

    Primary insurance: _____

    Secondary insurance: _____

28. Block 12 contains which signature? _____

29. Block 13 contains which signature? _____

30. The name of the referring provider, ordering provider, or other source that referred or ordered the service or procedure on the claim is entered in block 17. Explain the difference between a referring physician and an ordering physician.

    _____

    _____

    _____

32. Block 21 contains an important piece of information. What is it? _____

33. When entering the appropriate diagnosis or ICD-9-CM code or codes, what is the maximum number of codes that should be used on one claim form? _____

34. What number is placed in block 26 and who assigns this number? _____

35. What information is provided in block 28? _____

36. What information is provided in block 29? _____

37. What information is provided in block 30? _____

38. Many guidelines for reviewing a claim must be followed before a claim is submitted. List 10 of those guidelines.

a. _____

b. _____

c. _____

d. _____

e. _____

f. _____

g. _____

h. _____

i. _____

j. _____

39. The two main reasons for denial of payment are _____ and _____.

40. A clean claim is defined as _____.

41. A dirty (or dingy) claim is defined as _____.

42. A rejected claim is defined as _____.

SKILLS AND CONCEPTS

Part I: Completing Insurance Claim Forms

Complete a claim form using the patient information in each of the following scenarios. Use the claim forms in Work Products 21-1 through 21-5.

Answers: Please check the Work Products for accurate completion using the following information.

1. Claim Form 1 (Work Product 21-1)

Today's Date: 9-29-20XX

Mr. Jackson, an established patient, has suffered from situational depression since his wife of 47 years died last winter. He has a history of congestive heart failure and intermittent high blood pressure. He comes to the office on July 23, 20XX, for treatment of his depression. Dr. Swakoski sees Mr. Jackson and counsels him about medication for his condition. He is with the patient for about 25 minutes. He gives Mr. Jackson a week's worth of samples of Cymbalta and writes a prescription for the drug that is refillable for 3 months. The charge for the office visit is $85. File this claim with BC/BS.

Donald W. Jackson (patient and insured)
77834 High Road Way
Los Angeles, CA 90010
818-665-0098 (home)
SS# 567-99-0067

Insurance: BC/BS and Medicare
ID# 567990067
Employer: Retired
DOB: 3-8-1940

Diagnosis: Depression, CHF, HTN
Procedures: Office visit
Account Number: JAD0067

Family Health Center
120 E. Northwest Highway
Los Angeles, CA 90010
818-624-0112
Federal Tax ID# 75-6102034

BC/BS
11001 Spring Way, Suite 200
Sacramento, CA 90012
800-443-0033

Theodore Swakoski, MD
NPI# 6170421616
BS Provider# 621604211

2. Claim Form 2 (Work Product 21-2)

Today's date: 9-29-20XX

Mr. Adams, an established, married patient, comes to the office because of an episode of bronchitis. He states that he has felt poorly for about 1 week and that he is now having trouble getting a full breath of air. He has had moderate pain on coughing and admits that the cough has kept him awake or has awakened him. He says he has bronchitis about once a year in the fall. Dr. Abbott sees Mr. Adams for about 15 minutes in the office. She prescribes an antibiotic, a cough syrup, and Hycodan. Dr. Abbott knows that Mr. Adams is also diabetic, so she draws blood for a glucose test to make sure the levels are normal. She suggests that Mr. Adams stay home from work for the 2 days leading into the weekend and return to work on Monday. Dr. Abbott asks whether Mr. Adams is still having trouble sleeping, as reported on his last office visit. He admits that he is still suffering from insomnia even apart from the bronchitis. Mr. Adams also admits that his marriage is failing, and he says that the stress may be contributing to the insomnia. Dr. Abbott gives him a prescription for Ambien CR along with the other prescriptions. Mr. Adams is to return to the clinic in 1 week if he is not feeling better. The charge for the office visit is $77, and the blood sugar test is $12. Mr. Adams pays his $20 co-payment.

Benjamin C. Adams
55180 Grand Avenue Parkway
Austin, Texas 78706
512-998-1354 (home)
SS# 445-74-8363

Insurance: Humana PPO
ID# 445748363
Employer: Texas Department of Public Safety
DOB: 7-2-1954

Diagnosis: Acute bronchitis; diabetes mellitus type II, controlled; insomnia
Procedures: Office visit, blood glucose test
Account Number: ADB8363

Family Medical
1216 E. Lamar Blvd.
Austin, Texas 78704
512-624-0112
Federal Tax ID# 75-8210612

Clinic Humana
PO Box 3031103
Chicago, IL 60068
800-611-1216

Barbara Abbott, MD
NPI 4712678920

3. Claim Form 3 (Work Product 21-3)

Today's date: 9-29-20XX

Ms. Snell comes to the office complaining of severe pain in the lower left quadrant. She states that the pain came on suddenly and that she has a history of ovarian cysts. Ms. Snell is clearly in severe pain, so Dr. Jackman gives her an injection of Toradol. Once the medication has taken effect, he performs a pelvic examination and determines that the most likely cause of her pain is a ruptured ovarian cyst. Dr. Jackman sends Ms. Snell to the hospital for an ultrasound examination and will see her in the emergency department later in the afternoon. Ms. Snell has no other significant health problems. Her office visit is $85, and the injection is $25. Dr. Jackman spent about 40 minutes with her.

Suanne L. Snell
4545 Rustic
Los Angeles, CA 90002
818-445-9970 (home)
SS# 665-76-5568

Insurance: Aetna HMO
ID# 665765568
Employer: Marriott Hotels International
DOB: 9-3-1964

Diagnosis: Ruptured ovarian cyst
Procedures: Office visit, injection
Account Number: SNS5568

Medical Surgical Clinic
4800 S. Broadway Blvd.
Los Angeles, CA 90012
818-261-1122
Federal Tax ID# 75-6120662

James Jackman, DO
NPI 8216740292

Aetna
PO Box 310661
Sacramento, CA 90121
800-996-8445

4. Claim Form 4 (Work Product 21-4)

Today's date: 9-29-20XX

Ms. Huntington, a single female, arrives at the clinic today as a new patient. She was referred to Dr. Tyler by Dr. William R. Curry, a friend of Dr. Tyler from medical school. Ms. Huntington has been diagnosed with systemic lupus erythematosus and periodically experiences a great deal of pain. She arranged to forward her medical records to Dr. Tyler several weeks ago, and she made today's appointment before her move to New Rochelle. Dr. Tyler has worked with numerous patients who have lupus and is understanding about their needs and the challenges they face in living a normal life. Ms. Huntington states that she needs to refill her medications, and Dr. Tyler reviews them with her, agreeing to refill her prescriptions for Motrin (800 mg), Lortab (10 mg), and Phenergan suppositories (50 mg). Ms. Huntington says that she uses the Motrin almost every day but rarely uses the Lortab, although she prefers to keep a supply on hand for times when the disease strikes aggressively. She mentions that she has not had a well-woman examination in 2 years because of the sale of her home and the purchase of a new one in New Rochelle. Dr. Tyler performs the well-woman examination and writes Ms. Huntington an order for a mammogram. She also performs a breast examination, which is included in the well-woman examination. Dr. Tyler spends about 45 minutes with the patient. She asks Ms. Huntington to return in 3 months if she does not feel the need to do so before then. Ms. Huntington is charged $179 for the new patient office visit and $55 for the Pap smear and well-woman examination. She leaves with her prescriptions.

Celeste C. Huntington
554 Georgetown Way
New Rochelle, NY 10801
914-889-6675 (home)
SS# 433-99-2364

Insurance: United Health Care PPO
ID# 433992364
Employer: Loist and Earnest Law Firm
DOB: 9-3-1960

Diagnosis: Systemic lupus erythematosus
Procedures: Office visit, Pap smear
Account Number: HUC2364

New Rochelle Family Medicine
2002 Front Street, Suite 600
New Rochelle, NY 10800
914-661-0001
Federal Tax ID# 75-6234710

Rene Tyler, MD
NPI 6779354390
William R. Curry, MD
NPI 4619907217

United Healthcare
PO Box 292928
New York, NY 10021
212-660-1100

5. Claim Form 5 (Work Product 21-5)

Today's date: 9-29-20XX

Mrs. Saxton, a married female, has several health problems and is a frequent visitor to Dr. Handley's office. She is insured through her own policy with Unicare and also through her husband's policy with Assurant Health. She has Graves' disease, malignant HTN, bursitis of the right knee, and carpel tunnel syndrome. She arrives at the office today to have her blood pressure checked. In the waiting area, she develops mild chest pains, so the medical assistant brings her to the back office immediately and performs an ECG. Upon checking the strip, Dr. Handley thinks that Mrs. Saxton may recently have had a mild heart attack, so he refers her to Dr. Stern, a cardiologist. The office sets up an immediate appointment for Mrs. Saxton, and she leaves the clinic with her husband with instructions to drive directly to Dr. Stern's office. They promise to do so. Mrs. Saxton is charged for the office visit ($165) and an ECG ($45). She is with Dr. Handley for approximately 50 minutes.

Patricia N. Saxton
13104 Highway 798 South
Tyler, TX 75701
903-882-4453 (home)
SS# 334-88-9907

Insurance: Unicare PPO
ID# 334889907
Employer: Self-employed
Husband: Levern R. Saxton
Employer: Kelly Tires
SS# 621-12-6701
ID# 621126701
DOB: 7-8-1953

Diagnosis: Malignant HTN, Graves' disease, bursitis, carpel tunnel syndrome
Procedures: Office visit, ECG
Account Number: SAP9907

South Tyler Health Clinic
120 E. West Street
Tyler, Texas 75703
903-566-1112
Federal Tax ID# 75-2162704

Unicare
12000 Walker Blvd., St. 100
Dallas, Texas 75225
800-921-0091

Wendle Handley, DO
NPI 5682103541

Assurant Health
PO Box 704
Dallas, Texas 75229
800-621-1000

Part II: Determining Diagnosis and Procedure Codes

Determine the proper diagnosis and procedure codes.

1. Diagnosis: Lou Gehrig's disease; hydrocodone dependence

   _____

   Procedures: Office visit, new patient (10 minutes)

   _____

2. Diagnosis: Generalized osteoarthritis in the upper arm

   _____

   Procedures: Office visit, established patient (10 minutes); basic metabolic panel; lipid panel

   _____

3. Diagnosis: Foreign body in the ear

   _____

   Procedures: Office visit, established patient (10 minutes)

   _____

4. Diagnosis: Third-degree burn over 40% of body surface because of car accident with another vehicle; passenger in the car

   _____

   Procedures: Hospital admission, new patient, physician spends approximately 50 minutes treating the patient

   _____

5. Diagnosis: Rosacea

   _____

   Procedure: Office visit, established patient (15 minutes)

   _____

6. Diagnosis: Sunburn, third degree

   _____

   Procedures: Office visit, established patient (10 minutes)

   _____

7. Diagnosis: Tachycardia, neonatal

   _____

   Procedures: Hospital visit, 2 days, inpatient subsequent care (25 minutes)

   _____

8. Diagnosis: Pernicious anemia

   _____

   Procedures: Office visit, established patient, (25 minutes); sedimentation rate, automated; CBC, automated

   _____

9. Diagnosis: Attention deficit disorder with hyperactivity; acute cystitis

_____

   Procedures: Office visit, established patient (15 minutes); urinalysis

_____

10. Diagnosis: Mastitis after delivery of a baby

_____

   Procedures: Office visit, established patient (5 minutes)

_____

CASE STUDY

Research the history of the CMS-1500 claim form. Determine when it was first used and the changes that the form has undergone since its inception. Prepare a report that details these changes, including the most recent modifications to the CMS-1500 (08/05). Present the report to the class.

WORKPLACE APPLICATION OPTION

Complete this activity and, if appropriate, share your results with the class.

Collect several blank encounter forms from various medical specialties. Distribute the forms to classmates, sharing and trading the various forms. Mark several procedures on the forms and at least two diagnoses codes. Prepare a CMS-1500 claim based on information on the encounter forms. Share the information in class, and explain the coding choices that were made on each claim.

INTERNET ACTIVITY OPTIONS

Complete one or more of these activities and, if appropriate, share your results with the class.

1. Review the National Uniform Claim Committee website. Find the User Manual for the CMS-1500 Claim Form (08/05).

2. Find three companies that sell the CMS-1500 claim form. Compare costs and determine the least expensive place to order the form.

3. Research software applications that are available for completing CMS-1500 forms. Determine which of those applications that are available for purchase would be good investments for a physician's office.

22 Professional Fees, Billing, and Collecting

VOCABULARY REVIEW

Fill in the blanks with the correct vocabulary terms from this chapter.

1. Jesse has a(n) _____ _____ of $464, which represents the total amount she owes after her insurance paid a portion of her bill.

2. Mrs. Ramone has a(n) _____ on her account for an overpayment, so the office manager sent her a check for that amount.

3. Robert's mother is the _____ of his bill, because she promised to pay the full amount for her son.

4. Julia had to _____ collections proceedings on several accounts last month, because the patients had not made payments as promised.

5. One of the tasks Pamela enjoys is _____ payments that arrive in the mail to patient accounts.

6. _____ _____ are used more and more often for payments in the physician's office.

7. An organization under contract to the government to handle insurance claims from providers is called a(n) _____ _____.

8. Mrs. Richland called the office to get the balance on her _____.

9. The office staff has been debating whether they should continue to offer _____ _____ to other healthcare providers and their staff members.

10. A business _____, which is any exchange or transfer of goods, services, or funds, must always be recorded.

11. Anna made several _____ for various bills that were due last week.

12. Dr. Taylor's fee _____ is a compilation of the fees he has charged over the past fiscal year.

13. The Peete family was considered _____ _____, because they could not afford medical care even though they were able to pay basic living expenses.

14. Deb sometimes confuses a credit with a(n) _____, which is a deduction from a revenue, net worth, or liability account.

15. Jessica totaled the _____ for the day, which came from patient and insurance payments.

16. State Farm is considered a(n) _____ _____ _____, because Bethany's injuries were sustained in a car accident and State Farm will pay her medical bills.

17. Dr. Martin reviewed his fee _____, which is a compilation of preestablished fee allowances for given services or procedures.

18. The balances due to a creditor on an account are called _____.

19. The Blackburn Clinic uses a computer to determine patient account balances, but June remembers when they used a manual _____ _____.

20. When Madelyn received the denial from Mr. Paul's insurance company, she wondered if he had paid his _____.

SKILLS AND CONCEPTS

Part I: Fee Schedules and Billing Forms

1. Examine the fee schedule on the next page and answer the following questions.

    a. What is the charge for a consultation? _____

    b. What is the charge for a 99203? _____

    c. Why is the charge different for a 99213? _____

    d. What is the most expensive procedure on the list? CPT code _____

    e. Which injection is more expensive, insulin or vitamin B_{12}? _____

Use the same fee schedule to complete the billing forms in Work Products 22-1, 22-2, and 22-3. Circle the codes and fill in the charges for each patient. Assume that all the patients have a previous balance of zero.

2. Work Product 21-1: Marilyn Westmoreland, established patient, straightforward, penicillin injections (75 mg), diagnosis—acute tonsillitis.

3. Work Product 21-2: Jane Wells, consultation, high complexity, ECG, diagnosis—chest pain.

4. Work Product 21-3: Paula Johnson, new patient, detailed, Solu-Medrol injection IM, diagnosis—osteoarthritis.

FEE SCHEDULE

BLACKBURN PRIMARY CARE ASSOCIATES, PC
1990 Turquiose Drive
Blackburn, WI 54937
608-459-8857

Federal Tax ID Number:	00-0000000	**BCBS Group Number: 14982** **Medicare Group Number: 14982**

OFFICE VISIT, NEW PATIENT

Focused, 99201	$45.00
Expanded, 99202	$55.00
Intermediate, 99203	$60.00
Extended, 99204	$95.00
Comprehensive, 99205	$195.00
Consultation, 99245	$250.00

OFFICE VISIT, ESTABLISHED PATIENT

Minimal, 99211	$40.00
Focused, 99212	$48.00
Intermediate, 99213	$55.00
Extended, 99214	$65.00
Comprehensive, 99215	$195.00

OFFICE PROCEDURES

EKG, 12 lead, 93000	$55.00
Stress EKG, Treadmill, 93015	$295.00
Sigmoidoscopy, Flex; 45330	$145.00
Spirometry, 94010	$50.00
Cerumen Removal, 69210	$40.00
Collection & Handling	
Lab Specimen, 99000	$9.00
Venipuncture, 35415	$9.00
Urinalysis, 81000	$20.00
Urinalysis, 81002 (Dip Only)	$12.00
Influenza Injection, 90724	$20.00
Pneumococcal Injection, 90732	$20.00
Oral Polio, 90712	$15.00
DTaP, 90700	$20.00
Tetanus Toxoid, 90703	$15.00
MMR, 90707	$25.00
HIB, 90737	$20.00
Hepatitis B, newborn to age 11 years, 90744	$60.00
Hepatitis B, 11-19 years, 90745	$60.00
Hepatitis B, 20 years and above 90746	$60.00
Intramuscular Injection, 90788	
Penicillin	$30.00
Cephtriaxone	$25.00
Solu-Medrol	$23.00
Vitamin B-12	$13.00
Subcutaneous Injection, 90782	
Epinephrine	$18.00
Susphrine	$25.00
Insulin, U-100	$15.00

COMMON DIAGNOSTIC CODES

Ischemic Heart Disease	414.9
w/o myocardial infarction	411.89
w/coronary occlusion	411.81
Hypertension, Malignant	401.0
Benign	401.1
Unspecified	401.9
w/congest. heart failure	402.91
Asthma, Bronchial	493.9
w/COPD	493.2
allergic, w/S.A.	493.91
allergic, w/o S.A.	493.90
Kyphosis	737.10
w/osteoporosis	733.0
Osteoporosis	733.00
Otitis Media, Acute	382.9
Chronic	382.9

Part II: Ledgers and Computing Patient Balances

Work through the following information and record it on the ledger cards presented in the corresponding work product pages. Use one ledger for each exercise.

Ledger 1—work product 22-4

Meagan Joy Reynolds
5534 Joe Pool Lake Road #233
Cedar Hill, Texas 75884
972-334-0423 (home)
972-331-0934 (cell)
meaganjoy@internet4.com
MR# REYM3341

Entry #	Transaction
1	Meagan comes to the Blackburn Primary Care Clinic on April 12 as a new patient. Her initial charge is $375, because she had a series of x-ray examinations, which were used to diagnose a blockage in her small intestine. Dr. Lupez recommends that she have surgery to correct the blockage as soon as possible. Meagan pays her bill in full with check #7110, although she has insurance coverage through her own policy with Prudential and her husband's policy through Southwest United Healthcare.
2	Meagan checks into Mercy Hospital and has surgery on April 21. Dr. Lupez charges $7,500 for the surgery. This charge will be filed with Meagan's insurances.
3	Meagan returns to the clinic on April 30 for a follow-up office visit. The charge is $150, which she pays in full with check #7261. Dr. Lupez says that she is doing very well since her surgery and asks her to return in mid-May for another checkup.
4	On May 2 the clinic receives an insurance payment from Prudential in the amount of $6,200. This money is applied to Meagan's account. The check number is 617761.
5	On May 3 the clinic receives check #7313 in the mail from Meagan for $300, which is applied to her account.
6	Meagan returns to the clinic on May 14 for an office visit. The charge is $75, and she pays $50 with check #7512.
7	Southwest United sends a check to the clinic for $800 on May 27, which is applied to her account. The check number is 8710.
8	Meagan sends a check for $125 to be put toward her account. The check, #7915, is posted on June 2.
9	Meagan returns to the clinic for an office visit and laboratory work on June 17. Her charges total $352, and she pays $150 with check #8116.
10	On June 20 the clinic receives Meagan's check toward her account for $100. Her check number is 8411.
11	Meagan visits the clinic for treatment of a migraine headache on June 26. Her charge is $85, and she pays $50 with check #8626. She schedules a follow-up visit with Dr. Lupez for June 30.
12	When Meagan returns for her follow-up visit on June 30, her office visit is $85, but she is unable to make a payment.
13	On July 5 the clinic receives a payment from Prudential on behalf of Meagan for $276. The Prudential check number is 721146.
14	On July 18 the clinic receives a check #9210 from Southwest United on behalf of Meagan for $124.
15	On July 31 the clinic refunds Meagan's credit balance to her using clinic check #9425.
16	The previous transaction brings Meagan's account to zero.

How much was the refund check? _____

Chapter **22** **Professional Fees, Billing, and Collecting**

Ledger 2—work product 22-5

Zachary Paul Staley
2324 Hill Avenue Plaza
Grosse Pointe, MI 48230
313-445-9987 (home)
313-565-6623 (cell)
zachattack@aol.com
MR# STAZ9823

Entry#	Transaction
1	Zachary Staley visited the clinic on June 6 as a new patient and was diagnosed with diabetes. His charge was $215. He paid his $15 co-pay with check #126.
2	On June 12 a check arrived from Permian Health for $180 on Zachary's account. The check number was 21617.
3	Zachary returned to the clinic on June 15 for an office visit and laboratory work. The total charge was $128, and Zachary paid his $15 co-pay with check #214.
4	On June 16 Zachary returned to the clinic without an appointment, because he felt extremely dizzy and nauseated. Dr. Hughes determined that his blood sugar had dropped substantially. After his condition was stabilized, his wife picked him up and took him home. She paid his $15 co-pay with check #217. The total charge for the visit was $70.
5	On July 7 check #36171 arrived from Permian Health on Zachary's account in the amount of $142.
6	Bethany, an insurance biller, realized that a $7 charge was not allowed for a laboratory test on Zachary's account. The office policy allows disallowed charges under $10 to be written off, so Bethany adjusts his account by $7 on July 7.
7	Zachary returns to the clinic for a routine visit on July 26 and has laboratory work done. The total charge is $156, and Zachary pays his $15 co-pay with check #310.
8	On August 1 Zachary has a brief office visit and is charged $70. Zachary forgot his checkbook, so he did not pay his co-pay.
9	On August 16 Permian sends check #41217 in the amount of $102 toward Zachary's account.
10	On August 21 Permian sends check #42168 in the amount of $55 toward Zachary's account.
11	On August 30 the clinic receives check #561 from Zachary in the amount of $40 to be placed toward his account.
12	September 6 is Zachary's next office visit, and he is charged $70. He pays his $15 co-pay with check #587.
13	Zachary sends $40 toward his account, which the clinic received on September 9. His check number is 620.
14	Permian Health sends check #53121 in the amount of $98 to the clinic to be applied to Zachary's account on September 15.
15	On October 3 the clinic receives check #681 from Zachary, who remembers that he did not pay his co-pay on August 1. He guesses that he owes about $40 total but is unsure, so he sends $20.
16	The clinic realizes that Zachary has overpaid on his account and sends him a refund for his credit balance using check #6116 on October 4.

How much was the refund check? _____

Ledger 3—work product 22-6

Lynn Annette Wilson
755 South Wheeley #4A
Sacramento, CA 94203
209-552-5437 (home)
209-553-7789 (cell)
lynnannw@yahoo.com
MR# WILL8845

Entry#	Transaction
1	Lynn Annette is a single mother of four who has had a difficult year. She lost a job after contracting infectious mononucleosis and missing 3 weeks of work. She had barely recovered from that illness when she was diagnosed with ulcerative colitis. Her medical bills have become increasingly difficult to pay, although she did find a new job and recently became eligible for coverage through Aetna. She is a determined woman with the best of intentions but often must put rent, utilities, and food costs before the payment of her medical bills. She comes to the clinic for a regular office visit on July 7. Her charges are $125, and she is able to pay the entire bill, since she has been saving the money for several weeks. She pays with check #1205.
2	On July 12 Lynn Annette returns to the office and has laboratory work. Her charges are $89, and she pays her $20 co-pay with check #1314.
3	Bethany in the insurance office notices that Lynn Annette was charged $9 for a single laboratory chemistry test that is not covered by her insurance. Because Bethany knows that Lynn Annette has faced financial difficulties this year, she adjusts the bill so that Lynn Annette will not be responsible for the charge. She also makes a note for the physicians that Lynn Annette's insurance does not cover that particular laboratory test and explains that an alternate chemistry test that will produce the same results is covered. The adjustment is made on July 19.
4	Aetna sends an insurance payment (check #7611493) toward Lynn Annette's account that the clinic received on July 23. The payment is for $85.
5	Bethany processes a refund for Lynn Annette and sends her check #5612 from the clinic account on July 24. This brings her balance to zero.
6	Lynn Annette comes to the office for a regular visit on August 1. Her charges are $284, and she pays her co-pay of $20 with check #1517.
7	On August 18 the clinic receives a check from Aetna for $200 toward Lynn Annette's account. The check number is 8267484.
8	Lynn Annette sends check #1622 in the amount of $64 to clear her account on August 31.
9	On September 12 Lynn Annette's bank returns her recent check payment because of insufficient funds. The clinic adds a charge of $30 to her account as a returned check fee.
10	Lynn Annette comes to the clinic and apologizes for her recent returned check. She explains that she missed getting her paycheck into the bank in time to cover the payment. She brings a cashier's check to cover the check and the fee. The date is September 20.
11	Lynn Annette has minor surgery in the office on October 15. The charge is $750, and she pays a co-pay of $20 in cash.
12	On February 12 Lynn Annette sends a $20 payment on her account, using check #2612. She encloses a note that says she is still having financial difficulties and will send another payment as soon as she can.
13	On April 10 Lynn Annette sends a payment of $5 using check #2711.
14	On May 12 the clinic receives a payment from Lynn Annette in the amount of $5, using check #2781.
15	In accordance with the clinic policy of reporting accounts to a collection agency after 3 months of nonpayment, Bethany reluctantly reports Lynn Annette's account to Smith Collections. The full balance is written off.
16	On September 12 a payment of $100 is received from Lynn Annette. Bethany forwards the payment to the collection agency.

How much was written off of this account? _____

How is the payment noted on the account that was received after the write-off? _____

_____

Completing a Day Sheet

Complete the proofs in Work Product 22-7 using the figures given.

Part III: Short Answers

1. Define the following terms.

    a. Usual _____

    b. Customary _____

    c. Reasonable _____

2. List two billing methods commonly used in the physician's office.

    a. _____

    b. _____

3. What notation should be made under the return address on statement envelopes?

    _____

4. Briefly explain cycle billing.

    _____

    _____

5. What are the pitfalls of fee adjustments?

    _____

    _____

    _____

6. What three values are considered in determining professional fees?

    a. _____

    b. _____

    c. _____

7. Why are estimates useful in patient treatment?

    _____

    _____

    _____

8. List five general rules for telephone collecting.

    a. _____

    b. _____

    c. _____

    d. _____

    e. _____

9. List four ways payment for medical services is accomplished.

a. _____

b. _____

c. _____

d. _____

10. Explain why patients sometimes fail to pay their accounts.

_____

_____

_____

11. What is professional courtesy and why is it less common now than in years past?

_____

_____

_____

12. Briefly explain how "skips" can be traced.

_____

_____

_____

Part IV: Collection Letters

1. Create a collection letter for an account that is 30 days past due.

2. Create a collection letter for an account that is 60 days past due.

3. Create a collection letter for an account that is 90 days past due.

4. Create a collection letter for an account that is 120 days past due.

5. Create a collection letter for an account that is ready to be submitted to a collection agency.

Read back through the information about Lynn Annette Wilson in Ledger 3. How could the medical assistant help Ms. Wilson keep her account out of collections? What could be said to her during a friendly phone call to encourage her to be regular with her payments? Write two collection letters to Ms. Wilson. Make the first letter a gentle reminder. The second letter should express that the account will be placed for collection if regular payments are not forthcoming. Use the stationery provided in Work Products 22-8 and 22-9 to write the collection letters.

WORKPLACE APPLICATION OPTION

Complete this activity and, if appropriate, share your results with the class.

Mr. Sanchez comes to the desk to check out after seeing the physician. When Sarah tells him that his bill is $95, he complains that he only saw the physician for 10 minutes. The fee is in accordance with the evaluation and management guidelines. Explain the fees to Mr. Sanchez.

1. Write what you would say to him to explain his fees.

_____

_____

_____

_____

_____

_____

2. Write a dialogue that could be used to ask a patient for payment as the person is checking out.

_____

_____

_____

_____

_____

_____

_____

INTERNET ACTIVITY OPTIONS

Complete one or more of these activities and, if appropriate, share your results with the class.

1. Research medical billing companies on the Internet and compare the costs of the various services they offer. Prepare a report or presentation for the class.

2. Search for patient accounting software and explore the options available for the physician's office. Write a brief report on one software product and present it to the class.

3. Research the role of an accountant and why most physicians employ one to handle financials for the office. Discuss what the accountant does for the physician.

4. Investigate companies or banks that provide credit card financing for medical services in a physician's office. Talk about the types of offices that would most benefit from financing medical procedures.

5. Explore the fees that are often charged to the office for credit card transactions and discuss whether it is less expensive to process cards as debit cards or credit cards.

23 Banking Services and Procedures

VOCABULARY REVIEW

Fill in the blanks with the correct vocabulary terms from this chapter.

1. Judy was unaware that checks were processed through _____ before they arrived at her bank.

2. Because Alicia was the person who wrote the check, she was considered the _____.

3. When the Blackburn Clinic purchased the ultrasound machine, the clinic paid $10,000 toward the _____ in order to be charged less interest.

4. Pamela wrote a check to Samantha, so Pamela is the _____ and Samantha is the _____.

5. The _____ of a check is the person who presents it for payment and may not be the person named as the payee.

6. Grace studied the _____ _____ _____, which is a series of laws that regulates sales of goods, commercial paper, secured transactions in personal property, and many aspects of banking.

7. First National Bank is considered the _____ for Dr. Lupez's business checking accounts.

8. Instruments that are legally transferable to another party are considered _____.

9. Rhonda made several _____ from the clinic checking account to pay monthly bills and order supplies.

10. As soon as the monthly bank statement arrives, Rhonda does a(n) _____ _____ to make sure the statement and checkbook balances are in agreement.

SKILLS AND CONCEPTS

Part I: Short Answers

1. List the requirements of a negotiable instrument.

   a. _____

   b. _____

   c. _____

   d. _____

2. Name several advantages to online banking.

   _____

   _____

   _____

3. Why is customer service such an important aspect of today's medical offices?

   _____

   _____

   _____

177

4. List four types of checks.

   a. _____

   b. _____

   c. _____

   d. _____

5. Describe each type of endorsement.

   a. Blank

   _____

   b. Restrictive

   _____

   c. Special

   _____

   d. Qualified

   _____

6. List five reasons checks should be deposited promptly.

   a. _____

   b. _____

   c. _____

   d. _____

   e. _____

7. Provide five guidelines for check acceptance.

   a. _____

   b. _____

   c. _____

   d. _____

   e. _____

8. List three reasons an individual might stop payment on a check.

   a. _____

   b. _____

   c. _____

9. Explain the ABA number and what each part of the number means.

   _____

   _____

   _____

10. List the three basic steps for preparing a deposit slip.

   a. _____

   b. _____

   c. _____

11. Where is the routing number found on a check?

   _____

12. Define EFT.

   _____

   _____

   _____

13. Define ACH.

   _____

   _____

   _____

Part II: Writing Checks for Disbursement of Funds

Write checks to pay the following bills. The beginning balance in the checkbook is $4,562.79. Use the checks numbered 5648 to 5651. Determine the balance after the check is written.

1. Write check #5648 to the American Medical Association for $356 for new coding books. Balance _____

2. Write check #5649 to the Blackburn Utility Company for $46.90 to pay the water bill. Balance _____

3. Write a check for the office mortgage payment to First National Bank in the amount of $1,700. Use check #5650.

   Balance _____

4. Write check #5651 to pay a bill to United Drug and Supply of $98.34. Balance _____

5. A deposit of $1,358 was made. Balance _____

Part III: Writing Refund Checks

Write checks for the following refunds. Use the ending balance from Part II, question 5, to determine the final balance in the checking account. Use the checks numbered 5652 to 5655.

1. Ms. Patty Bailey should receive a refund in the amount of $34.55 for an overpayment. Use check #5652. Balance

   _____

2. Write a check for Julie Smithy for $224.12. Her insurance company paid more than expected, so she is entitled to a

   refund. Use check #5653. Balance _____

3. Cindy Chan paid $10 more than she owed when she was seeing Dr. Hughes. Refund her money using check #5654.

   The office manager deposited $7,246.12 in checks. Balance _____

4. Carter Graves decided to postpone his knee surgery when his wife suddenly became ill. Use check #5655 to refund

   his $500 deposit. Balance _____

Part IV: Preparing a Bank Deposit

Prepare a bank deposit detail using the following information. Record your answers on the figure in Work Product 23-1.

1. Cash includes six (6) $20 bills, one (1) $100 bill, one (1) $50 bill, two (2) $10 bills, one (1) $5 bill, and one (1) $1 bill.

   Total cash _____

2. Check payments were #2387 for $67 from Sue Patrick and #460 for $50 from Ronald Rodriguez. Total personal checks _____

3. Credit card payments were $100 and $250. Total credit cards _____

4. An insurance payment for Alejandro Sanchez arrived in the amount of $1,374.32. The payment was from Aetna and the check was #309. Total deposit _____

Part V: Reconciling a Bank Statement

Reconcile the bank statement using the following facts and figures. Use the worksheet on page 183 to show your work.

The checkbook balance is $4,616.96. The statement balance is $6,792.79 (this amount includes the deposit of $2,137.32—do not add that amount again).

1. Three checks are outstanding: check #5648 for $356; check #5649 for $46.90; and check #5650 for $1,770. What is the total for outstanding checks? _____

2. Does the checkbook reconcile with the statement? _____

3. What is the ending balance? _____

5648

DATE _____
TO _____
FOR _____

BALANCE BROUGHT FORWARD		
DEPOSITS		
BALANCE		
AMT THIS CK		
BALANCE CARRIED FORWARD		

BLACKBURN PRIMARY CARE ASSOCIATES, PC
1990 Turquoise Drive
Blackburn, WI 54937
608-459-8857

5648

94-72/1224

DATE _____

PAY TO THE
ORDER OF _____ $ _____

_____ DOLLARS

DERBYSHIRE SAVINGS
Member FDIC
P.O. BOX 8923
Blackburn, WI 54937

FOR _____

⑆055003⑆ 446782011⑆ 678800470

5649

DATE _____
TO _____
FOR _____

BALANCE BROUGHT FORWARD		
DEPOSITS		
BALANCE		
AMT THIS CK		
BALANCE CARRIED FORWARD		

BLACKBURN PRIMARY CARE ASSOCIATES, PC
1990 Turquoise Drive
Blackburn, WI 54937
608-459-8857

5649

94-72/1224

DATE _____

PAY TO THE
ORDER OF _____ $ _____

_____ DOLLARS

DERBYSHIRE SAVINGS
Member FDIC
P.O. BOX 8923
Blackburn, WI 54937

FOR _____

⑆055003⑆ 446782011⑆ 678800470

5650

DATE _____
TO _____
FOR _____

BALANCE BROUGHT FORWARD		
DEPOSITS		
BALANCE		
AMT THIS CK		
BALANCE CARRIED FORWARD		

BLACKBURN PRIMARY CARE ASSOCIATES, PC
1990 Turquoise Drive
Blackburn, WI 54937
608-459-8857

5650

94-72/1224

DATE _____

PAY TO THE
ORDER OF _____ $ _____

_____ DOLLARS

DERBYSHIRE SAVINGS
Member FDIC
P.O. BOX 8923
Blackburn, WI 54937

FOR _____

⑆055003⑆ 446782011⑆ 678800470

5651

DATE _____
TO _____
FOR _____

BALANCE BROUGHT FORWARD		
DEPOSITS		
BALANCE		
AMT THIS CK		
BALANCE CARRIED FORWARD		

BLACKBURN PRIMARY CARE ASSOCIATES, PC
1990 Turquoise Drive
Blackburn, WI 54937
608-459-8857

5651

94-72/1224

DATE _____

PAY TO THE
ORDER OF _____ $ _____

_____ DOLLARS

DERBYSHIRE SAVINGS
Member FDIC
P.O. BOX 8923
Blackburn, WI 54937

FOR _____

⑆055003⑆ 446782011⑆ 678800470

181

5652

DATE _____
TO _____
FOR _____

BALANCE BROUGHT FORWARD		
DEPOSITS		
BALANCE		
AMT THIS CK		
BALANCE CARRIED FORWARD		

BLACKBURN PRIMARY CARE ASSOCIATES, PC
1990 Turquoise Drive
Blackburn, WI 54937
608-459-8857

5652

94-72/1224

DATE _____

PAY TO THE
ORDER OF _____ $ _____

_____ DOLLARS

DERBYSHIRE SAVINGS
Member FDIC
P.O. BOX 8923
Blackburn, WI 54937

FOR _____

⑆055003⑆ 446782011⑆ 678800470

5653

DATE _____
TO _____
FOR _____

BALANCE BROUGHT FORWARD		
DEPOSITS		
BALANCE		
AMT THIS CK		
BALANCE CARRIED FORWARD		

BLACKBURN PRIMARY CARE ASSOCIATES, PC
1990 Turquoise Drive
Blackburn, WI 54937
608-459-8857

5653

94-72/1224

DATE _____

PAY TO THE
ORDER OF _____ $ _____

_____ DOLLARS

DERBYSHIRE SAVINGS
Member FDIC
P.O. BOX 8923
Blackburn, WI 54937

FOR _____

⑆055003⑆ 446782011⑆ 678800470

5654

DATE _____
TO _____
FOR _____

BALANCE BROUGHT FORWARD		
DEPOSITS		
BALANCE		
AMT THIS CK		
BALANCE CARRIED FORWARD		

BLACKBURN PRIMARY CARE ASSOCIATES, PC
1990 Turquoise Drive
Blackburn, WI 54937
608-459-8857

5654

94-72/1224

DATE _____

PAY TO THE
ORDER OF _____ $ _____

_____ DOLLARS

DERBYSHIRE SAVINGS
Member FDIC
P.O. BOX 8923
Blackburn, WI 54937

FOR _____

⑆055003⑆ 446782011⑆ 678800470

5655

DATE _____
TO _____
FOR _____

BALANCE BROUGHT FORWARD		
DEPOSITS		
BALANCE		
AMT THIS CK		
BALANCE CARRIED FORWARD		

BLACKBURN PRIMARY CARE ASSOCIATES, PC
1990 Turquoise Drive
Blackburn, WI 54937
608-459-8857

5655

94-72/1224

DATE _____

PAY TO THE
ORDER OF _____ $ _____

_____ DOLLARS

DERBYSHIRE SAVINGS
Member FDIC
P.O. BOX 8923
Blackburn, WI 54937

FOR _____

⑆055003⑆ 446782011⑆ 678800470

THIS WORKSHEET IS PROVIDED TO HELP YOU BALANCE YOUR ACCOUNT

1. Go through your register and mark each check, withdrawal, Express ATM transaction, payment, deposit, or other credit listed on this statement. Be sure that your register shows any interest paid into your account, and any service charges, automatic payments, or Express Transfers withdrawn from your account during this statement period.

2. Using the chart below, list any outstanding checks, Express ATM withdrawals, payments, or any other withdrawals (including any from previous months) that are listed in your register but are not shown on this statement.

3. Balance your account by filling in the spaces below.

ITEMS OUTSTANDING		
NUMBER	AMOUNT	
TOTAL	$	

ENTER

The NEW BALANCE shown on
this statement_____$

ADD

Any deposits listed in your register $
or transfers into your account $
which are not shown on this $
statement.   + $ _____

TOTAL

CALCULATE THE SUBTOTAL_____$

SUBTRACT

The total outstanding checks and
withdrawals from the chart at left_____-$

CALCULATE THE ENDING BALANCE

This amount should be the same
as the current balance shown in
your check register_____$

The Internet has changed the way business is conducted, both in the United States and beyond U.S. borders. Some individuals are quite comfortable making purchases and paying bills online. How safe are these practices? How can the medical assistant know that online bill paying services are safe and secure? Research this information and prepare a report for the class.

WORKPLACE APPLICATION OPTION

Complete this activity and, if appropriate, share your results with the class.

The more versatile the medical assistant is, the more valuable he or she will be to the physician employer. Often new graduates hesitate to ask patients to pay their accounts. However, a medical assistant who is able to collect patient accounts increases the cash flow in the office. How might the medical assistant succinctly explain the various ways a patient can make a payment?

INTERNET ACTIVITY OPTIONS

Complete one or more of these activities and, if appropriate, share your results with the class.

1. Explore several types of billing software. Determine which seems to be the best option for a medium-sized family practice clinic. Pay special attention to software that has banking features.

2. Investigate the history of banking and prepare a report for the class.

3. Research safety measures designed to keep confidential banking information private. How do privacy policies affect Internet banking? How can the medical assistant ensure that private information remains private? Prepare a paper or report for the class on this subject.

4. Explore which banks offer apps that allow the users to deposit checks using their smart phone. Explain how the process is done and how long the process takes before the bank receives the information and credits the deposit to the user's account.

5. Research the federal Check 21 law. Determine how it affects individuals and businesses. Share the information with the class.

24 Financial and Practice Management

VOCABULARY REVIEW

Fill in the blanks with the correct vocabulary terms from this chapter.

1. Jenna told Andrea that a(n) _____ year is often different from a calendar year.

2. Julia works with the accounts _____ _____, which is the money that is owed to the physicians.

3. Anna works with the accounts _____ _____, which is the money the physicians owe to others.

4. Once a year Dr. Medina has his accountant total his _____ _____, which include the entire properties subject to the payment of debts.

5. Larry is the supervisor of the _____ _____ department, which records all business and accounting transactions.

6. The _____ _____ in question was sent last month, but the equipment never arrived, so Julia questions whether she should pay the entire balance due.

7. The Rosales Clinic uses the _____ _____ basis of accounting, in which income is recorded when received and expenses are recorded when paid.

8. When the total ending balance of patient ledgers equals the total of accounts receivable control, the two are said to be _____ _____.

9. The accountant prepared a(n) _____ _____ sheet for December 31, which showed the total assets, liabilities, and capital for the clinic.

10. The Tyler Clinic uses the _____ _____ basis of accounting, in which income is recorded when earned and expenses are recorded when incurred.

11. Alice keeps a(n) _____ _____ on her desk that summarizes accounts paid out.

12. Each patient receives a(n) _____ _____ every month if the balance on his or her account is more than $5.

13. Running a(n) _____ _____ is one method of checking the accuracy of accounts.

14. Joy takes minor expenses, such as those for sodas and small donations, from the _____ _____ fund.

15. Dr. Lupez asked his accountant to prepare a statement of _____ and _____ for the previous fiscal year.

16. A standard of comparison to make sure answers obtained are accurate is a(n) _____.

17. A(n) _____ _____ _____ is a summary for a specific period that shows a beginning balance, an ending balance, and all the expenditures during that particular period.

18. Angelique keeps a record of all accounts paid out in a(n) _____ _____.

19. Something that is owed, or a debt, is called a(n) _____.

20. The monetary value of a property or of an interest in a property in excess of claims or liens against it is called _____.

21. The office manager sent a strong _____ to employees about legible writing in charts and on phone messages.

SKILLS AND CONCEPTS

Part I: Short Answers

1. What items should appear on the financial records of any business at all times?

   a. _____

   b. _____

   c. _____

   d. _____

2. When writing numbers, keep the columns straight and write _____ _____ _____.

3. What item must be shown on the manual disbursement journal?

   a. _____

   b. _____

   c. _____

4. Name two common accounting systems used in medical offices.

   a. _____

   b. _____

5. Differentiate between accounting and bookkeeping.

   _____

   _____

   _____

6. List three cardinal rules of bookkeeping.

   a. _____

   b. _____

   c. _____

7. List two disadvantages of a single-entry system.

   a. _____

   b. _____

8. The Internal Revenue Service (IRS) requires that complete records be kept on all employees. Which records must be included?

a. _____

b. _____

c. _____

d. _____

9. What is Form 940 used for and when must it be filed?

_____

_____

_____

10. List seven expense categories often found in a physician's office budget.

a. _____

b. _____

c. _____

d. _____

e. _____

f. _____

g. _____

Part II: Bookkeeping Systems

Briefly explain the three types of bookkeeping systems.

1. Single-entry system

_____

_____

_____

2. Double-entry system

_____

_____

_____

3. Pegboard/write-it-once system

_____

_____

_____

4. Which of the three systems do you think would be the easiest to work with in the medical office? Why?

_____

_____

_____

_____

Part III: Forms

Briefly explain the use of each of the following forms.

1. SS-5

_____

_____

_____

2. W-2

_____

_____

_____

3. W-3

_____

_____

_____

4. W-4

_____

_____

_____

Read the case study and complete the exercise following it.

Kristy Stephens works for Dr. Mitchell, who has a small office in a suburban area just outside Birmingham, Alabama. The longer that Kristy works for Dr. Mitchell, the more she learns about accounting and the business side of running a successful medical practice. Kristy is a very organized person and wants to make sure she follows the right procedures and understands why a certain task must be done a certain way. She wants to establish a calendar that shows what duties should be done at what times.

Determine when all the forms in Part III must be turned in or filed. Add tax day to the calendar. Print the calendar, showing all filing dates on it. If a template will help, use one from the Microsoft Office home page.

WORKPLACE APPLICATION OPTIONS

Complete the following math review test. Turn it in to your instructor for grading or grade it in class.

Solve the following addition problems.

1. 99 + 104 = _____

2. 78 + 57 = _____

3. 98 + 128 = _____

4. 187 + 233 = _____

5. 284 + 440 = _____

6. 306 + 291 = _____

7. 204 + 278 = _____

8. 409 + 246 = _____

9. 15 + 74 = _____

10. 181 + 369 = _____

Solve the following subtraction problems.

1. 290 − 303 = _____

2. 231 − 263 = _____

3. 453 − 156 = _____

4. 459 − 325 = _____

5. 318 − 105 = _____

6. 398 − 294 = _____

Solve the following multiplication problems.

1. 46 × 24 = _____

2. 11 × 49 = _____

3. 48 × 17 = _____

4. 26 × 24 = _____

5. 42 × 15 = _____

6. 5 × 49   = _____

7. 47 × 12 = _____

8. 26 × 34 = _____

9. 45 × 21 = _____

Solve the following division problems.

1. 1,950 ÷ 13 = _____

2. 50,350 ÷ 53 = _____

3. 12,105 ÷ 15 = _____

4. 9,712 ÷ 16 = _____

5. 13,500 ÷ 20 = _____

INTERNET ACTIVITY OPTIONS

Complete one or more of these activities and, if appropriate, share your results with the class.

1. Investigate bookkeeping software on the Internet and use any tutorials or trial software available. Determine a good program for use in the medical office and be able to defend your decision in a class presentation.

2. Look for math worksheet sites and work through some of the sheets for practice.

3. Find the IRS form W-4 and review the Personal Allowances Worksheet. Following the directions, determine the deductions that you could personally claim, based on your situation while in school. Also, review the Deductions and Adjustments Worksheet as well as the Two Earners/Multiple Jobs Worksheet. Determine if either of these worksheets would apply to your personal situation.

4. On the IRS website, find pages that answer questions about quarterly and annual returns. How can the medical assistant learn more about the tax requirements for a physician's office?

VOCABULARY REVIEW

Fill in the blank with the correct vocabulary term from this chapter.

1. Dr. Hughes enjoys offering _____ to employees who perform over and above the call of duty.

2. Lucia told a(n) _____ lie to her supervisor, which almost resulted in termination of her employment.

3. The staff enjoys _____ talks and recently traveled to North Dallas to hear a famous motivational speaker.

4. Employee _____ can indicate the working conditions at a facility; when the staff is happy with their jobs, they tend to remain in their positions for a number of years.

5. Mrs. Gordon has always been a great promoter of employee _____, never failing to offer her smile and a kind word to others.

6. Ruth Ann was written up for _____ after she and Sue Lynn, her supervisor, had a rather loud and tense discussion last week.

7. The marketers _____ young women in their latest advertisements to promote the hospital expansion in the labor and delivery department.

8. New employees may find it helpful to be assigned a(n) _____, who will assist them as they learn the office routines and responsibilities.

9. The office manager assigned several new duties to Ann, including development of meeting _____.

10. Sandy had 17 performance _____ to give over the course of the week.

11. People in the medical field sometimes experience _____ and feel a need to separate themselves from the profession for a time.

12. Paul was charged with _____ after he took money from the physical therapy clinic where he formerly worked.

13. The doctors and management personnel have worked hard to develop such a(n) _____ team.

14. A(n) _____ of _____ is necessary in any organization, even smaller ones.

15. Barbara is _____ with her paperwork and seldom makes an error.

Part I: Office Managers

1. Why is it a good idea to have one person in charge of office operations?

   _____

   _____

   _____

2. Most management problems can be prevented by carefully defining which areas?

   a. _____

   b. _____

3. What usually happens if a manager helps employees get what they want and need from a job?

   _____

   _____

   _____

4. Managers who have a group of outstanding employees are usually looked upon as _____

   _____.

5. List the three basic types of leaders.

   a. _____

   b. _____

   c. _____

6. List and explain three types of power.

   a. _____

   b. _____

   c. _____

7. The office manager must always have enough written _____ when terminating an employee.

8. List five ways to motivate employees.

   a. _____

   b. _____

   c. _____

   d. _____

   e. _____

9. What is a "yes" person?

   _____

   _____

10. What is one of the most effective ways to improve employee morale?

_____

_____

Part II: Hiring and Terminating Employees
Fill in the blank with the best answer.

1. One of the most effective methods of finding new employees is through word of _____.

2. When calling a job candidate to schedule an interview, the office manager has an opportunity to judge how well the person speaks on the _____.

3. The job candidate should fill out the application at the office by hand so that the applicant's _____ can be evaluated.

4. If the job candidate feels at _____, he or she will be able to share strengths and will communicate better during the interview.

5. Relationships with those who work in the medical office should, above all else, be _____.

6. Candidates may be required to submit to a(n) _____ check, especially if they will be handling office finances.

7. One of the most critical errors in bringing a new staff member to the team is not providing fair and adequate

   _____ and _____.

8. Well-written job _____ list the essential functions of the job and specify the chain of command that should be followed in the office.

9. A dismissed employee should never be left in the office _____.

10. Always check at least _____ references when hiring a new employee.

Part III: Leading During Transitions and Change
Add the appropriate word to the following sentences about change.

1. Change _____.

2. _____ with the change.

3. _____ change.

4. _____ to change quickly.

5. _____ change.

6. Anticipate _____.

Part IV: Meeting Agendas
Number these activities in the correct order for a staff meeting.

____ Discussion of unfinished business
____ Adjournment
____ Discussion of problems in the administrative area
____ Discussion of new business
____ Reading of the minutes from the last meeting
____ Discussion of problems in the clinical area
____ Discussion of problems in the common areas

Read the case study and perform the exercise following it.

Belinda is a single mom with two children. She recently was divorced from her husband and is in the process of rebuilding her life. She enrolled in medical assisting school 8 months ago and is now preparing for graduation. Throughout her time in classes, she has researched medical facilities on the Internet and found several that are close to her apartment complex.

Belinda has several goals in life, and the most important ones involve her family. She wants to find a job that will allow her to take care of her children, provide them a good education, and save for their college education. She knows that she needs to find a job that offers health benefits. Belinda is a loyal employee and has a work history, so she is hopeful that her positions from graduation forward will be such that she is able to make steady progress toward reaching her goals.

What goals do you have for your life after graduation? Assess your own personal situation and determine five long-term (life) goals, five short-term goals (1 year or more away), and 10 immediate goals (for the next 6 months). Write the goals down. For the long- and short-term goals, include a few sentences that explain why the goal is important to you. Make sure all the immediate goals are attainable in a 6-month period.

Look over your list daily. Write down all the progress you have made toward the goals, and celebrate when you attain each one. It may be beneficial to keep a journal that details the progress you make toward your goals, as well as the new ones you set as your original goals are met.

WORK APPLICATION OPTIONS

Complete one or more of these activities and, if appropriate, share your results with the class.

1. Revise or write a new patient information booklet and assign different groups of classmates to work on different sections of the booklet. Plan a staff meeting, and send a memo to each classmate who should attend. Write an agenda for the meeting, set a time limit, and determine a general subject to discuss. Each group should discuss its part of the booklet during the meeting.

2. Compose a rough draft of your résumé. Allow three classmates to proof the document and make suggestions. Draft a final copy and turn it in to the instructor for a grade.

INTERNET ACTIVITY OPTIONS

Complete one or more of these activities and, if appropriate, share your results with the class.

1. Develop a manager's checklist for all of the paperwork that a new hire needs to complete. Search the Internet for examples of forms and checklists.

2. Search the Internet for employment laws that pertain specifically to your state.

3. Select one employment law from this chapter and research it on the Internet. Look for real-life cases in which the law was breached, including any court action or rulings that pertain to the law. Share the information you find with the class.

4. Find team-builder exercises designed to promote and build teamwork for a group of employees. Share the exercises with the class and select several of them to try among classmates. Briefly critique each one, determining how the exercise benefits the employees.

26 Medical Practice Marketing and Customer Service

VOCABULARY REVIEW

Fill in the blanks with the correct vocabulary terms from this chapter.

1. Dr. Julie Todd and Dr. Robert Todd truly enjoy _____, because it provides an opportunity to reach and involve diverse audiences using key messages and effective programs.

2. Monica has identified several _____ _____ and has a strong idea for marketing efforts that she plans to implement over the next year.

3. When you are developing a marketing plan, clearly establish _____ and think about the long- and short-term goals for the practice.

4. Monica wants to develop a(n) _____ business plan that is workable and will be flexible if changes become necessary.

5. One area Monica hopes to improve is the _____ laboratory, because much of the equipment is outdated and needs to be replaced.

6. _____ is the process of creating a unique name and image in a customer's mind using a consistent theme.

SKILLS AND CONCEPTS

Part I: Short Answers

1. List the three steps generally followed in preparing to implement or change medical marketing strategies.

   a. _____

   b. _____

   c. _____

2. What is meant by "reaching the target market"?

   _____

   _____

   _____

3. List five specific planning steps that are effective for developing marketing strategies.

   a. _____

   b. _____

   c. _____

   d. _____

   e. _____

4. List several phrases that should never be used with patients, especially when attempting to provide exceptional customer service.

a. _____

b. _____

c. _____

d. _____

5. Explain the concept that good customer service is a commitment.

_____

_____

_____

6. What are the four Ps of marketing?

a. _____

b. _____

c. _____

d. _____

7. How does the provider determine what services to offer at the practice?

_____

_____

_____

8. Provide five examples of community involvement that may help a medical practice grow.

a. _____

b. _____

c. _____

d. _____

e. _____

9. What is the difference between advertising and public relations?

_____

_____

_____

10. List the four basic steps of creating a website.

a. _____

b. _____

c. _____

d. _____

11. What is the goal of any business?

_____

_____

_____

12. Why is it necessary for medical assistants to provide a high level of customer service to those who visit the physician's office?

_____

_____

_____

13. Define and provide two examples of branding.

_____

_____

_____

Part II: Website Evaluation

Research various websites for healthcare organizations, preferably in your geographic area. Rate the websites from 1 to 10 (10 being the best), by putting your ranking on the line to the left of the website name. Then fill in the chart that follows, putting the websites in the order in which you ranked them.

Rank	Website Name	Rank	Website Name
_____	_____	_____	_____
_____	_____	_____	_____
_____	_____	_____	_____
_____	_____	_____	_____
_____	_____	_____	_____

Website	Overall Appeal	Content	Ease of Navigation	Fonts	Consistency	Comments
1						
2						
3						
4						
5						
6						
7						
8						
9						
10						

Part III: Customers in the Physician's Office

1. Who are some of the customers who visit the medical office?

   _____

   _____

   _____

2. Explain how to provide patients and other guests in the office with exceptional customer service.

   _____

   _____

   _____

Part IV: Ethics, Marketing, and Public Relations

1. Do you think that any advertising for medical services is ethical? Why or why not?

   _____

   _____

   _____

2. Why has advertising become necessary in today's health industry?

   _____

   _____

   _____

CASE STUDY

Read the case study and answer the question at the end.

Lorendia has worked for Dr. Johnson for more than 15 years. Recently she was forced to cut her hours from 40 a week to 35, because she has been diagnosed with chronic fatigue syndrome, and she struggles toward the end of the week because of the symptoms of the disease. Lorendia has become more and more impatient with the people who come to the physician's office, and she often makes a snippy remark when she is behind in her duties. Her attitude has alienated her from most of the clinic's staff. Although her job performance is not acceptable now, for most of her career her work has been above reproach.

How can this situation be resolved so that Lorendia can keep her job yet improve her performance?

_____

_____

_____

WORKPLACE APPLICATION OPTION

Complete this activity and, if appropriate, share your results with the class.

Providing exceptional customer service can actually interfere with job duties. Some workers use customer service as an excuse to chat with patients and avoid other duties. Determine how the medical assistant can strike a balance between providing the customer service that patients deserve and completing all the tasks required each day.

INTERNET ACTIVITY OPTIONS

Complete one or more of these activities and, if appropriate, share your results with the class.

1. Research customer service and develop your own, original definition of the concept of customer service. Present your thoughts to the class by creating a professional presentation.

2. Research public relations and make a list of the various "free" ways publicity can be generated for the office. Choose five ideas you feel are the best. E-mail these ideas to each of your classmates. If the entire class participates, everyone will have numerous fresh ideas to use once they begin their career. Write the ideas on index cards and keep them in a box or develop a portfolio of ideas.

3. Design a fictional website using free software on the Internet. If appropriate, share the site with classmates and compare ideas.

4. Create a fictional medical clinic and explain how social media could be used to enhance its web presence. Provide examples of specific ways in which social media would drive patients to use the website or the actual facility.

5. Choose one type of social media and research its history on the Internet. Prepare a detailed report for the class with information about the media's beginnings, changes or modifications, and outlook for future use.

27 Infection Control

Define the following terms.

1. Anaphylaxis

   _____

2. Antibody

   _____

3. Antigen

   _____

4. Antiseptic

   _____

5. Autoimmune

   _____

6. Contaminated

   _____

7. Coagulate

   _____

8. Fomite

   _____

9. Germicides

   _____

10. Interferon

    _____

11. Palliative

    _____

12. Parenteral

    _____

13. Pathogenic

    _____

14. Permeable

_____

15. Relapse

_____

16. Remission

_____

17. Spores

_____

18. Urticaria

_____

19. Vector

_____

Match the following terms with the correct definition.

_____ 20. Disinfection

_____ 21. Medical asepsis

_____ 22. Surgical asepsis

_____ 23. Sanitization

_____ 24. Sterilization

a. Removal of disease-causing organisms or destruction of the organisms after they leave the body

b. Destruction of all microorganisms

c. Destruction of organisms before they enter the body

d. A cleansing process that reduces the number of microorganisms to a safe level as dictated by public health guidelines

e. The process of killing pathogenic organisms or rendering them inactive

Define the following terms as they relate to disease processes.

25. Chronic

_____

26. Latent

_____

27. Acute

_____

SKILLS AND CONCEPTS

Part I: Short Answers

1. Describe the five conditions needed for microorganisms to grow.

   a. _____

   b. _____

   c. _____

202

d. _____

e. _____

2. List five groups of infectious organisms.

   a. _____

   b. _____

   c. _____

   d. _____

   e. _____

3. Label the chain of infection diagram with the following terms. Place the correct number in the chain of infection next to the corresponding letters that follow.

   a. Reservoir host _____

   b. Entry (any body opening) _____

   c. Transmission mode (air, food, hand, insects, body fluid) _____

   d. Exit mode (mouth, skin, rectum, body fluid) _____

   e. Susceptible host _____

4. The human body has several natural protective mechanisms to defend itself from infections. Summarize them here.

   _____

   _____

   _____

   _____

   _____

5. Describe the impact of the inflammatory response on the body's ability to defend itself against infection.

_____

_____

_____

6. Explain the difference between cell-mediated immunity and humoral immunity.

_____

_____

_____

7. List six common errors of disinfection.

a. _____

b. _____

c. _____

d. _____

e. _____

f. _____

8. Explain the five major areas included in the Occupational Safety and Health Administration (OSHA) Compliance Guidelines.

a. _____

b. _____

c. _____

d. _____

e. _____

9. List five bodily fluids that have been identified as potentially infectious by the Centers for Disease Control and Prevention (CDC).

a. _____

b. _____

c. _____

d. _____

e. _____

10. Identify four safety rules that should be followed in the ambulatory care setting to comply with OSHA's environmental protection guidelines.

a. _____

b. _____

c. _____

d. _____

11. Place a check mark beside the procedures that require the use of disposable gloves.

_____ Assisting with a vaginal examination

_____ Performing a routine urinalysis

_____ Measuring a patient's temperature, pulse, and respirations

_____ Performing a patient interview

_____ Drawing blood from a 6-year-old child

CASE STUDIES

1. Rosa is explaining the signs and symptoms of inflammation to a patient. List the four classic symptoms.

   a. _____

   b. _____

   c. _____

   d. _____

2. A patient asks Rosa why the physician did not prescribe an antibiotic for her viral illness. What should Rosa say to the patient? Include in your discussion the physician's concerns about antibiotic resistance.

   _____

   _____

   _____

   _____

3. Mrs. Beck has been diagnosed with the flu. Explain why she might be ordered either over-the-counter (OTC) or prescribed medication as a palliative treatment for this viral infection. Give an example of an OTC that the physician might recommend to relieve her discomfort.

   _____

   _____

   _____

   _____

4. While performing venipuncture, Rosa receives an accidental needle stick. Describe the postexposure instructions and follow-up procedures.

   _____

   _____

   _____

   _____

5. Rosa realizes that her patient needs to be educated about proper asepsis. However, in a busy office, the staff does not have a lot of extra time. What can Rosa do during her time with the patient to educate the person properly about aseptic technique? Explain the difference between an antiseptic and a disinfectant.

   _____

   _____

   _____

   _____

6. Rosa is responsible for teaching a new member of the staff to sanitize and disinfect properly the instruments used throughout a typical day in the facility. What PPE should the employee use to protect herself from possible contamination? What are the important steps in cleaning instruments so that all biologic material is removed? What are some reasons disinfection might not occur? How can the medical assistant prevent these errors?

_____

_____

_____

_____

_____

WORKPLACE APPLICATION OPTIONS

Complete one or more of these activities and, if appropriate, share your results with the class.

1. Employers with workers who are at risk for occupational exposure to blood or other infectious materials must implement an Occupational Safety and Health Administration (OSHA) Exposure Control Plan that details employee protection procedures. List seven items that should be included in the plan.

a. _____

b. _____

c. _____

d. _____

e. _____

f. _____

g. _____

2. Rosa is concerned that she may be allergic to latex. For what signs and symptoms should she look when she puts on latex gloves? Is Rosa's employer required to supply her with latex-free gloves if she does have a latex allergy? Why or why not?

_____

_____

_____

_____

3. Rosa is helping to update the OSHA Exposure Control Plan in her office. She wants to include a policy for wearing gloves. List six different times gloves should be worn.

a. _____

b. _____

c. _____

d. _____

e. _____

f. _____

4. To prevent cross contamination of infectious materials among patients, herself, and other staff members, it is vital that Rosa understand and follow the CDC's recommendations for adequate hand hygiene. Summarize these guidelines.

_____

_____

_____

_____

5. Review Procedure 27-4: Performing Medical Aseptic Hand Washing in your textbook. What did you learn? Practice proper hand washing for the next 24 hours. Note any new habits you have formed. Do you see any improvement? Have you noticed the hand-washing behaviors of others? Explain the difference between resident and transient bacteria.

_____

_____

_____

6. Rosa is assisting the physician with a dressing change when a patient suspected of having tuberculosis coughs, and mucus splatters into Rosa's eyes. Based on what you learned in Procedure 27-2, what should Rosa do?

_____

_____

_____

INTERNET ACTIVITY OPTIONS

Complete one or more of these activities and, if appropriate, share your results with the class.

1. Visit www.osha.gov. Review the OSHA Bloodborne Pathogens Standards. What can you do in your workplace to prevent accidental exposure to blood-borne pathogens? Did you find anything surprising in the guidelines or on the website? Prepare to discuss your answers in class.

2. Visit the Infection Control area of the CDC site at www.cdc.gov/ncidod/dhqp/index.html. Investigate the material on healthcare-associated infections and summarize what you have learned.

28 Patient Assessment

VOCABULARY REVIEW

Fill in the blanks with the correct vocabulary terms from this chapter.

1. Lilly's _____ for seeing the physician today is a sore throat.

2. A(n) _____ is the conclusion the physician reaches after evaluating all the findings, including laboratory and other test results.

3. "IBS vs. Gastroenteritis" listed under the impression is an example of a(n) _____.

4. _____ means pertaining to the operation of the mind by which we become aware of perceiving, thinking, and remembering.

5. _____ is the relationship of harmony and accord that exists between the patient and the healthcare provider.

6. A(n) _____ healthcare approach considers all aspects of an individual's life when treating a physical problem.

7. An important part of therapeutic communications is to establish _____ between verbal and nonverbal messages.

SKILLS AND CONCEPTS

Part I: Short Answers

1. Describe some factors that influence a person's value system. Do you think these factors have influenced your values?

   _____

   _____

   _____

   _____

2. Define the three processes of active listening.

   a. _____

   b. _____

   c. _____

3. Identify four important rules to remember when preparing the appropriate environment for patient interaction.

   a. _____

   b. _____

   c. _____

   d. _____

4. List and describe the six components of the medical history.

a. _____

b. _____

c. _____

d. _____

e. _____

f. _____

5. Define the three stages of the patient interview.

a. _____

b. _____

c. _____

6. Therapeutic nonverbal behaviors are key to a successful interview process. Summarize four examples of nonverbal behavior that enhance therapeutic communication with patients.

a. _____

b. _____

c. _____

d. _____

7. Label the following questions as either open ended or closed ended.

_____ a. How have you been feeling?

_____ b. Do you have a headache?

_____ c. Have you ever broken a bone?

_____ d. What brings you to the physician?

_____ e. Are you feeling better?

_____ f. Do you have high blood pressure?

_____ g. Tell me about your back pain.

_____ h. When did the nausea start?

_____ i. Did your mother have a history of cancer?

_____ j. Do you smoke?

8. Describe the difference between a patient's signs of a disease and his or her possible symptoms.

_____

_____

_____

9. Label the following as "subjective" (symptom) or "objective" (sign).

a. Pain _____

b. Nausea _____

c. Dizziness _____

d. Elevated blood pressure _____

210

e. Labored respirations _____

f. Headache _____

g. Temperature of the skin _____

h. Back pain _____

i. Color of the skin _____

j. Abdominal pain _____

10. Describe the four components of the POMR.

a. _____

b. _____

c. _____

d. _____

11. Identify and explain four questions that could be used to clarify a patient's perception of pain.

a. _____

b. _____

c. _____

d. _____

12. Identify the defense mechanism displayed by these patients.

a. A patient who refuses to believe she has breast cancer.

_____

b. A 5-year-old child who starts to suck his thumb again when he is ill.

_____

c. A patient who accuses you of being disrespectful when he has acted that way himself.

_____

d. A patient who explains that she missed her appointment because she was so busy and she really didn't need to follow up on the biopsy results anyway.

_____

13. The first letter of each part of the progress note makes up the word SOAPE. Explain the meaning of each of these letters.

S _____

O _____

A _____

P _____

E _____

14. What is a SOMR? How is it organized? What is the major disadvantage of this system?

_____

_____

_____

15. What is an EHR? What are some advantages and disadvantages of this type of medical record?

_____

_____

_____

16. Define the following abbreviations.

ac _____   bid _____

BP _____   CAD _____

CHF _____   CVA _____

CXR _____   dc _____

DVT _____   Dx _____

f/u _____   fx _____

hs _____   HTN _____

Hx _____   MI _____

NKA _____   NPO _____

prn _____   pt _____

RBC _____   R/O _____

Rx _____   stat _____

URI _____   VS _____

17. Define the following medical word parts.

a- _____   aden/o _____

adip/o _____   -algesia _____

-algia _____   arthro _____

brady- _____   cardi/o _____

cephal/o _____   -clast _____

cyan/o _____   gastr/o _____

hem/o _____   hepat/o _____

hyper- _____   hyster/o _____

inter- _____   intra- _____

leuk/o _____   lith/o _____

-malacia _____   -penia _____

phleb/o _____   -pnea _____

py/o _____   -sclerosis _____

-stenosis _____   cyst/o _____

cyt/o _____   -ectomy _____

-emia _____   morph/o _____

my/o _____   olig/o _____

supra- _____   tachy- _____

thorac/o _____   viscer/o _____

In the following case studies, what types of interview barriers are indicated? Explain how these statements are dangerous and may interfere with the patient interview.

1. Mrs. Miller is expressing her concern about a changing mole in her left axillary region. Chris, the medical assistant obtaining her health history, makes the statement, "Mrs. Miller, the dysplastic nevus found in the left axillary region looks as if it could be malignant. You have not been using sunscreen, have you?"

   _____

   _____

   _____

2. Mr. Sunsari is being seen today for a suspicious mass in his left lung. The physician has recommended a biopsy of the mass; however, Mr. Sunsari prefers to postpone the procedure. He asks Chris what he should do about scheduling the procedure. Chris states, "I would do it right away."

   _____

   _____

   _____

3. Carmen Largosi is a diabetic patient who is very concerned about her blood glucose levels. Her mother was a diabetic and had to have her left leg amputated. When Carmen expresses her fears, Chris responds with, "I wouldn't worry about that. The doctor is very good with diabetic patients."

   _____

   _____

   _____

How can you display sensitivity to the diverse influences on the patients in the following case studies? Explain the rationale behind your behavior.

1. Mrs. Nyguen Xu will not establish eye contact with you during the patient interview. Do you think this means Mrs. Xu is not telling the truth?

   _____

   _____

   _____

2. Carl Worth, a 78-year-old patient, is hard of hearing and does not appear to be paying attention when you ask questions for the patient history. His daughter is in the examination room with him, so would it be better to gather patient information from her? Why or why not?

   _____

   _____

   _____

3. Theo Lang is being seen today for a surgical follow-up visit. He asks that his partner, David, accompany him into the examination room. What should you do?

   _____

   _____

   _____

213

WORKPLACE APPLICATION OPTIONS

Complete one or more of these activities and, if appropriate, share your results with the class.

1. The receiver of a message attaches meaning to the message based on verbal and nonverbal communication. Provide examples of each and describe how the receiver may put his or her own interpretation on them.

2. Body language plays a significant role in therapeutic communications. Describe positive nonverbal behaviors that enhance interactions with patients.

3. Chris Isaccson, CMA (AAMA), is updating the office's policies and procedures handbook. One of the items he would like to include is communication using an age-specific approach. Create a list of the important guidelines to follow when interacting with a child.

4. Chris Isaccson, CMA (AAMA), is to present an in-service lecture, "Proper Charting Methods." What type of information should Chris include when preparing his presentation? Include both technical format and documenting patient signs and symptoms.

5. Chris has been asked by one of the physicians in the practice to summarize changes that need to be made to comply with Health Insurance Portability and Accountability Act (HIPAA) guidelines regarding patient confidentiality. What details should Chris include in the summary?

6. As a member of the healthcare team, Chris is responsible for practicing sound risk management principles. Summarize four principles he should consistently practice.

INTERNET ACTIVITY OPTIONS

Complete one or more of these activities and, if appropriate, share your results with the class.

1. EHRs are increasingly becoming part of the medical office. Visit the site www.eclinicalworks.com and choose "online demo" to view the different ways electronic health records can be used in the medical office. What are some of the most important features? How will EHRs improve patient care?

2. Go to the Health and Human Services site, www.hhs.gov/ocr/privacy/hipaa/understanding/, to learn more about HIPAA. Summarize this information for your peers.

MEDICAL RECORD ACTIVITIES

1. Gather a patient history from your partner in your lab class using the Patient History form found in the Medical Record while completing Procedure 28-1.

2. Document the following scenarios in the progress notes section of the medical record using POMR practices.

    a. Patient c/o chest pain of 4 on a 1-10 scale and sweating for the past 2 hours. The patient states taking nitroglycerin for relief of symptoms. VS are T–99°, P–68/minute, R–24/minute, with an irregular pulse and left arm pain.

    S: _____

    O: _____

    b. Patient c/o a sore throat with pain of 7 on a 1-10 scale and fever for 2 days. The patient has been taking OTCs and gargling with warm salt water for relief of symptoms. VS are T–102.4°, P–108/minute, R–20/minute. Patient also has an erythremic papular rash across the chest. The patient states exposure to strep last week.

    S: _____

    O: _____

    c. Patient c/o a headache with pain of 8 on a 1-10 scale and nausea for 3 days. The patient has been taking Lortab 5 mg for relief of symptoms. VS are T–97.6°, P–110/minute, R–20/minute. Also c/o dizziness and pain in the eyes. Patient appears pale with damp skin.

    S: _____

    O: _____

    d. Patient fell off a ladder 2 days ago and c/o low back pain of 5 on a 1-10 scale. He has been taking Advil for relief of symptoms. VS are T–98.7°, P–98/minute, R–20/minute. Patient also has ecchymosis across the flank and c/o blood in urine.

    S: _____

    O: _____

29 Patient Education

VOCABULARY REVIEW

Fill in the blanks with the correct vocabulary terms from this chapter.

The holistic model suggests that healthcare workers should take into consideration all aspects of a patient's life, including

patients' _____, _____, _____, _____, and _____ needs.

SKILLS AND CONCEPTS

Part I: Short Answers

1. List six guidelines for patient education.

   a. _____

   b. _____

   c. _____

   d. _____

   e. _____

   f. _____

2. Explain seven patient factors that influence learning.

   a. _____

   b. _____

   c. _____

   d. _____

   e. _____

   f. _____

   g. _____

3. Summarize eight approaches to language barriers.

   a. _____

   b. _____

   c. _____

   d. _____

   e. _____

   f. _____

   g. _____

   h. _____

4. One of the most important aspects of patient teaching is to be _____ and provide information about _____ patients want to know _____ patients want to know it.

5. List 10 barriers to patient learning.

   a. _____

   b. _____

   c. _____

   d. _____

   e. _____

   f. _____

   g. _____

   h. _____

   i. _____

   j. _____

6. Identify five guidelines for ordering educational materials.

   a. _____

   b. _____

   c. _____

   d. _____

   e. _____

7. What does the role of the medical assistant educator include?

   a. _____

   b. _____

   c. _____

   d. _____

   e. _____

   f. _____

   g. _____

   h. _____

8. Effective teaching methods include use of _____ materials, videos, and approved _____ sites to gather information; referral to community _____ and experts; _____ demonstration of medical skills; examination of patients' records of events; and involving _____ in the education process.

9. Use the following checklist to design and present a program for a patient during your externship or role-play with a fellow classmate.

   a. Conduct a patienst assessment.
      - Consider pertinent patient factors.
      - Identify barriers to learning.
      - Prioritize patient information.
      - Determine immediate and long-term needs.
      - Decide on appropriate teaching materials and methods.

      Complete _____

   b. Prepare the teaching area and assemble necessary equipment and materials.
      - Use supplies and equipment the patient will use at home.
      - Provide positive feedback for correct display of skills.

      Complete _____

   c. Maintain an adequate, not too fast, pace.

      Complete _____

   d. Repeatedly ask for patient feedback to confirm understanding.
      - Eliminate barriers to learning.
      - Address immediate learning needs.
      - Use repetition and rephrasing to promote understanding.

      Complete _____

   e. Summarize the material learned or the skill mastered at the end of each teaching interaction.

      Complete _____

   f. Outline a plan for the next meeting.

      Complete _____

   g. Evaluate the teaching plan.
      - Was there enough time to complete the lesson?
      - Was the patient physically and psychologically ready for the information?
      - Were the goals for the session reached?

      Complete _____

   h. Document the teaching intervention.
      - Material covered.
      - Patient response or level of skill performance.
      - Plans for next session.
      - Community referrals.

      Complete _____

WORKPLACE APPLICATION OPTIONS

Complete one or more of these activities and, if appropriate, share your results with the class.

1. Gather a list of community resources for patients in your area. To what groups are the resources geared? What is the contact information? What services do the organizations offer?

2. Taylor, a medical assistant for a family practice office, has been asked by Dr. Norberger to create patient education files for each examination room. The file should contain handouts on chronic disease, nutrition, exercise, and a healthy lifestyle. Create a list of 15 topics that should be included in this file. Why did you choose them? How may they be helpful to the doctor and the patients?

3. As Taylor begins to obtain and develop educational supplies for the patient education files, what are some guidelines she should follow as she reviews the information available? What other teaching materials should she consider using in addition to the handouts?

4. Based on what you have learned about the Health Belief Model, complete the blank spaces in the following table.

The Health Belief Model

Principles	Definition	Application to Patient Education
Perceived susceptibility		Supply information on risk level; individual risk based on _____ _____
Perceived _____	_____ on the seriousness of the condition and its health risks	Outline the potential _____ of the disease
Perceived benefits	Patient's belief in _____	Emphasize the _____ that can occur if patient is compliant with health care recommendations
Perceived _____	Patient's opinion of the _____ and psychological costs of compliance	Identify _____ and work to reduce them through patient education, family outreach, _____
_____	Methods developed to activate patient compliance	
Self-efficacy	Patient has the confidence to take action toward a healthier state	

5. Identify Dr. Elisabeth Kübler-Ross's stages of grief and include in your explanation a suggestion for therapeutic interaction with a patient in each stage.

a. _____

_____

_____

b. _____

_____

_____

c. _____

_____

_____

d. _____

_____

_____

e. _____

_____

_____

6. Explain how the medical assistant can perform patient education for the following patients with special needs.

a. Antonio DeMendez, a 68-year-old patient, has profound hearing loss in his left ear. He needs to be taught how to take his blood pressure medication accurately.

_____

_____

_____

b. Christina Wu, a 48-year-old patient, is legally blind. She is a new patient who is visiting the office for the first time and needs to complete a health history form. The physician recommends that she follow a low-sodium diet.

_____

_____

_____

c. Julio Gonzales is 17 and has limited English skills. He is scheduled for diagnostic testing at the hospital and must be taught how to prepare for the studies.

_____

_____

_____

7. One of the roles of the medical assistant is to help patients in need of community health education or support services. To prepare for this role, collect a minimum of 25 community resources that are available in your area. Include in your directory the name of the group and the services provided; the contact person; telephone number, address, meeting times, and locations; and a related website if available. Choose one of these resources and investigate the services it provides in greater detail, either by interviewing an individual who works or volunteers in the organization or by attending one of the group's sponsored meetings. Summarize your experience and share it with your classmates.

8. For the following scenarios, write "Yes" on the line if the medical assistant's actions are acceptable practice according to Health Insurance Portability and Accountability Act (HIPAA) guidelines or "No" if they are not acceptable.

_____ The mother of a 19-year-old patient, Sue Collins, calls the office. Even though the mother is not listed as Sue's PHI, Taylor answers her questions about Sue's illness.

_____ The patient requests that only her husband receive information about her health status. Taylor receives a call from the patient's adult daughter, who insists on learning her mother's diagnosis. Taylor feels bad for the daughter and answers her questions.

Internet Activity Options

Complete this activity and, if appropriate, share your results with the class.

Visit the Interactive Tutorial Site at www.nlm.nih.gov/medlineplus/tutorial.html. Click on any of the topics you find interesting. Do you think this site would be a good patient education choice for individuals who have access to the Internet?

MEDICAL RECORD ACTIVITIES

1. Mary Ann has recently been diagnosed with hypercholesterolemia. As Taylor is discussing diet and exercise recommendations, Mary Ann replies that she doesn't think the cholesterol is something she should be concerned about, and what with working two jobs, she is "forced" to dine out and eat "on the run" most days. What type of barriers will Taylor need to overcome? What type of patient education material should Taylor provide? Document the patient education intervention.

_____

_____

_____

2. Describe how the patient's chronologic age and developmental age result in the need to adapt the teaching plan for the following patients. What changes will you make to the methods of delivery? Are any learning barriers present that must be overcome? What types of patient information will you provide to each person? Document the patient education intervention.

a. A 74-year-old woman was recently diagnosed with diabetes type 2. Before her diagnosis, she had not seen a doctor in 20 years. She loves to cook for her large family but complains of difficulty reading recipes, because the diabetes has resulted in diabetic retinopathy.

_____

_____

_____

b. An 11-year-old boy was recently diagnosed with diabetes type 1. He loves to play sports and is very active. His father complains that he plays so much that getting him to eat properly is difficult. The boy is afraid of needles, and the doctor has ordered him to begin using insulin and a Glucometer immediately.

_____

_____

_____

30 Nutrition and Health Promotion

Match the following terms with the correct definition.

_____ Turgor

_____ Cholesterol

_____ Free radicals

_____ Hydrogenated oils

_____ Vertigo

_____ Diabetes type 1

_____ Diverticulosis

_____ Digestion

_____ Triglyceride

_____ Diabetes type 2

_____ Psyllium

_____ Nutrient deficiency

_____ Amino acids

_____ Neural tube defects

a. Beta cells in the pancreas no longer produce insulin, meaning the patient must follow complicated dietary and medication treatment plans

b. Water-soluble fiber found in some cereals, dietary supplements, and bulk fiber laxatives

c. Fatty acid and glycerol compound that combines with a protein molecule to form high- or low-density lipoprotein

d. Process of converting food into chemical substances that the body can use

e. Conditions caused by a below-normal intake of a particular substance

f. Skin tension test that can reveal dehydration

g. Organic compounds that form the chief constituents of protein and are used by the body to build and repair tissues

h. Any of a group of congenital anomalies of the brain and spinal column caused by failure of the neural tube to close during embryonic development

i. Oils that are combined with hydrogen, making them more saturated

j. Nonessential nutrient produced by the liver that can result in atherosclerotic plaques with excessive dietary intake

k. Dizziness

l. Presence of pouchlike herniations through the muscular layer of the colon

m. Unstable compounds believed to damage cells, resulting in cancer, heart disease, and other disorders

n. Inability of the body to use glucose for energy as a result of either a lack of insulin production in the pancreas or a resistance to insulin on the cellular level

Describe the dietary imbalances that contribute to each of the following health problems.

1. Anemia

_____

_____

2. Cancer

_____

_____

3. Constipation

_____

_____

4. Diabetes

_____

_____

5. Hypercholesterolemia

_____

_____

6. Hypertension

_____

_____

7. Osteoporosis

_____

_____

Fill in the blanks with the appropriate terms.

1. A(n) _____ nutrient, such as cholesterol, can be created in the body and does not need to be included in the diet.

2. _____ are chemical organic compounds composed of carbon, hydrogen, and oxygen and are primarily plant products in origin. They are divided into three groups based on the complexity of their molecules: simple sugars, complex carbohydrates (starch), and dietary fiber.

3. _____ is a storage form of fuel that is used to supplement carbohydrates as an available energy source.

4. _____ is produced by the liver and is found in animal foods; it can produce atherosclerotic plaque deposits in arteries.

5. _____ are composed of units known as *amino acids*, which are the materials the body uses to build and repair tissues.

6. Vitamins are divided into two groups: _____-soluble vitamins (A, D, E, and K) and_____-soluble vitamins (B complex and C).

7. The _____ is the amount of energy needed by fasting, resting individuals to maintain vital function.

8. Dietary fiber is commonly called _____.

Define the following terms.

1. Metabolism

_____

2. Anabolism

_____

3. Catabolism

_____

4. High-density lipoprotein (HDL)

_____

5. Low-density lipoprotein (LDL)

_____

6. Trans fats

_____

SKILLS AND CONCEPTS

Part I: Short Answers

1. How does culture influence our dietary choices? Why is this important to note when providing nutrition education to patients?

_____

_____

_____

_____

Examine the nomogram below and answer the following questions.

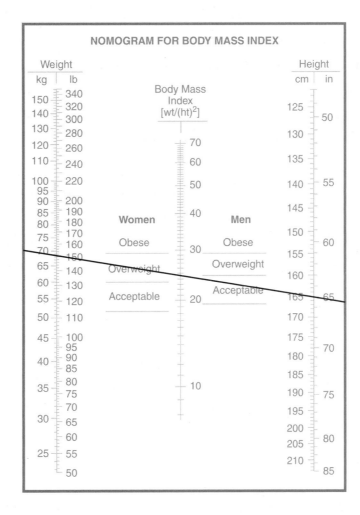

2. What is the purpose of the nomogram?

   _____

   _____

3. How much does this patient weigh in pounds? In kilograms?

   lb _____ kg _____

4. What is the patient's height in inches? In centimeters?

   in _____ cm _____

5. What is the patient's body mass index (BMI)?

   _____

6. Use the nomogram to calculate your own BMI.

   _____

7. List four functions of water.

   a. _____

   b. _____

   c. _____

   d. _____

8. List four functions of proteins.

   a. _____

   b. _____

   c. _____

   d. _____

9. What is the Glycemic Index? How is it used to manage blood sugar levels?

   _____

   _____

   _____

   _____

10. Investigate the MyPlate.gov site. How does the new design differ from the previous food guide pyramid? Do you think the new design is a good educational tool for the general public?

   _____

   _____

   _____

   _____

Examine the nutrition facts label and answer the following questions.

Nutrition Facts		
Serving size: 1¼ cups (30 g)		
Servings per container: About 16		
Amount per serving	Cereal	Cereal with ½ cup skim milk
Calories	110	190
Calories from fat	0	0
	% Daily value**	
Total fat 9 g*	0%	0%
Saturated fat 0 g	0%	1%
Cholesterol 0 mg	0%	1%
Sodium 270 mg	11%	14%
Total carbohydrate 26 g	9%	11%
Dietary fiber less than 1 g	0%	0%
Sugars 3 g		
Other carbohydrate 22 g		
Protein 2 g		
Vitamin A	0%	6%
Vitamin C	10%	10%

Continued

Nutrition Facts

		Cereal	Cereal with ½ cup skim milk
Calcium		0%	15%
Iron		50%	50%
Thiamin		25%	25%
Niacin		25%	25%
Vitamin B_6		25%	25%
Folate		25%	25%
Vitamin B_{12}		25%	30%
Amount per serving		**Cereal**	**Cereal with ½ cup skim milk**
Calories		2000	2500
Total fat	Less than	65 g	60 g
Saturated fat	Less than	20 g	25 g
Cholesterol	Less than	300 mg	300 mg
Sodium	Less than	2400 mg	2400 mg
Total carbohydrate		300 g	375 g
Dietary fiber		25 g	30 g

Calories per gram:

Fat 9 • Carbohydrate 4 • Protein 4

*Amount in cereal. One half cup skim milk adds an additional 40 calories. Less than 5 mg cholesterol, 65 mg sodium, 6 g total carbohydrate (6 g sugars), and 4 g protein.

**Percent daily values are based on 2000-calorie diet. Your daily values may be higher or lower depending on your calorie needs.

11. What is the normal serving size? _____

12. How many calories are in one serving without milk? _____

13. How many grams of fiber are in one serving? _____

14. This food is high in _____ and _____.

15. What is the total number of carbohydrates for 2½ cups of cereal? _____

16. If one serving of CHO equals 15 g, then how many servings of CHO are in 1¼ cups of cereal?

17. Examine the following table and fill in the blank spaces with the appropriate numbers.

Total Cholesterol				Low-Density Lipoprotein (LDL) Cholesterol		
Age (yr)	Acceptable	Borderline	High	Acceptable	Borderline	High
2 to 20	<170	170-199		<110	110-129	
>20			>240		130-159	

18. The main function of carbohydrate is to supply _____.

19. What are the recommended ranges for percentage of daily intake for the primary nutrients?

Carbohydrates _____

Proteins _____

Fats _____

20. The best types of oils to use in food preparation are either _____ or _____.

21. _____ may interfere with the action of anticoagulant medications.

22. Patients who have had gastric bypass surgery may require certain supplements, including vitamin _____.

23. Adequate intakes of both _____ and _____ are needed to prevent osteoporosis.

24. Examine the tables that follow and fill in the blank spaces with the correct information about vitamins and minerals.

Vitamins

Vitamin	Best Sources	Functions	Deficiency Symptoms
A, carotene		Formation and maintenance of skin, hair, and mucous membranes; aids vision in dim light; bone and tooth growth	
B₁, thiamine	Fortified cereals and oatmeal, meat, rice and pasta, whole grains, liver		Heart irregularity, fatigue, nerve disorders, mental confusion
B₂, riboflavin		Helps the body release energy from protein, fat, and carbohydrates during metabolism	
B₆, pyridoxine	Fish, poultry, lean meat, bananas, prunes, dried beans, whole grains, avocados		Convulsions, dermatitis, muscular weakness, skin cracks, anemia
B₁₂, cobalamin		Aids cell development, functioning of the nervous system, and metabolism of protein and fat	
Biotin	Cereal and grain products, yeast, legumes, liver		Nausea; vomiting; depression; hair loss; dry, scaly skin
Folate folacin, folic acid			Gastrointestinal disorders, anemia, cracked lips
Niacin	Meat, poultry, fish, enriched cereals, peanuts, potatoes, dairy products, eggs	Involved in carbohydrate, protein, and fat metabolism	
Pantothenic acid	Lean meat, whole grains, legumes, vegetables, fruits		Fatigue, vomiting, stomach stress, infections, muscle cramps
C, ascorbic acid		Essential for structure of bones, cartilage, muscle, and blood vessels; also helps maintain capillaries and gums and aids absorption of iron	
D		Aids bone and tooth formation; helps maintain heart action and nervous system	
E			Muscular wasting, nerve damage, anemia, reproductive failure
K			Bleeding disorders in newborns and those taking blood-thinning medications

Minerals

Functions	Sources	Deficiency Symptoms	Toxicity Symptoms
Calcium			
	Primarily found in milk and milk products; also found in dark green, leafy vegetables; tofu and other soy products; sardines; salmon with bones; and hard water		Kidney stones
Chloride			
Involved in the maintenance of fluid and acid-base balance; provides an acid medium in the form of hydrochloric acid for activation of gastric enzymes		Disturbances in acid-base balance with possible growth retardation, psychomotor defects, and memory loss	Disturbances in acid-base balance
Magnesium			
Helps build strong bones and teeth; activates many enzymes; participates in protein synthesis and lipid metabolism; helps regulate heartbeat		Rare but in disease states may lead to central nervous system problems (confusion, apathy, hallucinations, poor memory) and neuromuscular problems (muscle weakness, cramps, tremor, cardiac arrhythmia)	
Phosphorus			
		Rare but with malabsorption can cause anorexia, weakness, stiff joints, and fragile bones	Hypocalcemic tetany (muscle spasms)
Potassium			
		May cause impaired growth, hypertension, bone fragility, central nervous system changes, renal hypertrophy, diminished heart rate, and death	
Sodium			
Plays a key role in the maintenance of acid-base balance; transmits nerve impulses and helps control muscle contractions; regulates cell membrane permeability		Hyponatremia (too little sodium in the blood)	
Chromium			
Activates several enzymes; enhances the removal of glucose from the blood		Weight loss, abnormalities of the central nervous system, and possible aggravation of diabetes mellitus	

Functions	Sources	Deficiency Symptoms	Toxicity Symptoms
Copper			
Aids in the production and survival of red blood cells; parts of many enzymes involved in respiration; plays a role in normal lipid metabolism	Shellfish (especially oysters), liver, nuts and seeds, raisins, whole grains, and chocolate		In Wilson's disease and Huntington's chorea (both hereditary diseases), copper accumulation causes neuron and liver cell damage
Fluorine			
	Fluoridated water (and foods cooked in fluoridated water), fish, tea, gelatin		Fluorosis and mottling of teeth
Iodine			
			Little toxic effect in individuals with normal thyroid gland functioning
Iron			
	Heme sources: organ meats, especially liver, red meat, and other meats Nonheme sources: iron-fortified cereals; dark green, leafy vegetables; legumes; whole grains; blackstrap molasses; dried fruit; and foods cooked in iron pans		Idiopathic hemochromatosis, which can lead to cirrhosis, diabetes mellitus, skin pigmentation, arthralgias (joint pain), and cardiomyopathy
Manganese			
		None observed in humans	Iron-deficiency anemia through inhibiting effect on iron absorption; pulmonary changes, anorexia, apathy, impotence, headaches, leg cramps, and speech impairment; in advanced stages of toxicity, resembles Parkinson's disease
Selenium			
Part of an enzyme system; acts as an antioxidant with vitamin E to protect the cell from oxygen		Keshan disease (a human cardiomyopathy) and Kashin-Bek disease (an endemic human osteoarthropathy)	Physical defects of the fingernails and toenails and hair loss
Zinc			
	Whole grains, wheat germ, crabmeat, oysters, liver and other meats, brewer's yeast		Severe anemia, nausea, vomiting, abdominal cramps, diarrhea, fever, hypocupremia (low blood serum copper), malaise, fatigue

25. In your textbook, refer to Table 30-5, which identifies the body mass index (BMI) for individuals as a ratio of their height and weight, and Table 30-6, which classifies disease risk based on the BMI. Determine the BMI of patients in the following scenarios and identify their disease risk.

a. Kelly Anderson, a 12-year-old patient, is 61 inches tall and weighs 148 pounds.

_____

b. Anthony Noel, a 21-year-old patient, is 76 inches tall and weighs 279 pounds.

_____

c. Anna Garcia, 46 years old, is 64 inches tall and weighs 126 pounds.

_____

26. Marcia is working with a teenager who shows evidence of having anorexia nervosa. What the characteristics are typically seen in patients with anorexia nervosa? How do these compare with the characteristics seen in patients with bulimia?

_____

_____

_____

_____

CASE STUDIES

1. Mrs. Barton has been recently diagnosed with diabetes mellitus type 2. At her office visit today, she tells Marcia, the medical assistant, that her glucometer readings 2 hours after eating breakfast have been running, on average, 230 to 300 mg/dL. Mrs. Barton's food diary for breakfast is as follows:

Monday Breakfast	Tuesday Breakfast	Wednesday Breakfast
1½ cup cereal 4 ounces OJ	2 pancakes 2 tablespoons syrup 4 ounces OJ	1 blueberry muffin 1 banana 1 cup of tea

What should Marcia notice from the food diary? What conclusions can Marcia draw from Mrs. Barton's breakfast choices and the resulting blood glucose readings?

_____

_____

_____

Mrs. Barton has asked Marcia to create a sample breakfast menu for the next 3 days. Create the menu on the following chart. Why do you think this will better regulate Mrs. Barton's blood glucose level?

Thursday Breakfast	Friday Breakfast	Saturday Breakfast

2. Mr. Hawthorne is trying to make changes in his diet but is confused about how to choose a healthy type of bread at the grocery store. Based on what Marcia knows about bread labels, how should she explain the healthiest bread choice?

_____

_____

_____

_____

3. Lucretia Lang, a 38-year-old patient who has been told to increase her fiber intake to treat chronic constipation and hypercholesterolemia, is having difficulty understanding the difference between soluble and insoluble fiber. Explain the functions of each and name good dietary sources of the two types of fiber.

_____

_____

_____

4. Marcia has a patient on the phone who thinks he may have eaten contaminated food. What questions should Marcia ask to gather more details? What gastrointestinal symptoms occur with food poisoning? What food contaminants are most likely to cause health problems?

_____

_____

_____

_____

_____

WORKPLACE APPLICATION OPTIONS

Complete one or more of these activities and, if appropriate, share your results with the class.

1. Marcia is gathering material for a patient education brochure describing the importance of fiber consumption. What is the function of fiber in the diet? Include the difference between soluble and insoluble fiber. What is the daily dietary recommendation for fiber intake? Create a list of foods high in fiber for Marcia to include in her brochure.

2. Marcia has been asked to assist the physician with research for a journal article, "The Importance of Antioxidants." Prepare a list of foods high in antioxidants to be included in the article.

3. The internal medicine clinic where Marcia works frequently sees patients with hypertension. The recommended treatment for lowering blood pressure is the Dietary Approaches to Stop Hypertension (DASH) diet. Describe the guidelines included in the DASH diet.

4. Obesity is at epidemic proportions in the United States. The practice where Marcia works is considering starting an obesity support program, which will include patients who are planning on or who have recently undergone bariatric surgery. Summarize the facts about obesity in the United States, the relationship to the BMI, and the facts about bariatric procedures that Marcia must understand to provide care for this patient population.

5. Marcia has been asked to prepare a patient education handout for each of the therapeutic diets that may be recommended for patients in the practice. Summarize the details of the therapeutic diets discussed in the text.

INTERNET ACTIVITY OPTIONS

Complete one or more of these activities and, if appropriate, share your results with the class.

1. The "5 A Day for Better Health" Program is one of the nation's largest initiatives for nutrition. The goal of the program is to increase the national fruit and vegetable consumption to five per day by 2010. Visit the program's website at www.5aday.org. Why is the consumption of fruits and vegetables so important? Keep a food diary for 1 week. Have you met the goal of "5 A Day"? If not, how do you plan to add more fruits and vegetables to your diet?

2. Visit www.choosemyplate.gov. Click on the SuperTracker and create your personal profile. View and print your personalized profile to answer the following questions.

   a. The results are based on a calorie pattern of how many calories?

   b. What is the recommended amount of grains?

   c. What tips do you find will enable you to fulfill these requirements?

   d. What is your daily recommendation for physical activity?

   e. Do your current eating and exercise habits support the results found on your personalized SuperTracker?

   f. What areas in your diet need modification?

   g. How could the MyCoach center help you or your patients stay on target to achieve health goals?

   h. How could this site be used for patient education purposes?

MEDICAL RECORD ACTIVITIES

Document the following scenarios in the progress notes section of the medical record using POMR practices.

1. Suzie's recent blood work results show an LDL of 176 mg/dL and a total cholesterol of 256 mg/dL. Suzie does not seem concerned with these results and wonders why the physician wants her to follow a low-cholesterol diet. What can Marcia tell Suzie about the risks of hyperlipidemia? What are the recommended ranges for total cholesterol and LDL? Document the teaching intervention in the patient's medical record.

_____

_____

_____

2. Ms. Lily Lu is a new patient in the practice who was recently diagnosed with hypertension and hypercholesterolemia. What culturally sensitive suggestions could Marcia make about choosing foods low in sodium and fat? Document the teaching intervention in the patient's medical record.

_____

_____

_____

3. Tony Madaloni is a 67-year-old patient who must lose weight and restrict salt intake to lower his disease risk. What might be some of the reasons Mr. Madaloni chooses the foods he does? What suggestions could Marcia make about changes in eating habits? Document the teaching intervention in the patient's medical record.

_____

_____

_____

4. Ajah Simone is a 22-year-old pregnant patient who is a vegan. The physician asks Marcia to reinforce his discussion on eating foods that provide a nutritionally balanced approach to incomplete proteins. What food combinations could Marcia suggest to Ms. Simone? What resources might reinforce Ms. Simone's implementation of a healthy diet during her pregnancy? Include details about the patient education intervention in the patient's medical record.

_____

_____

_____

31 Vital Signs

VOCABULARY REVIEW

Define the following medical terms.

1. Apnea

   _____

2. Arrhythmia

   _____

3. Arteriosclerosis

   _____

4. Bradycardia

   _____

5. Bradypnea

   _____

6. Dyspnea

   _____

7. Febrile

   _____

8. Hyperlipidemia

   _____

9. Hypertension

   _____

10. Hyperventilation

   _____

11. Hypotension

   _____

12. Orthopnea

   _____

13. Peripheral

   _____

14. Pyrexia

_____

15. Rales

_____

16. Rhonchi

_____

17. Syncope

_____

18. Stertorous

_____

19. Tachycardia

_____

20. Tachypnea

_____

21. Vertigo

_____

SKILLS AND CONCEPTS

Part I: Short Answers

1. List the four cardinal vital signs.

   a. _____

   b. _____

   c. _____

   d. _____

2. What anthropometric measurements are included?

   a. _____

   b. _____

   c. _____

   d. _____ and _____

Part II: True or False
Indicate which statements are true (T) and which are false (F).

1. _____ A change in one or more of the patient's vital signs may indicate a change in general health.

2. _____ Sometimes vital sign measurements must be obtained a second time, after the patient is calmer or more comfortable.

3. _____ Body temperature is regulated by the hypothalamus.

4. _____ Body temperature ranges from being highest in the morning to being lowest in the late afternoon.

5. _____ Patients with a febrile condition exhibit pyrexia and can be treated with an antipyretic.

6. _____ An individual with hypertension may have a bounding pulse.

7. _____ A contraindication for taking a temporal artery temperature is bilateral impacted cerumen.

8. _____ Primary or essential hypertension is idiopathic.

9. _____ The difference between tachypnea and hyperpnea is that respirations are rapid and shallow with hyperpnea.

10. _____ A patient with orthostatic hypotension experiences a rapid drop in blood pressure when she stands too quickly.

11. _____ Otitis externa is known as "swimmer's ear."

12. _____ Frequent spirometer studies will be ordered for a patient diagnosed with chronic obstructive pulmonary disease (COPD) to determine the person's breathing capabilities.

13. _____ Individuals with advanced kidney disease always develop secondary hypertension.

Part III: Temperatures
Use the correct terms to fill in the blanks.

1. A(n) _____ fever rises and falls only slightly during a 24-hour period. It remains above the patient's average normal range.

2. A(n) _____ fever comes and goes, or it spikes and then returns to the average range.

3. A(n) _____ fever fluctuates greatly (more than 3° F) but does not return to the average range.

4. _____ temperatures are approximately 1° F (0.6° C) lower than accurate oral readings.

5. _____ thermometers are an accurate means of taking temperatures in adults and older children because of the closeness to the hypothalamus.

6. _____ temperatures are an easy, noninvasive, and accurate alternative to taking rectal temperatures in infants.

7. Medication to reduce a fever is called a(n) _____.

8. Tympanic thermometers should not be used if the patient has _____ or _____.

9. _____ should not be used in a healthcare setting, because they are not as accurate as other methods.

10. Temperatures considered febrile include the following:

    a. Aural (ear) temperatures higher than _____ ° F (38° C)

    b. Oral temperatures higher than _____ ° F (37.5° C)

    c. Axillary temperatures higher than _____ ° F (37° C)

11. Use the following formulas to convert the temperatures in the chart from one system to the other.

$$° C = (° F - 32) \times \frac{5}{9}$$

$$° F = (° C \times \frac{9}{5}) + 32$$

a. 98.6° F = _____ ° C   f. 36° C = _____ ° F

b. 37° C = _____ ° F   g. 42° C = _____ ° F

c. 97.6° F = _____ ° C   h. 42° C = _____ ° F

d. 99.4° F = _____ ° C   i. 102° F = _____ ° C

e. 43° C = _____ ° F   j. 41° C = _____ ° F

12. List and describe three factors that may affect body temperature.

a. _____

b. _____

c. _____

Part IV: Pulse

1. List eight pulse sites and label their correct locations on the following figure.

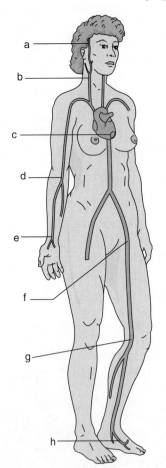

a. _____

b. _____

c. _____

d. _____

e. _____

f. _____

g. _____

h. _____

2. What three characteristics should the medical assistant note while measuring a pulse?

   a. _____

   b. _____

   c. _____

3. A patient with a significant difference between the apical and brachial pulse counts has a(n) _____.

4. A well-conditioned athlete may have a pulse rate below 60 beats per minute. The medical term for this is _____.

5. A patient who is anxious or in pain may have an increase in the pulse rate, which is called _____.

6. The brachial pulse, which is palpated before the blood pressure is taken, is located in the _____ of the elbow.

7. When the heart rate varies with respirations, this is known as _____.

8. The _____ pulse is the most accurate method of taking the pulse of infants and of patients with an arrhythmia.

9. Pedal and popliteal pulses may be checked with a sonogram device called a(n) _____.

Part V: Respirations
Complete the following sentences with the correct terms.

1. One full respiration includes both _____ and _____.

2. The exchange of oxygen and carbon dioxide in the lungs is called _____.

3. Carlos counts eight respirations for 30 seconds. The rate is _____ per minute.

4. A bluish discoloration of the skin caused by increased CO_2 buildup is called _____.

5. Breathing rates are controlled by the respiratory center, which is located in the _____ of the brain.

6. Patients typically have a ratio of _____ pulse beat(s) to _____ respiration(s).

7. List the three characteristics of respirations.

   a. _____

   b. _____

   c. _____

Part VI: Blood Pressure
Complete the sentences with the correct terms.

1. Blood pressure is a reflection of the pressure of the blood against the walls of the _____.

2. The difference between the systolic and diastolic pressures is the _____.

3. Blood pressure is recorded as a fraction; the _____ reading is the numerator (top number) and the _____ reading is the denominator (bottom number).

4. _____ is the amount of blood in the arteries.

5. A(n) _____ is the instrument used to measure the pressure of blood in the arteries.

6. _____ is the contraction of the heart.

7. _____ describes the relaxation of the heart.

8. Complete the following table.

Blood Pressure	Normal	Prehypertension	Hypertension
Systolic (mm Hg)	Less than	120-139	
Diastolic (mm Hg)	Less than		90 or higher

9. Describe some common signs and symptoms of hypertension.

_____

_____

_____

10. Summarize the American Heart Association's recommendations for the prevention and treatment of hypertension.

a. _____

_____

b. _____

_____

c. _____

_____

d. _____

_____

11. List and define the five Korotkoff phases.

a. _____

_____

b. _____

_____

c. _____

_____

d. _____

_____

e. _____

_____

12. The systolic pressure may be checked by the _____ method if the medical assistant is unable to auscultate the patient's blood pressure.

13. Explain four common causes of errors in blood pressure readings.

a. _____

b. _____

c. _____

d. _____

Part VII: Anthropometric Measurements

Use the formulas to convert the following weights from one system to the other.

1 kg = 2.2 lb

1 lb = 0.45 kg

1. 145 lb = _____ kg

2. 54 kg = _____ lb

3. 60 kg = _____ lb

4. 112 lb = _____ kg

5. 50 lb = _____ kg

WORKPLACE APPLICATION OPTIONS

Complete one or more of these activities and, if appropriate, share your results with the class.

1. Mrs. Parker has just arrived at the office. She states that she is on her way home from work and would like to have her blood pressure (BP) checked. Should Carlos take her blood pressure right away? If he should wait, why and for how long?

_____

_____

_____

a. Carlos has obtained a BP reading of 150/94 mm Hg in the left arm and 160/98 mm Hg in the right arm. Concerned about the readings, Carlos decides the patient should see the physician. What type of questions might Carlos want to ask Mrs. Parker?

_____

_____

_____

b. Document the finding using the SOAPE format.

S: _____

O: _____

2. Sarah, an 18-month old patient, is being seen today for a possible ear infection. The best method of taking her temperature is _____. Her mother is concerned, because Sarah's temperature has been fluctuating between normal and high levels for 2 days; this is called a(n) _____ fever. Carlos should take Sarah's pulse using the _____ method. Dr. Xu recommends that Sarah's mother give her Tylenol to relieve her fever. Tylenol is classified as a(n) _____ drug. Sarah's mother has a digital thermometer at home.

    a. What would be the best method she could use to take the baby's temperature and why?

    _____

    b. What patient education should Carlos give Sarah's mother about taking axillary temperatures accurately?

    _____

3. Carlos is responsible for training a new medical assistant in the Occupational Safety and Health Administration (OSHA) guidelines for preventing disease transmission when taking vital signs. What important factors should Carlos include?

    _____

    _____

    _____

INTERNET ACTIVITY OPTIONS

Complete one or more of these activities and, if appropriate, share your results with the class.

1. Visit the American Heart Association site at www.heart.org/HEARTORG. Click on the "Conditions" link and then the link for "High Blood Pressure." Using the "Understand Your Risk for High Blood Pressure" tool, evaluate your risk of developing hypertension. You will need a current blood pressure reading, so work with a partner to measure your most recent blood pressure. Are you at risk? What type of lifestyle changes should you consider to avoid increasing your risk?

2. Investigate the patient education materials available at the American Lung Association's site, at www.lung.org/lung-disease/copd, for individuals with COPD. Summarize what you learned for the class.

MEDICAL RECORD ACTIVITIES

Vital signs are documented with temperature (T) first, pulse (P) second, and respirations (R) last; the blood pressure is recorded after the TPR. Correctly document the following information. Date and sign each entry as you would on a patient record.

1. Oral temperature of 98.7, apical pulse of 60, respirations 22, and orthostatic blood pressure of 152/98 supine and 114/76 standing.

    _____

    _____

2. Tympanic temperature of 96.8, radial pulse of 86, respirations 18, and bilateral blood pressure of 132/76 in the left arm and 128/80 in the right arm with a body mass index (BMI) of 29.

    _____

    _____

3. Aural temperature of 101.2, pulse of 100 and irregular, respirations 20, and blood pressure of 126/70.

_____

_____

4. Axillary temperature of 97.5, apical pulse of 98, respirations 24, and palpated blood pressure of 62.

_____

_____

5. Temporal artery temperature of 102.6, respirations 24, and apical pulse 98.

_____

_____

32 Assisting with the Primary Physical Examination

VOCABULARY REVIEW

Match the following terms with their definitions.

_____ 1. Bruit   a. Abnormal sound or murmur heard on auscultation

_____ 2. Gait   b. White part of the eye

_____ 3. Intercellular   c. Movement of the body by applied force

_____ 4. Mastication   d. Physical injury caused by violence

_____ 5. Trauma   e. Style of walking

_____ 6. Sclera   f. Chewing

_____ 7. Manipulation   g. Rhythmic contraction of involuntary gastrointestinal (GI) muscles

_____ 8. Peristalsis   h. Pertaining to the area between cells

Use the appropriate vocabulary word to complete each sentence.

9. The physician uses _____ to assess the sinuses.

10. A patient with advanced heart or lung disease may develop _____ because of a lack of oxygen to the tissues.

11. A faulty heart valve creates a(n) _____.

12. A(n) _____ is a small lump, lesion, or swelling felt when the skin is palpated.

13. A(n) _____ is an abnormal sound auscultated over a blood vessel.

14. The process of _____ creates blood cells in the bone marrow.

15. The lumen size of an artery decreases in size when _____ occurs.

16. In a(n) _____ procedure, the physician uses a fiberoptic instrument to view the inside of the large intestine.

SKILLS AND CONCEPTS

Part I: Short Answers

1. Histology is the study of tissues. Explain the four types of tissue in the human body.

     a. _____

     _____

     b. _____

     _____

c. _____

_____

d. _____

_____

2. Describe the structural organization of the human body.

_____

_____

_____

3. Identify three responsibilities of the medical assistant in room preparation.

a. _____

b. _____

c. _____

4. Explain three responsibilities of the medical assistant in patient preparation.

a. _____

b. _____

c. _____

5. Detail three responsibilities of the medical assistant in assisting the physician.

a. _____

b. _____

c. _____

Part II: Application of Learning

Describe the following methods of assessment.

1. Inspection

_____

_____

2. Palpation

_____

_____

3. Percussion

_____

_____

4. Auscultation

_____

_____

5. Mensuration

_____

_____

6. Manipulation

_____

_____

7. Summarize the major guidelines for proper body mechanics.

_____

_____

_____

_____

8. Outline the principles of safe lifting techniques.

_____

_____

_____

_____

9. Describe how to transfer a patient safely from a wheelchair to the examination table.

_____

_____

_____

_____

10. Describe the typical physical examination sequence.

_____

_____

_____

_____

11. Complete the following table, which outlines the organization of body systems.

Body System	Cells, Organs, and Structures	Functions
Blood	Arteries, arterioles, veins, venules, white blood cells, red blood cells, platelets, plasma	
Cardiovascular	Heart, valves, arteries, arterioles, veins, venules	
Endocrine	Pituitary, pineal, hypothalamus, thyroid, pancreas, adrenal cortex and medulla, parathyroid, thymus, ovaries, testes	
Integumentary	Skin, subcutaneous tissue, sweat and sebaceous glands, hair, nails, sense receptors	
Gastrointestinal	Mouth, tongue, teeth, pharynx, esophagus, stomach, small intestine, large intestine, liver, gallbladder, pancreas, appendix	

Body System	Cells, Organs, and Structures	Functions
Lymphatic and immune	Lymph, lymph vessels, lymph nodes, thymus, tonsils, spleen, lymphocytes, antibodies	
Musculoskeletal	Bones, joints, muscles, tendons, ligaments, cartilage	
Nervous	Brain, spinal cord, neurons, neuroglial cells, peripheral nerves, autonomic nerves	
Reproductive	*Female:* Estrogen and progesterone, ovum, ovaries, fallopian tubes, uterus, vagina, vulva, mammary glands *Male:* Testosterone, sperm, epididymis, vas deferens, prostate gland, testes, scrotum, penis, urethra	
Respiratory	Nose, sinuses, pharynx, larynx, trachea, bronchi, lungs, bronchioles, alveoli	
Sensory	Eyes, ears, taste buds, olfactory receptors, sensory receptors	
Urinary	Nephron unit, bilateral kidneys, ureters, urinary bladder, urethra	

CASE STUDIES

Read the case studies and answer the questions that follow.

1. The first patient of the day is coming in for a complete physical examination; she has a suspicious breast mass. What type of equipment should the medical assistant prepare in the examination room? What method should be used to gown and position the patient?

   _____

   _____

   _____

   _____

2. Joan comes to the office today complaining of lumbar spine pain. Discuss how the patient should be gowned and positioned.

   _____

   _____

   _____

   _____

3. An adult patient complains of chest congestion, fever, and cough that have lasted for 3 days. What vital signs should be measured? Describe the gowning and positioning of the patient.

   _____

   _____

   _____

   _____

4. A 47-year-old patient is being prepared for a rectal exam. What position would you place the patient in for this exam and how should he be gowned and draped?

   _____

   _____

   _____

   _____

5. A 20-year-old patient is being seen today for her first Pap smear. How should the patient be prepared for the exam? Include in your discussion how to gown, drape, and position the patient appropriately.

_____

_____

_____

_____

WORKPLACE APPLICATION OPTIONS

Complete one or more of these activities and, if appropriate, share your results with the class.

1. How can the medical assistant ensure patient privacy while preparing the patient for the physical examination?

_____

_____

_____

2. Identify the instruments needed for the physical examination that are shown in the following figures.

   a. _____

   b. _____

c. _____

d. _____

e. _____

f. _____

g. _____

h. _____

Chapter **32** **Assisting with the Primary Physical Examination**

3. Label the positions for examination shown in the following figures and give an example of a physical examination that is appropriate for each.

a. _____

b. _____

c. _____

d. _____

Chapter **32 Assisting with the Primary Physical Examination**

e. _____

f. _____

g. _____

h. _____

33 Principles of Pharmacology

Define the following medical terms.

1. Angina pectoris

   _____

2. Bronchodilator

   _____

3. Cirrhosis

   _____

4. Formulary

   _____

5. Hypercholesterolemia

   _____

6. Metabolic alkalosis

   _____

7. Spermicide

   _____

8. Therapeutic range

   _____

9. Benefit-to-risk ratio

   _____

10. Controlled Substance Act

    _____

11. Physical drug dependency

    _____

12. Habituation

    _____

13. Chemical name

    _____

14. Trade name

_____

15. PDR

_____

16. USP

_____

17. Systemic effect

_____

18. Subscription

_____

19. Inscription

_____

20. Signature

_____

21. Superscription

_____

22. Antagonism

_____

23. Synergism

_____

24. Potentiation

_____

25. Sublingual

_____

26. Intrathecal injection

_____

27. Diurnal rhythms

_____

Match the following definitions with the correct terms.

_____ 1. Drugs used to treat and cure a disorder; for example, antibiotics cure bacterial infections

_____ 2. Drugs that do not cure a disorder but relieve pain or symptoms related to the condition; for example, use of an antihistamine for allergic symptoms

_____ 3. Drugs that prevent the occurrence of a condition; for example, vaccines prevent the occurrence of specific infectious diseases

_____ 4. Drugs that help determine the cause of a particular health problem; for example, injection of antigen serum for allergy testing

_____ 5. Drugs that provide substances the body needs to maintain health; for example, estrogen replacement therapy for menopausal women and administration of insulin to patients with diabetes

_____ 6. Medications sold without prescription

_____ 7. Drugs that are not protected by trademark

_____ 8. Pertaining to a gluelike substance

_____ 9. Denoting any medication route other than the gastrointestinal route

_____10. Space within a vessel or tube

_____11. Drug formulation in which tablets are coated with a special compound that does not dissolve until the tablet is exposed to the fluids of the small intestine

a. Prophylactic

b. Therapeutic

c. Replacement

d. Palliative

e. Diagnostic

f. Parenteral

g. Colloidal

h. Generic

i. Enteric-coated

j. Over the counter

k. Lumen

SKILLS AND CONCEPTS

For each of the following terms, define the type of drug action and the typical side effects; then give an example of that type of drug.

1. Analgesic

_____

_____

2. Anesthetic

_____

_____

3. Antibiotic

_____

_____

4. Antidepressant

_____

_____

5. Antihistamine

_____

_____

6. Antihypertensive

_____

_____

7. Antiinflammatory

_____

_____

8. Antimigraine

_____

_____

9. Antipruritics

_____

_____

10. Antipsychotics

_____

_____

11. Central nervous system stimulants

_____

_____

12. Diuretics

_____

_____

13. Hypnotics

_____

_____

14. Lipid-lowering agents

_____

_____

15. Oral hypoglycemics

_____

_____

16. Osteoporosis treatment

_____

_____

17. Anticoagulants

_____

_____

18. Antifungals

_____

_____

Fill in the blank with DEA, FDA, or FTC.

19. The _____ regulates over-the-counter drug advertising.

20. The _____, a division of the Department of Health and Human Services, was created in 1936 to regulate the development and sale of all prescription and over-the-counter drugs.

21. The _____ was established in 1973 as part of the Department of Justice to enforce federal laws on the use of illegal drugs.

22. Every medical practice should have a copy of the controlled substances regulations. The medical assistant may obtain this list from a regional office of the _____.

23. In addition to approving new drugs for the marketplace, the _____ is also responsible for establishing standards for their purity and strength during the manufacturing process and for ensuring that generic brands are effective and safe.

24. Each physician who prescribes controlled substances or has them on site must register with the _____ for a Controlled Substance Registration Certificate. The physician receives a specific registration number that must be included on all prescriptions for controlled substances.

25. List five specific guidelines for prescription orders for controlled substances.

a. _____

b. _____

c. _____

d. _____

e. _____

Indicate which statements are true (T) and which are false (F).

_____ 26. The chemical name represents the drug's exact formula.

_____ 27. The generic drug name is assigned by the manufacturer and is protected by copyright.

_____ 28. Brand names are capitalized.

_____ 29. The PDR is the most commonly used drug reference book.

_____ 30. A prescription is an order written by the physician for the compounding or dispensing and administration of drugs to a particular patient.

Chapter **33** **Principles of Pharmacology**

31. List six factors that can affect a drug's action.

    a. _____

    b. _____

    c. _____

    d. _____

    e. _____

    f. _____

32. Explain the difference between an antitussive medication and an expectorant.

_____

_____

_____

33. Complete the following classification of controlled substances table.

Schedule	Guidelines	Drug Examples
	No accepted medical use High potential for abuse Possession of these drugs is illegal	
II		
	Accepted for medical use Potential for abuse less than for schedule I or II drugs May cause moderate to low physical dependence or high psychological dependence	
IV	Accepted for medical use Low potential for abuse May cause limited physical or psychological dependence	
		Cough medicines containing codeine, kaolin and pectin belladonna, Donnagel, Lomotil, buprenorphine

34. Complete the following pregnancy risk categories table.

Category of Risk	Category Description
A	
B	
C	
	Proven risk of fetal harm Human studies show proof of fetal damage _____

35. Summarize the Joint Commission's (formerly JCAHO) "Do Not Use" abbreviations list.

_____

_____

_____

36. Choose five of the top 10 frequently prescribed medications shown in Table 33-5. Using a PDR, create medication cards for each, including the following information:

    a. Indications

    b. Precautions

    c. Adverse reactions

    d. Dosage and administration

    e. Patient education factors

37. Complete the following table of herbal products.

Name	Use	Side Effects and Cautions
	Weight-loss and anti-aging; antioxidant	
Black cohosh	To relieve symptoms of menopause and to treat menstrual irregularities	
Echinacea		
	Laxative; to treat hot flashes and breast pain; arthritis; to prevent high cholesterol and cancer	
Garlic		Some evidence indicates garlic can slightly lower blood cholesterol levels and may slow development of atherosclerosis.
		Short-term use can safely relieve pregnancy-related nausea and vomiting. Side effects most often reported are gas, bloating, heartburn, and nausea.
Asian ginseng		
	To treat asthma, bronchitis, fatigue, and tinnitus; Alzheimer's disease and other types of dementia; decrease intermittent claudication; to treat sexual dysfunction and multiple sclerosis	
	To treat arthritis and joint pain	
	To treat sleep disorders	
Milk thistle (silymarin)	To promote liver health; treat cirrhosis, chronic hepatitis, and gallbladder disorders; lower cholesterol; reduce insulin resistance	
Saw palmetto		
	Traditionally used to treat mental disorders and nerve pain	

Read the case studies and answer the questions that follow.

1. The first patient of the day for Martha, the medical assistant, has some prescriptions that need to be refilled. Look up each of the following drugs in the PDR to become familiar with the drug's indications and possible side effects. Then prepare the prescriptions for the physician's signature:

   a. Crestor 10 mg; take one pill daily. Dispense 90 tablets with three refills.

   b. Atenolol 50 mg; take one and a half pills by mouth every morning. Dispense 1-month supply with one refill.

   c. Xanax 0.5 mg; take one to two tablets at bedtime as needed. Dispense 30 tablets with no refills.

   d. OxyContin 20 mg; take one tablet as needed for relief of pain. Dispense 15 tablets.

DEA#: 8543201   John Jones, M.D.   Tel: 917-544-8976
                          108 N. Main St.
                          City, State

Patient _____ DATE _____

ADDRESS _____

Rx:

Disp:

Sig:

Refill _____ Times
Please label ☑ _____

DEA#: 8543201   John Jones, M.D.   Tel: 917-544-8976
                          108 N. Main St.
                          City, State

Patient _____ DATE _____

ADDRESS _____

Rx:

Disp:

Sig:

Refill _____ Times
Please label ☑ _____

```
DEA#: 8543201          John Jones, M.D.   Tel: 917-544-8976
                       108 N. Main St.
                       City, State

Patient _____  DATE _____

ADDRESS _____


Rx:

Disp:

Sig:



Refill _____ Times
Please label ☑   _____
```

```
DEA#: 8543201          John Jones, M.D.   Tel: 917-544-8976
                       108 N. Main St.
                       City, State

Patient _____  DATE _____

ADDRESS _____


Rx:

Disp:

Sig:



Refill _____ Times
Please label ☑   _____
```

2. The physician has recommended OTC medication for treatment of symptoms of the common cold. What types of things should Martha encourage her patients to do when they are choosing an OTC?

_____

_____

_____

3. What types of medication should the medical assistant consider when obtaining a medical history. What information about these medications should be documented in the patient's chart?

_____

_____

_____

4. Simon Carmacci, age 78, has been prescribed several medications, including Tenormin, Lasix, Lipitor, and Actos. Based on what you have learned about these medications and about the physiologic changes associated with aging, summarize the potential complications of multiple prescriptions for this patient. Should you consider any patient education factors? If so, what are they?

_____

_____

_____

WORKPLACE APPLICATION OPTIONS

Complete one or more of these activities and, if appropriate, share your results with the class.

1. Martha has noticed that the other medical assistants in the office are unsure of the drug classifications for controlled substances. Prepare an educational handout for the office staff to use as a resource. The handout should include the definition of a controlled substance, an explanation of each schedule (I to V), the potential for abuse or addiction, and some examples of drugs in each schedule. Note whether the prescription can be written or oral.

_____

_____

_____

2. The route of administration used for a drug depends on the intended use of the drug. What route of administration would Martha expect for each of the following illnesses or medications (oral, topical, inhaled, sublingual, mucous membrane, or parenteral route)? Why?

   a. Annual flu vaccination

   _____

   b. Bronchodilator for treatment of an acute asthma attack

   _____

   c. Hyperlipidemia

   _____

   d. Nitroglycerin used for angina

   _____

   e. Dermatitis

   _____

   f. Allergic rhinitis

   _____

   g. Insulin

   _____

   h. Tinea pedis

   _____

   i. Conjunctivitis

   _____

3. You are working for a practice that has just started implementing e-prescriptions. What are the benefits of electronic prescriptions for the patient and the practice?

4. One of your routine responsibilities as a medical assistant will be to telephone prescription orders into the patient's pharmacy. Explain safe methods for doing so and include in your answer the information that must be included for each medication order.

INTERNET ACTIVITY OPTIONS

Complete one or more of these activities and, if appropriate, share your results with the class.

1. Search the Internet for articles on prescription drug abuse. What are some steps the medical assistant can take to help prevent the abuse of prescription drugs?

_____

_____

_____

2. Using either the PDR or Rx List online service, look up 10 of the most prescribed medications from Table 33-5. Make medication cards for these drugs. Be prepared to discuss the indication, side effects, typical dosage levels, route of administration, and patient education factors for these drugs.

3. The American College of Physicians has developed multiple resources to help internal medicine physicians incorporate e-prescribing into their practices. If you are hired as a practice manager, you will be involved in developing and maintaining e-prescription services. Refer to the following website for details, and report your findings to the class: www.acponline.org/running_practice/technology/eprescribing.

4. Search the Internet for information on homeopathic medicine. Refer to the American Institute of Homeopathy at www.homeopathyusa.org. Under "Evidence Based Homeopathy," click on a link to one of the conditions listed. Summarize what you have learned about the homeopathic approach to one of these common conditions.

MEDICAL RECORD ACTIVITIES

1. Mrs. Jones calls the office and states that she wants to discontinue her Diovan 80 mg because she has no prescription coverage. She states, "I feel fine and don't even know why I'm taking this medication!" What patient education can Martha provide to Mrs. Jones to make her understand the importance of continuing her current medication? Is there anything Martha can do to help Mrs. Jones's drug coverage? Document your conversation for the physician's review and recommendations.

_____

_____

_____

2. A patient comes to the office today for a refill of Vicodin ES 7.5/500 mg, one pill every 8 hours as needed with food. After checking the medical record, you notice the patient had a prescription written 5 days ago for the same drug and was dispensed 30 pills at that time. Is it too early for this drug to be refilled? Provide your documentation to the physician. What type of information should you include?

_____

_____

_____

34 Pharmacology Math

Define the following terms.

1. Dispense

   _____

2. Stat

   _____

3. Unit dose

   _____

4. Nomogram

   _____

5. Surface area

   _____

6. Route

   _____

7. Numerator

   _____

8. Denominator

   _____

9. Proper fraction

   _____

10. Improper fraction

    _____

Fill in the blanks with basic drug label terms.

11. The size or amount of the drug available in the drug package is the _____.

12. _____ is the potency of the drug.

13. A(n) _____ is the pure drug that is dissolved in a liquid to form a solution.

14. Usually sterile water or saline, the _____ is the liquid that dissolves the solute.

1. Complete these statements using the following label.

FOR ORAL USE ONLY.
Store dry powder below 86°F (30°C).
PROTECT FROM FREEZING.
DOSAGE AND USE
See accompanying prescribing information.
MIXING DIRECTIONS:
Tap bottle to loosen powder.
Add 15 mL of water to the bottle.
After mixing, store suspension at
41° to 86°F (5° to 30°C).
Oversized bottle provides extra space
for shaking.
After mixing, use within 10 days. Discard
after full dosing is completed.
SHAKE WELL BEFORE USING.
Contains 1200 mg azithromycin.

NDC 0069-3140-19
30 mL (when mixed)
Zithromax®
(azithromycin for oral suspension)
CHERRY FLAVORED
200 mg* per 5 mL
Pfizer Pfizer Labs
Division of Pfizer Inc, NY, NY 10017

* When constituted as directed, each teaspoonful (5 mL) contains azithromycin dihydrate equivalent to 200 mg of azithromycin.

Rx only

6424
MADE IN USA

05-5015-32-1

a. The brand name of the medication is _____.

b. The drug's generic name is _____.

c. The manufacturer of the medication is _____.

d. The manufacturer's NDC code is _____.

e. The lot number is _____.

f. The lot number is used to _____.

g. The specific storage requirements include _____.

h. Identify any warnings or cautions on the label. _____.

i. The total number of units of medication in the container is _____.

j. Each unit of medication contains a dosage strength of _____.

k. Look the drug up in a PDR. The typical pediatric dose of Zithromax is _____.

2. Explain the difference between proper and improper fractions.

_____

_____

3. Review the following examples. Identify the proper and improper fractions. If the fraction is improper, perform the math to get the whole number equivalent.

a. $\frac{2}{3}$ _____

b. $\frac{27}{9}$ _____

c. $\frac{14}{7}$ _____

d. $\frac{5}{6}$ _____

e. $\frac{15}{5}$ _____

f. $\frac{19}{20}$ _____

4. Reduce the following fractions to their lowest terms.

a. $\frac{15}{20}$ _____

b. $\frac{14}{42}$ _____

c. $\frac{120}{180}$ _____

d. $\frac{7}{49}$ _____

e. $\frac{12}{16}$ _____

f. $\frac{4}{36}$ _____

5. Perform the following calculations and reduce the answers to the lowest terms.

a. $\frac{2}{3} \times \frac{9}{8} =$

b. $\frac{7}{9} \div \frac{3}{4} =$

c. $\frac{12}{14} \times \frac{1}{2} =$

d. $\frac{5}{12} \div \frac{6}{14} =$

6. Convert the following fractions into decimals.

   a. $\frac{1}{3}$ = _____   b. $\frac{7}{23}$ _____   c. $\frac{16}{84}$ = _____   d. $\frac{2}{9}$ = _____   e. $\frac{26}{34}$ = _____

7. The act of dividing a fraction results in a decimal number. Decimal numbers can then be converted to percentages by moving the decimal two spaces to the right, as follows:

   $$0.25 = 25.0\%, \text{ commonly written } 25\%$$

   Convert the following decimals to percentages. Show your work in the space to the right of the questions.

   a. 0.75 = _____ %

   b. 0.33 = _____ %

   c. 0.25 = _____ %

   d. 1.0 = _____ %

   e. 0.50 = _____%

   Convert the following decimals into percentages.

   a. 0.45 = _____   b. 1.37 = _____   c. 0.97 = _____   d. 2.59 = _____   e. 0.62 = _____   f. 1.05 = _____

8. A proportion is written as follows:

   $\frac{4}{16}$ = $\frac{1}{4}$ or 4:16::1:4

   Use cross-multiplication to solve for *x*. Show your work in the space to the right of the questions.

   a. 3:4 = *x*:12

   b. 1:2 = *x*:6

   c. 2:5 = *x*:100

   d. 2:6 = *x*:12

   e. 1:3 = *x*:75

   Solve for *x* in the following problems and prove that your answer is correct.

   a. 5:4 = *x*:12 _____

   b. 3:15 = *x*:25 _____

   c. 4:28 = *x*:84 _____

   d. 9:*x* = 5:250 _____

   e. 100:*x* = 10:50 _____

9. What are the correct doses of the following medications, rounded to the nearest tenth?

   a. 1.28 mL = _____   b. 5.76 g = _____   c. 14.74 mcg = _____   d. 3.62 mL = _____

   e. 0.18 mL = _____   f. 1.44 (unscored) tabs = _____   g. 2.11 cc = _____   h. 0.54 (scored) tab = _____

10. What three basic steps must the medical assistant complete to accurately calculate a prescribed dose?

   a. _____

   b. _____

   c. _____

Part I: Metric System

Consider the following fundamental units of the metric system:

Mass or weight: gram (g) *always lowercase*
Volume: liter (L) *always capitalized*
Length: meter (m) *always lowercase*

Consider the following equivalents:

Mass and Weight	Volume
1 kg = 1,000g	1 kL = 1,000 liters
1 g = 1,000 mg	1 L = 1,000 mL (or cc)
1 mg= 1,000 µg	1 mL (or cc) = 1,000 µL
1 dg = 0.1 g or 1/10 g	1 dL = 0.1 L or 1/10 L
1 cg = 0.01 g or 1/100 g	1 cL = 0.01 L or 1/100 L
1 mg = 0.001 g or 1/1,000 g	1 mL = 0.001 L or 1/1,000 L

Write the prefix for the following (remember to write the prefixes in lowercase).

1. _____ 1/100 of a unit

2. _____ 1/10 of a unit

3. _____ 1/1,000 of a unit

4. _____ 1/1,000,000 of a unit

5. _____ 10 units

6. _____ 100 units

7. _____ 1,000 units

Convert the following by moving the decimals, by multiplication, or by division. Show your work in the space to the right of the questions.

8. 1.5 L = _____ mL

9. 500 mg = _____ g

10. 3 g = _____ mg

11. 2,000 mg = _____ g

12. 2.5 g = _____ mg

13. 0.5 g = _____ mg

14. 500 mL = _____ L

15. 0.75 g = _____ mg

16. 1 kg = _____ g

17. 1,000 mg = _____ g

18. Complete the following abbreviation table.

Apothecary System		Metric System	
Min (M)			Gram
	Dram		Liter
f dr		cc	
	Ounce		Milliliter
fl oz			
Gr			

Part II: Apothecary System and Household Measurements

1. The basic unit of weight in the apothecary system for a solid measurement is the _____.

2. The basic unit of volume in the apothecary system for a liquid measurement is _____.

3. Household measurements are not precisely accurate, so they should never be used in the medical setting.

    a. True

    b. False

4. The household measurement for weight is _____.

5. In household measurements, liquid oral medications are taken by the drop, teaspoon, or tablespoon and are supplied in bottles labeled in ounces or pints.

    a. True

    b. False

6. Supply the abbreviations or symbols for these metric, apothecary system, and common household units.

    a. ounce _____

    b. teaspoon _____

    c. milligram _____

    d. grain _____

    e. pint _____

    f. dram _____

    g. tablespoon _____

Use the conversions to complete the questions that follow.

Mass and Weight	Volume
1 cup = 8 oz	1 tsp = 5 mL (cc)
1 oz = 2 Tbsp	1 Tbsp = 15 mL (cc)
1 Tbsp = 3 tsp	1 fl oz = 30 mL (cc)
1 tsp = 60 drops	1 grain = 60 mg

7. A standard teaspoon equals 5 mL. If a liquid drug has 100 mg/teaspoon, how many milligrams are in each milliliter? _____

   How did you determine your answer?

   _____

   _____

   _____

8. You are asked to give 2 teaspoons of cough medicine to a child. How many milliliters will you give?

   _____

9. How many teaspoons are in 1 oz? _____

10. Now that you know that 5 mL is the same as 1 tsp, how many milliliters are in 1 oz?

    _____

11. Complete the following household equivalents table.

60	gtt	=			
3		=	1 T		
180	gtt	=		=	½ oz
	T	=	1 oz	=	6 t (or tsp)
360	gtt	=			
1	oz	=			
	oz	=	1 tsp		
8	oz	=			
2	c	=	1 pt	=	oz
	pt	=	1 qt	=	32 oz
4	c	=	1 qt	=	oz
	qt	=	1 gal	=	128 oz

Part III: Conversion between Systems of Measurement

Units of measurements can also be converted by using the following formula:

$$\text{Have} \times \frac{\text{Wanted}}{\text{have}} \text{ (conversion)} = \text{Unit wanted in new system}$$

Perform the following conversions. The conversion factor is 1 kg = 2.2 lb. Show your work in the space to the right of the questions.

1. 150 lb = _____ kg

2. 78 lb = _____ kg

3. 18 kg = _____ lb

4. 210 lb = _____ kg

5. 71 kg = _____ lb

6. 198 lb = _____ kg

7. 112 lb = _____ kg

8. 163 lb = _____ kg

9. 21 kg = _____ lb

10. 4.4 lb = _____ kg

11. 6 lb 10 oz = _____ kg

Convert inches to centimeters. The conversion factor is 2.5 cm/inch. Show your work in the space to the right of the questions.

12. 62 inches = _____ cm

13. 34 inches = _____ cm

14. 97 inches = _____ cm

15. 5′0″ = _____ inches = _____ cm

16. 6′2″ = _____ inches = _____ cm

17. The following formula provides a method of converting drug orders from the ordered unit of measurement to the label unit:

$$\text{Drug have} \times \frac{\text{Wanted}}{\text{have}} = \text{Unit wanted in new system}$$

Use this formula to convert the following drug orders. Show your work next to the problem.

    a. 30 gr = _____ g

    b. 0.25 gr = _____ mg

    c. 8 fl oz = _____ mL

    d. 12 mL = _____ fl dr

    e. 180 mg = _____ gr

    f. 60 mg = _____ gr

18. The standard formula for calculating dosage is:

$$\frac{\text{Available strength}}{\text{Ordered strength}} = \frac{\text{Available amount}}{\text{Amount to give}}$$

Using the standard formula, calculate the following dosages. Show your work beneath the problem.

    a. Physician's order: Bicillin 400,000 units IM; Label: 1,200,000 units per 2 mL

_____

    b. Physician's order: 75 mg Demerol IM stat; Label: 100 mg per cc

_____

c. Physician's order: 200 mcg Vitamin B$_{12}$ SC; Label: 1000 mcg per mL

_____

d. Physician order: Amoxicillin solution 250 mg; Label: 0.5 g per 2 cc

_____

19. An alternative formula for calculating drug dosages is: D/H × Q

    D—Desired dose (the physician's order)

    H—What is on hand (the dosage strength listed on the medication label)

    Q—Quantity in the unit (identified on the label as one tablet, 5 mL, and so on)

Using this formula, calculate the following dosages. Show your work beneath the problem.

    a. Physician's order: Compazine 12 mg IM. On hand is a 15 mL vial that contains 4 mg/mL.

_____

    b. Physician's order: Depro-Medrol 25 mg IM. On hand is a 10 mL vial that contains 80 mg/mL.

_____

    c. Physician's order: 250 mg Amoxil PO. On hand are 500 mg scored tablets.

_____

    d. Physician's order: 15 mg Coumadin PO. On hand are 7.5 mg tablets.

_____

CASE STUDIES

Calculate the following doses of medication. Remember to use the standard formula:

$$\frac{\text{Available strength}}{\text{Ordered strength}} = \frac{\text{Available amount}}{\text{Amount to give}}$$

Physician's Order	Label Reads	Amount to Give	Practice Charting
Keflex 500 mg	250 mg capsule		
Lasix 40 mg	20 mg tablet		
Zoloft 75 mg	25 mg tablet		
Claritin 30 mg	10 mg tablet		
Prilosec 40 mg	10 mg capsule		
Celebrex 200 mg	100 mg capsule		
Vioxx 12.5 mg	25 mg		
Lanoxin 0.125 mg	0.25 mg tablet		
Coumadin 20 mg	5 mg tablet		
Augmentin 250 mg	500 mg per 5 mL		

Physician's Order	Label Reads	Amount to Give	Practice Charting
Prednisone 40 mg	5 mg tablet		
Prozac 20 mg	10 mg capsule		
Synthroid 0.44 mg	88 mcg per tablet		
Zocor 60 mg	20 mg tablet		
Glucophage 1 g	500 mg tablet		
Zestril 2.5 mg	5 mg tablet		
Norvasc 10 mg	2.5 mg tablet		
Cipro 750 mg	250 mg tablet		
Zyrtec syrup 4 mg	5 mg/5 mL		
Zovirax 200 mg	400 mg tablet		

Pediatric Dosages

Clark's rule

Clark's rule is based on the weight of the child. It uses 150 lb (70 kg) as the average adult weight and assumes that the child's dose is proportionately less. The formula is as follows:

$$\text{Pediatric dose} = \frac{\text{Child's weight in pounds}}{150 \text{ lb}} = \text{Adult dose}$$

Order	Adult Dose	Child's Weight	Amount to Give
Penicillin	100,000 units	22 lb	
Benadryl	50 mg	13 lb	
Tylenol	500 mg	54 lb	
Sudafed	60 mg	37 lb	

West's Nomogram

West's nomogram uses a calculation of the body surface area (BSA) of infants and young children to determine the pediatric dose.

$$\text{Pediatric dose} = \frac{\text{(BSA) of child in } m^2}{1.7 m^2 \text{ (average adult BSA)}} = \text{Adult dose}$$

Order	Adult Dose	Child's BSA	Amount to Give
Penicillin	100,000 U	0.5 m^2	
Benadryl	50 mg	0.3 m^2	
Tylenol	500 mg	0.6 m^2	
Sudafed	60 mg	0.7 m^2	

WORKPLACE APPLICATION OPTIONS

Use Clark's rule, West's nomogram, or the body weight method to answer the following questions.

1. A child weighs 42 lb. The physician orders 1 mg of medication per kilogram. How many kilograms does the child weigh? How many milligrams of medication do you need to give?

_____

2. An infant weighs 14 lb. The adult dose is 100 mg. When Clark's rule is used, how much is the pediatric dose?

_____

3. The physician orders 5 mg of medication per kilogram of body weight. The patient weighs 145 lb. How many milligrams do you give?

_____

4. The child has a BSA of 0.9 m^2, and the adult dose is 200 mg. According to West's nomogram, what is the pediatric dose?

_____

5. The nurse practitioner orders 250 mg of Rocephin to be given by injection. The vial contains Rocephin at a concentration of 500 mg/mL. How much medication will the medical assistant draw into the syringe?

_____

6. The patient takes 5,000 units of heparin by injection each day. The vial contains heparin, 10,000 units/mL. How much heparin needs to be drawn into the syringe?

_____

7. The patient weighs 163 lb. The order is for 2 mg/kg. How much medicine does the patient need?

_____

8. The physician orders Phenergan 12.5 mg by mouth. You have Phenergan syrup in a concentration of 25 mg/5 mL. How many milliliters will you give?

_____

9. You need to give a 500-unit injection of vitamin B_{12}. You have on hand vitamin B_{12} at a concentration unit of 1,000 units/mL. How much will you measure in the syringe?

_____

INTERNET ACTIVITY OPTIONS

Complete this activity and, if appropriate, share your results with the class.

Use the Internet or a drug reference book to collect information and make index cards for 20 of the top 50 prescribed drugs identified in Table 33-5. Include the following information:

Brand name
Generic name
Schedule (if appropriate)
Type of drug or drug classification
Usual dose
Route of administration
Typical use
Warnings or precautions

MEDICAL RECORD ACTIVITIES

Document the following scenarios in the progress notes section of the medical record using POMR practices.

1. An infant who weighs 11 lb is ordered Amoxil q 6 hr. The label reads 250 mg in 5 cc of suspension. The recommended range of the medication for an infant is 15 mg/kg/day. How much should the child receive per dose? Document the administration of this medication.

_____

_____

_____

2. An infant who weighs 12 lb 5 oz is ordered Diflucan qid for the treatment of thrush. The label reads 150 mg in 3 cc of suspension. The recommended range of the medication is 3 mg/kg/day. How much should the child receive per dose? Document the administration of this medication.

_____

_____

_____

3. An infant is ordered Zantac bid. The infant weighs 35 lb. The label reads 300 mg in 5 cc of suspension. The recommended range of the medication is 10 mg/kg/day. How much should the child receive per dose? Document the administration of this medication.

_____

_____

_____

35 Administering Medications

VOCABULARY REVIEW

Match the following terms with their definitions.

_____ 1. Angled tip of a needle

_____ 2. Narrowing of the bronchiole tubes

_____ 3. Abnormal accumulation of fluid in the interstitial spaces of tissues

_____ 4. A coating added to an oral medication that resists the effects of stomach juices; designed so that medicine is absorbed in the small intestine

_____ 5. Sealed so that no air is allowed to enter

_____ 6. Low blood pressure

_____ 7. Administering repeated injections of diluted extracts of the substance that causes an allergy; also called *desensitization*

_____ 8. An abnormally hard, inflamed area

_____ 9. Administering a double dose for the first dose of the medication; usually done with antibiotic therapy to reach therapeutic blood levels quickly

_____ 10. Inflammation of a vein; may lead to thrombus formation

_____ 11. The curved formation of liquids in a container

_____ 12. Excretion of an unusually large amount of urine

_____ 13. Drug in pill form manufactured with an indentation for division through the center

_____ 14. Increase in the diameter of a blood vessel

_____ 15. The quality of being thick; property of resistance to flow in a fluid

_____ 16. Referring to an explosive substance's capacity to vaporize at a low temperature

_____ 17. Localized area of edema or a raised lesion

a. Bevel

b. Scored tablet

c. Hypotension

d. Polyuria

e. Volatile

f. Wheal

g. Viscosity

h. Vasodilation

i. Immunotherapy

j. Loading dose

k. Edema

l. Meniscus

m. Bronchoconstriction

n. Induration

o. Enteric coated

p. Phlebitis

q. Hermetically sealed

Solid Oral Forms

Define the following terms.

1. Scored

_____

2. Tablet

_____

3. Buffered

_____

4. Capsule

_____

5. Caplet

_____

6. Time released

_____

Liquid Oral Forms
Define the following terms.

1. Syrup

_____

2. Aromatic waters

_____

3. Liquors

_____

4. Suspension

_____

5. Emulsion

_____

6. Gel or magma

_____

7. Tinctures

_____

8. Elixirs

_____

Mucous Membrane Forms
List the site of absorption indicated by the following terms.

1. Buccal

_____

2. Sublingual

_____

3. Inhalation

_____

Topical Forms

Describe or define the following.

1. Lotion

_____

2 Liniment

_____

3. Ointment

_____

4. Transdermal

_____

Parenteral Forms

Define or describe the following.

1. Vial

_____

2. Ampule

_____

3. Multiuse

_____

4. Prefilled

_____

5. Cartridge system

_____

SKILLS AND CONCEPTS

1. List and explain the seven rights of drug administration.

   a. _____

     _____

   b. _____

     _____

   c. _____

     _____

   d. _____

     _____

e. _____

_____

f. _____

_____

g. _____

_____

2. When should the medical assistant check the drug label?

_____

_____

_____

3. List four additional steps the medical assistant can take to ensure the safety of medication administration.

a. _____

b. _____

c. _____

d. _____

4. Summarize four guidelines for the administration of medications to geriatric patients.

a. _____

b. _____

c. _____

d. _____

5. List a minimum of five guidelines for the administration of parenteral medications.

a. _____

b. _____

c. _____

d. _____

e. _____

Label the following statements as either "ampule" or "vial."

6. Has a rubber stopper _____

7. Has sharp edges after it is opened _____

8. Is always single use. _____

9. Air must be injected into it before medicine can be removed. _____

10. Can be multiuse _____

11. A filtered needle is required to avoid getting glass in the syringe. _____

12. Has a vacuum after it is opened _____

13. Extra care is required to prevent contamination. _____

14. Always discarded in a sharps container _____

15. Gauze or an unopened alcohol prep should be used to prevent injury as the neck breaks away. _____

16. List four routes of parenteral administration; include approved abbreviations and how to locate the sites anatomically.

    a. _____

    _____

    b. _____

    _____

    c. _____

    _____

    d. _____

    _____

Part I: Parenteral Medication Equipment

Indicate which statements about needles are true (T) and which are false (F).

1. _____ Needles may be purchased separately or as part of a needle-syringe unit.

2. _____ The diameter or lumen size of a needle is called its *gauge*.

3. _____ The larger the gauge number, the smaller the diameter of the needle.

4. _____ Gauges 25 and 26 are commonly used for subcutaneous injections.

5. _____ Gauges 20 to 23 usually are necessary for intramuscular injections when the medication is thick (e.g., penicillin).

6. _____ Needles that are ½ or ⅝ inch long are used for intramuscular injections.

7. _____ Needles that are ½ or ⅝ inch long are used for subcutaneous injections.

8. _____ A contaminated needle should be recapped before disposal in a sharps container.

9. _____ The parts of the needle are the barrel, calibrated scale(s), plunger, and tip.

10. _____ Longer needles are necessary for depositing drugs intradermally.

11. In the following examples, identify whether the best choice is an insulin syringe, a TB syringe, or a 3-cc syringe.

    a. 2.1 mL   _____

    b. 0.14 mL   _____

    c. 14 U   _____

    d. 1.1 mL   _____

    e. 38 U   _____

    f. 0.76 mL   _____

12. Label the syringes in the following figure.

a. On the insulin syringe, draw a line at 62 units.

b. On the tuberculin syringe, draw a line at 0.3 mL.

c. On the 3-cc Luer-Lok syringe, draw a line at ½ cc.

d. On the 10-cc slip-tip syringe, draw a line at 4.8 cc.

e. Insulin syringes can be purchased in 30 U, 50 U, and 100 U sizes. Which one is pictured?

f. The angle of an insulin injection is _____, and the angle of injection for an intradermal administration
   is _____.

g. What gauge and length of needle would be used for a TB skin test? _____ For an insulin
   injection? _____ For an intramuscular (IM) injection? _____

h. The 1-mL TB syringe is calibrated at _____ mL per line. The 3-mL syringe is calibrated at
   _____ mL per line.

i. A(n) _____ injection may be used to help prevent irritation of surrounding tissues and leakage of the
   medication to the surface of the injection.

Part II: Injection Sites

Label the intramuscular, intradermal, and subcutaneous injection sites correctly on the following figure.

ANTERIOR

POSTERIOR

a. Deltoid

b. Ventrogluteal

c. Adult vastus lateralis

d. Gluteal (dorsogluteal)

e. TB skin test

f. Insulin injection site

Chapter **35** **Administering Medications**

Part III: Pediatric Sites

1. On the following figure, label and name the appropriate IM injection site for an infant and young child.

2. Explain why infant IM injections are limited to the vastus lateralis site. Describe the anatomic location of a pediatric injection site.

   _____

   _____

   _____

Part IV: Therapy Terms

1. Define the following terms.

   a. isotonic solutions

   _____

   b. hypertonic solutions

   _____

   c. hypotonic solutions

   _____

   d. infiltration

   _____

2. Discuss the role of the medical assistant in IV therapy.

   _____

   _____

   _____

WORKPLACE APPLICATION OPTIONS

Complete one or more of these activities and, if appropriate, share your results with the class.

1. Dorothy, the medical assistant, has been asked by Dr. Thau to update the medication abbreviation list to be included as part of the policy and procedures manual. Use the following list to spell out each abbreviation.

   a. q 4 hr _____

   b. tid _____

   c. qid _____

   d. bid _____

   e. q 3 hr _____

   f. HS _____

   g. AC _____

   h. PC _____

   i. PRN _____

   j. PO _____

   k. NPO _____

   l. PR _____

   m. IV _____

   n. SC (SQ) _____

   o. IM _____

   p. SL _____

   q. QD _____

   r. QAM _____

   s. QPM _____

2. Dorothy is in charge of organizing a newly constructed examination room. The room will be used for medication administration, and Dorothy wants to make sure it is fully equipped. What supplies must Dorothy order to fulfill Occupational Safety and Health Administration (OSHA) guidelines? What other items may she want to make sure are in the room to make patients as comfortable as possible?

   _____

   _____

   _____

   _____

3. Dorothy has been asked to perform a two-step tuberculin skin test on a new employee. Why is this being done? Explain the procedure to the new co-worker.

   _____

   _____

   _____

   _____

4. Dorothy is responsible for reading and documenting the outcome of a Mantoux test that was administered 2 days ago. Explain the criteria for a positive test result, including the reasons a result may be considered positive even if the induration is less than 15 mm.

_____

_____

_____

_____

INTERNET ACTIVITY OPTIONS

Complete one or more of these activities and, if appropriate, share your results with the class.

1. Investigate the FDA's site on drug safety at www.fda.gov/Drugs/DrugSafety/default.htm. Click on the link to "Medication Errors," and summarize what you think the medical assistant could do to eliminate medication errors in the ambulatory care center.

2. Review the information available from the Centers for Disease Control and Prevention (CDC) on medication safety at www.cdc.gov/medicationsafety. Summarize what you learn for the class.

3. Investigate the National Patient Safety Foundation's site at www.npsf.org. Review an article that summarizes research on medication safety, and share the material with your classmates.

MEDICAL RECORD ACTIVITIES

1. Dorothy is administering DTaP 0.5 mL intramuscularly to a 5-year-old patient. What site should she use? What steps would help her administer the medication with the least amount of trauma to the child and her mother? Document the procedure.

_____

_____

_____

2. You have just administered allergy injections to a patient. As you are informing the patient that he must wait in the office for 20 minutes so that he can be monitored for any reactions, the patient informs you that he is unable to remain in the office. What should you do? Document your answer.

_____

_____

_____

3. You are providing instruction on the use of an Epipen to a patient who is allergic to bee venom. Provide step-by-step instructions for the patient. Using your knowledge of patient education, what are some points to remember with demonstration? What types of materials should you give the patient to take home? Document your session with the patient in the medical record.

_____

_____

_____

4. You are getting ready to administer IM penicillin to a patient as ordered. Just as you are about to inject the medication, the patient tells you she is allergic to penicillin. What should you do? Provide the appropriate documentation in the patient record.

_____

_____

_____

5. You are gathering a new patient history for Dr. Thau. What types of questions should you ask the patient about his or her use of medications? Role-play with a partner, interviewing each other about medication use. Document your findings.

_____

_____

_____

_____

36 Emergency Preparedness and Assisting with Medical Emergencies

VOCABULARY REVIEW

Define the following terms.

1. Cyanosis

_____

2. Diaphoresis

_____

3. Dyspnea

_____

4. Ecchymosis

_____

5. Emetic

_____

6. Fibrillation

_____

7. Hematuria

_____

8. Mediastinum

_____

9. Myocardium

_____

10. Necrosis

_____

11. Photophobia

_____

12. Polydipsia

_____

13. Polyuria

_____

14. Transient ischemic attack

_____

Fill in the blanks with the correct terms.

15. _____ is defined as the immediate care given to a person who has been injured or has suddenly become ill.

16. AED stands for _____.

17. CPR stands for _____.

18. CVA stands for _____.

19. TIA stands for _____.

20. MI stands for _____.

21. _____ is the most dangerous form of heat-related injury and results in a shutdown of body systems.

22. _____ are the initial signs of a heat-related emergency.

23. Patients with _____ appear flushed and report headaches, nausea, vertigo, and weakness.

24. _____ are medications that may be administered to dissolve a blood clot.

25. A patient who has experienced a sudden cardiac arrest will show a(n) _____ pattern on the electrocardiogram (ECG).

26. The medical term for extensive bruising of the skin is _____.

27. If the physician diagnoses a disease that has no known cause, it is called _____.

28. _____ is a pulse rate below 60 beats per minute.

SKILLS AND CONCEPTS

1. Summarize a minimum of four methods of maintaining a safe environment for both staff and patients.

   a. _____

   b. _____

   c. _____

   d. _____

2. Identify five methods for preventing fires in the ambulatory care center.

   a. _____

   b. _____

   c. _____

   d. _____

   e. _____

3. Explain the procedure for effectively discharging a fire extinguisher.

_____

_____

_____

4. List the criteria that should be included in a healthcare facility's evacuation plan.

_____

_____

_____

_____

5. Ambulatory care practitioners should be prepared to contact community emergency services as needed. Identify five resources available in your community for emergency preparedness. Include the services provided and contact information for each.

a. _____

_____

b. _____

_____

c. _____

_____

d. _____

_____

e. _____

_____

6. Standard precautions are crucial for preventing the transmission of diseases associated with bioterrorism. Summarize infection control procedures that should be implemented in the event a bioterrorism incident may have occurred.

_____

_____

_____

7. Summarize the recommendations of the Centers for Disease Control and Prevention (CDC) to help minimize the negative psychological effects of an emergency situation on both staff members and patients.

_____

_____

_____

8. The Occupational Safety and Health Administration (OSHA) recommends multiple factors that can help promote staff safety. Explain six accident prevention behaviors that should be followed in a healthcare setting.

a. _____

b. _____

c. _____

d. _____

e. _____

f. _____

9. You are responsible for placing and labeling biohazard waste containers in the physician's office where you work. Explain the methods for proper disposal of hazardous material in the physician's office.

_____

_____

_____

_____

10. Discuss the role of medical assistants in emergency preparedness and the ways they can help if a natural disaster or other emergency occurs in their community.

_____

_____

_____

_____

_____

11. List five classic symptoms of a heart attack.

a. _____

b. _____

c. _____

d. _____

e. _____

12. What is the difference between classic myocardial signs and symptoms and those that may be experienced by female patients?

_____

_____

_____

13. List and explain seven types of shock.

a. _____

b. _____

c. _____

d. _____

e. _____

f. _____

g. _____

14. What four interventions can be used to treat sprains and strains?

a. _____

b. _____

c. _____

d. _____

15. Give five examples of situations in which patients with abdominal pain should be seen by a healthcare provider immediately.

a. _____

b. _____

c. _____

d. _____

e. _____

16. Screening emergency telephone calls is an important role of the medical assistant in the ambulatory care setting. List a minimum of two questions the medical assistant should ask for the following health problems.

a. Syncope (fainting)

_____

_____

b. Head injury

_____

_____

c. Insect bites or stings

_____

_____

d. Burns

_____

_____

e. Wounds

_____

_____

f. Animal bites

_____

_____

g. Asthma

_____

_____

h. Poisoning

_____

_____

CASE STUDIES

Read the case studies and answer the questions that follow.

1. Sally calls the office complaining of lumbar pain that has been present for the past 2 weeks. What type of screening questions should you ask the patient? When should the patient be seen in the office? Provide the appropriate documentation.

_____

_____

_____

2. Mr. Walker, a 64-year-old patient of Dr. Bendt, calls the office complaining of shortness of breath, pressure in the chest, and sweating for the past hour. Upon checking the patient's chart, you find that Mr. Walker is a smoker and obese. What advice should you give the patient? Show your documentation.

_____

_____

The physician refers Mr. Walker to the emergency department, but he refuses to go, stating, "I don't feel well enough to drive to the hospital." What should be done to meet the needs of the patient? Document your conversation.

_____

_____

3. A patient calls, stating that she has found a tick on her left forearm. Explain the proper technique for removal of the tick. Also, you should advise the patient to watch for what signs and symptoms? Document your conversation.

_____

_____

_____

4. A 19-year-old patient sitting in the waiting room experiences a grand mal seizure. What should Cheryl, the medical assistant, do to prevent injury to the patient? After the seizure, the patient needs to be placed in the recovery position to maintain her airway. Explain how to place her in this position.

_____

_____

_____

5. The mother of a 10-year old child comes running into the office with her son. He is bleeding profusely from a gash in his left forearm. She states he fell on some glass at the playground and she just rushed him to the physician's office. What should be done immediately to control the bleeding from the wound? Include in your discussion OSHA precautions for possible contamination.

_____

_____

_____

WORKPLACE APPLICATION OPTIONS

Complete one or more of these activities and, if appropriate, share your results with the class.

1. You learned in your text about factors that are crucial for patient safety and a few of the most common mistakes that can be made by healthcare workers that result in injury to a patient. Develop a handout that summarizes patient safety factors and share it with the class.

2. At a recent office meeting, telephone screening difficulties were addressed. Dr. Bendt asks you to review the current procedures and policies that are followed when patients call the office with emergencies and offer suggestions on how possible questions might be improved. In addition, the physician would like you to make a list of "home care advice" to go along with the symptoms. The work should also include "if" and "how soon" the patient should be seen in the office or under what circumstances the patient should be referred to the emergency department. Include the following situations in your project.

Asthma	Insect bites and stings
Wounds	Head injuries
Burns	Chest pain
Diabetic coma	Hypoglycemia
Back pain	Dysuria
Burns	Syncope
Hyperglycemia	High blood pressure

3. As a medical assistant, you understand that medical emergencies have many different signs and symptoms. Dr. Bendt has asked you to create an informative brochure to educate patients about the importance of early detection and treatment. The brochure should include the following:

a. Definition of illness

b. Importance of early detection

c. Signs and symptoms

d. Risk factors

e. Prevention recommendations

f. What patients should do if they think they are experiencing this condition

4. Cheryl is in charge of establishing the office crash cart. What type of supplies should be stocked in the cart? What medications should be included? How should the cart and supplies be maintained? Where should the cart be kept?

_____

_____

_____

_____

_____

5. The medical assistant can play an integral role in a community's response to natural or human-created disasters. Summarize how the medical assistant can contribute to the community response to an emergency.

_____

_____

_____

_____

6. The daughter of an elderly stoke victim is very concerned about her father's potential for choking. Explain to the daughter what to do if her father experiences an obstructed airway. Include in your explanation the techniques for both responsive and unresponsive adults.

_____

_____

_____

_____

INTERNET ACTIVITY OPTIONS

Complete one or more of these activities and, if appropriate, share your results with the class.

1. You notice that your CPR for the professional certification is about to expire. Search for a list of certification sites in your area. Make a list of the contact information and share the locations with your classmates.

2. Perform a search for the poison control center in your area. Search for and create a list of ideas for ways to prevent poisoning. Create an informative poster to display in your physician's office.

3. Investigate the CDC's site for emergency preparedness planning at www.bt.cdc.gov/planning/#healthcare.

4. Search the CDC's Emergency Operations Center site at www.cdc.gov/phpr/eoc.htm.

MEDICAL RECORD ACTIVITIES

Documentation of an onsite emergency includes the following information:

- Patient's name, address, age, and health insurance information
- Allergies, current medications, and pertinent health history
- Name and relationship of any person with the patient
- Vital signs and chief complaint
- Sequence of events, beginning with how the problem occurred, any changes in the patient's overall condition, and any observations made regarding the patient's condition
- Details of procedures or treatments performed on the patient

300

Document the details of the following cases.

1. Charise Mourning calls at 4 p.m., just after the physician has left for the day, and reports that her husband, Sam, fell going down the steps and can't bear weight on his left leg. Mrs. Mourning is 78 years old and does not know how to drive. What questions should you ask? How should you handle the situation? Document pertinent information in Mr. Mourning's medical record.

_____

_____

_____

_____

_____

2. Lynne Franklin, the 17-year-old mother of a 9-month-old son, calls, hysterical and crying. She states that the baby is "jerking and shaking all over the crib." She states, "I tried to hold him down, and I heard something snap! What should I do? He looks like he is turning blue!" Lynne tells you he had a fever all night. The last time she took his temperature it was 103° F axillary. She is alone with the baby. How should the situation be handled? Document the details in the baby's medical record.

_____

_____

_____

_____

_____

3. Charles Drysden, a 42-year-old patient, calls when the rest of the office is out to lunch. He is at work and is experiencing heaviness in his chest, difficulty breathing, indigestion, sweating, and minor jaw discomfort. He reports that the discomfort in his chest started about 30 minutes ago, after he ate a large lunch. Mr. Drysden took Mylanta for the indigestion but is not feeling any better. He wants to drive himself to the office even though a co-worker has offered to take him to the emergency department (ED). His pain is getting worse, but he doesn't think he needs to go to the ED. What should you do? Document the important details in Mr. Drysden's medical record.

_____

_____

_____

_____

_____

4. You are working in the administrative area of the office when a patient enters the waiting room screaming for attention. She insists the physician ordered the wrong medication, and she wants to talk to the doctor immediately. The physician is not in the office today, so you attempt to handle this very angry patient. Using the skills discussed in Procedure 36-3, try to work out a solution with the patient. Document the patient interaction in the woman's health record.

_____

_____

_____

_____

_____

37 Assisting in Ophthalmology and Otolaryngology

VOCABULARY REVIEW

Match the term with the correct definition.

_____ 1. Adjustment of the eye for seeing various sizes of objects at different distances

_____ 2. Reduction or dimness of vision with no apparent organic cause; often referred to as *lazy eye syndrome*

_____ 3. An allied healthcare professional specializing in evaluation of hearing function, detection of hearing impairment, and determination of the anatomic site of impairment

_____ 4. Structures found in the retina that make the perception of color possible

_____ 5. A small pit in the center of the retina that is considered the center of clearest vision

_____ 6. Any substance or medication that causes constriction of the pupil

_____ 7. A region at the back of the eye where the optic nerve meets the retina; considered the blind spot of the eye because it contains only nerve fibers and no rods or cones and therefore is insensitive to light

_____ 8. The second cranial nerve, which carries impulses for the sense of sight

_____ 9. The formation of spongy bone in the labyrinth of the ear, often causing the auditory ossicles to become fixed and unable to vibrate when sound enters the ear

_____ 10. A substance or medication that damages the eighth cranial nerve or the organs of hearing and balance

_____ 11. Abnormal sensitivity to light

_____ 12. A usually chronic, recurrent skin disease marked by bright red patches covered with silvery scales

_____ 13. Structures located in the retina of the eye and forming the light-sensitive elements

_____ 14. An excessive discharge of sebum from the sebaceous glands, forming greasy scales or cheesy plugs on the body

_____ 15. An instrument used to measure intraocular pressure

_____ 16. A topical ophthalmic medication that dilates the pupil; used in diagnostic procedures of the eye and treatment for glaucoma

_____ 17. A noise sensation of ringing heard in one or both ears

a. Cones

b. Accommodation

c. Seborrhea

d. Psoriasis

e. Rods

f. Audiologist

g. Amblyopia

h. Photophobia

i. Optic nerve

j. Otosclerosis

k. Ototoxic

l. Fovea centralis

m. Optic disc

n. Miotic

o. Mydriatic

p. Tinnitus

q. Tonometer

Fill in the blanks with the correct terms.

18. A(n) _____ is a licensed medical physician who can diagnose eye disorders, prescribe medication, conduct eye screenings, prescribe glasses or contact lenses, and perform otic surgery.

19. _____ are trained to fill prescriptions written for corrective lenses by grinding the lenses and dispensing eyewear.

20. A(n) _____ can perform eye examinations, diagnose vision problems and eye diseases, and treat visual defects through corrective lenses and eye exercises.

21. A(an) _____ is a procedure that uses an optical instrument with mirrors that helps the healthcare provider visualize the anterior chamber of the eye to aid in the diagnosis of glaucoma.

22. The _____ of the eye secretes vitreous fluid and also changes the shape of the lens depending on the amount of light exposure.

23. The _____ of the eye is where light receptors are transformed into nerve impulses.

24. The _____ produce tears.

25. The abbreviation PERRLA means

_____

_____

SKILLS AND CONCEPTS

1. On the following figure, label the structures of the outer eye.

2. Name the two disorders of the outer eye pictured in the following figures.

a. _____

304

Chapter **37** **Assisting in Ophthalmology and Otolaryngology**

b. _____

3. List and define three refractive errors.

a. _____

b. _____

c. _____

4. List three signs and symptoms of refractive errors.

a. _____

b. _____

c. _____

5. Compare and contrast strabismus and amblyopia.

_____

_____

_____

6. Explain how a corneal abrasion is diagnosed and treated.

_____

_____

_____

7. Differentiate between otitis media and otitis externa.

_____

_____

_____

8. Summarize five risk factors for otitis media.

a. _____

b. _____

c. _____

d. _____

e. _____

9. Explain the difference between the Weber and Rhinne tuning fork tests for hearing loss.

_____

_____

_____

_____

10. Label the anatomy of the ear in the following picture using the terms listed.

a. Pinna

b. External auditory canal

c. Ear lobe

d. Cartilage

e. Bone (skull)

f. Tympanic membrane

g. Malleus

h. Incus

i. Stapes

j. Round window

k. Eustachian tube

l. Semicircular canals

m. Vestibule

n. Cranial nerve VIII

o. Cochlea

p. External ear

q. Middle ear

r. Inner ear

CASE STUDIES

Read the case studies and answer the questions that follow.

1. Amy, the medical assistant, has a patient who is interested in a surgical procedure to correct her myopia. What can Amy tell her patient about the different types of corrective procedures?

_____

_____

_____

_____

2. Joe, a 5-year-old patient, is brought to the office with itchy, watery eyes with a purulent discharge. His mother states that Joe's older brother recently was seen in the office with the same symptoms. What type of problem do you think Joe has? Is it contagious? How should Amy educate Joe and his mother to prevent the spread of infection? Document the patient education intervention.

_____

_____

_____

3. Kiasha Johnson, 4 years old, is being seen today for suspected otitis media. The physician decides to delay prescribing antibiotics to see how the child does in the next day or so. Mrs. Johnson doesn't understand why her child is not being given an antibiotic. Help reinforce the physician's recommendations and document the patient education intervention.

_____

_____

_____

_____

4. You are conducting a health history on a patient in the ear, nose, and throat (ENT) specialty office. What are some questions you should ask about the history of the patient's ear or hearing problems?

_____

_____

_____

_____

WORKPLACE APPLICATION OPTIONS

Complete one or more of these activities and, if appropriate, share your results with the class.

1. Kim asks Amy to create a list of common disorders of the eyeball. Prepare the list, defining the disorder, identifying the common signs and symptoms of the disorder, and describing the treatment involved.

_____

_____

_____

2. Amy is learning to perform a Snellen examination. What type of guidelines should she keep in mind while performing this procedure?

_____

_____

_____

3. After learning how to perform a throat swab, Amy attempts to gather a specimen from a 4-year-old patient. The young child appears scared and apprehensive. What can Amy do to calm the patient's fears? Explain the verbal and nonverbal communication Amy can use with the child to perform the procedure.

_____

_____

_____

4. You are hired to work in an ENT specialty office. Summarize the communication skills that would be most helpful to use with patients who have suffered a hearing loss.

_____

_____

_____

INTERNET ACTIVITY OPTIONS

Complete one or more of these activities and, if appropriate, share your results with the class.

1. Use a drug reference book or the Internet to make drug cards for the following medications.

   a. Carbamide peroxide (Debrox)

   b. Cortisporin otic

   c. Pilocarpine ophthalmic

   d. Betoptic

   e. Diamox

   f. Acular

   g. Livostin

   h. Tobrex

   i. Bleph-10

   j. Timoptic

   k. Garamycin ung

      l. Viroptic

      m. Alphagan

      n. Xalatan

      o. Voltaren

2. Investigate the Americans with Disabilities site at www.ada.gov. How might these regulations apply to patients with vision or hearing deficits?

_____

_____

_____

_____

MEDICAL RECORD ACTIVITIES

1. A patient comes to the office complaining of pain and swelling in the left eye. While obtaining the history, Amy finds that the patient may have wood chips in her eye. The physician orders an eye irrigation. Amy administers 100 cc of sterile saline into the patient's left eye. Document the case and the procedure using the SOAPE format.

    S: _____

    O: _____

    A: _____

    P: _____

    E: _____

Refer to the charts in the following figure to answer the next group of questions.

2. Your patient can read line number 8 with the right eye, line number 9 with the left eye, and line number 8 with both eyes on the Snellen chart. Document your findings. Use appropriate abbreviations. Be sure to include the date and your signature.

_____

_____

_____

_____

3. Your patient cannot read English. He indicates that he can see line number 6 with the right eye, line number 5 with the left eye, and line number 6 with both eyes on the E chart. How will you have your patient respond so that you know your findings are accurate? Document your findings.

_____

_____

_____

_____

4. You are ordered to perform a bilateral ear irrigation on a 72-year-old patient with impacted cerumen. In the right ear, a large amount of dark brown cerumen completely covers the tympanic membrane; in the left ear, a moderate amount of golden brown cerumen covers the side of the tympanic membrane. After the procedure, both membranes are visible. The patient had no complaints of discomfort. Document the procedure.

_____

_____

_____

_____

38 Assisting in Dermatology

VOCABULARY REVIEW

Define the following terms.

1. Alopecia

   _____

2. Cryosurgery

   _____

3. Debridement

   _____

4. Ecchymosis

   _____

5. Electrodesiccation

   _____

6. Eschar

   _____

7. Exacerbation

   _____

8. Hyperplasia

   _____

9. Jaundice

   _____

10. Keratin

   _____

11. Leukoderma

   _____

12. Opaque

   _____

13. Postherpetic neuralgia

_____

14. Remission

_____

Fill in the blanks with the correct terms.

15. Sebaceous glands release _____, an oily substance that lubricates the skin.

16. The epidermis is the thin uppermost layer, and the _____ is the thicker layer beneath.

17. A variety of microorganisms, called normal or resident _____, are found on the skin and may increase the risk of integumentary system infections.

18. _____ is a common, contagious, superficial infection caused by streptococci or *Staphylococcus aureus.*

19. _____ is a disorder of the hair follicle and sebaceous gland unit.

20. _____ is characterized by a vesicular, pruritic rash on the face, neck, elbows, and posterior knees and behind the ears.

21. Individuals with _____, an inherited recessive trait, are unable to produce melanin, so they have white hair and skin and lack pigment in the iris.

22. Cancer cells are undifferentiated and _____ in nature.

23. Jaundice is caused by deposits of _____ in the tissues, which creates an orange discoloration of the skin.

24. A patient with an extremely pruritic skin rash may scratch so much that the area becomes _____.

25. A(n) _____ is a raised, firm scar caused by overgrowth of collagen at the site of a skin injury.

26. A patient who is given an antipruritic cream for an itchy skin lesion is receiving _____ treatment.

27. Small purple hemorrhages under the skin that may resemble a rash are called _____.

28. Accutane is an extremely dangerous _____ that is contraindicated in women of childbearing age.

29. A(n) _____ disorder is one that has no known cause.

30. Ischemia of the extremities that results in cyanosis and pain is called _____.

31. SLE is a(n) _____ disorder that results when the immune system attacks the body's connective tissue.

SKILLS AND CONCEPTS

1. Describe the major functions of the skin.

_____

_____

_____

2. Label the three layers of the skin in the following drawing.

_____ — A

_____ — B

_____ — C

Define and give an example of the following skin lesions.

3. Macule

_____

_____

4. Papule

_____

_____

5. Plaque

_____

_____

6. Fissure

_____

_____

7. Pustule

_____

_____

8. Vesicle

_____

_____

9. Bulla

_____

_____

10. Cyst

_____

_____

11. Ulcer

_____

_____

12. Wheal

_____

_____

13. List and describe four types of inflammatory skin disorders.

a. _____

_____

b. _____

_____

c. _____

_____

d. _____

_____

14. List and describe two types of autoimmune disorders.

a. _____

_____

b. _____

_____

15. Identify six criteria used in the diagnosis of SLE.

a. _____

b. _____

c. _____

d. _____

e. _____

f. _____

16. List and describe the three different types of burns.

a. _____

_____

b. _____

_____

c. _____

_____

17. Complete the following table.

Characteristic	Benign Tumor	Malignant Tumor
Cellular structure		
Type of growth		
Rate of growth		
Destruction of localized tissue		

18. Explain the seven warning signs of cancer.

a. C _____

b. A _____

c. U _____

d. T _____

e. I _____

f. O _____

g. N _____

19. Describe the early warning signs of malignant melanoma.

a. _____

b. _____

c. _____

d. _____

e. _____

20. List and describe three ways to perform allergy testing.

a. _____

b. _____

c. _____

21. Explain three procedures for appearance modification.

a. _____

b. _____

c. _____

22. Explain the connection between chickenpox and herpes zoster, and describe the typical signs and symptoms of shingles. Name the two vaccines used to prevent shingles. Who should receive them?

_____

_____

_____

_____

23. Explain the difference between basal cell and squamous cell carcinoma.

_____

_____

_____

_____

24. Describe how to perform a wound culture procedure. Include in your description the difference between aerobic and anaerobic microorganisms.

_____

_____

_____

_____

CASE STUDIES

Read the case studies and answer the questions that follow.

1. Alicia Ramsey, 16 years old, is being seen today for complaints of acne breakouts. What are the typical causes of acne vulgaris and how is it treated? Would the physician prescribe Accutane for this patient? Why?

_____

_____

_____

316

2. Mrs. Rosa Philippe complains of frequent flushing across the nose, forehead, cheeks, and chin with pustule formation. The physician's diagnosis is rosacea. What happens as the condition progresses? Explain to Mrs. Philippe the signs and symptoms of the condition and the treatment prescribed by the physician.

_____

_____

_____

3. A patient calls and states that she has redness on her upper arm. What questions do you need to ask before scheduling the appointment? What vital signs should be obtained for the patient? Why? With a partner, role-play the case and document your findings.

_____

_____

_____

4. A 6-year-old patient comes to the office today with a red, raised area around the mouth and nose. As Melissa, the medical assistant, examines the area, she notices that it is moist, inflamed, and crusted. What type of infection do these symptoms represent? With your knowledge of this infection, what education can you provide the patient and parents for stopping the spread of the infection? What types of medications are used to treat this infection?

_____

_____

_____

5. A 15-year-old patient comes to the office today with several boils forming on his anterior forearm. The physician is concerned about the development of cellulitis in the area. The patient's mother doesn't understand what the physician told her about her son's problem. Explain cellulitis to the mother, including the primary concerns about the infection, and the treatment typically prescribed.

_____

_____

_____

WORKPLACE APPLICATION OPTIONS

Complete one or more of these activities and, if appropriate, share your results with the class.

1. Patient education is an important part of Melissa's job as a medical assistant. Often patients are not aware of the medical terms used for common infections. Examine the following list of mycotic infections and provide the common name for each.

   a. Tinea pedis

   b. Tinea cruris

   c. Tinea corporis

   d. Tinea unguium

   What type of medication is used to treat mycotic infections?

2. Scabies (itch mite) and pediculosis (lice) are the two most common parasites that infest people. Dr. Lee has asked Melissa to develop a patient education handout on how to prevent the spread of these infestations. Include common medications used for treatment and how they are taken. What can patients do around the house to eliminate mites or lice? Who should be treated?

3. One of Melissa's duties is to assist the physician during tissue biopsies. What should she do to prepare for such procedures?

4. Understanding the processes of staging and grading of tumors is an important part of patient care for patients diagnosed with a malignancy. Define the two terms and explain how they are performed.

5. Describe what should be included when educating a patient scheduled for allergen skin testing.

INTERNET ACTIVITY OPTIONS

Complete one or more of these activities and, if appropriate, share your results with the class.

1. Search the Internet for a list of sun safety recommendations. How can you reduce the risk of skin cancer? Create a list of ideas and compare it with those of your classmates.

2. Locate an article online on the treatment and management of different types of burns. Summarize the article and be prepared to share your findings in class.

3. Investigate the National Cancer Institute's recommendations for the prevention of skin cancer. Develop a patient education brochure on this topic.

4. Choose a condition or disease from the dermatology chapter that interests you. Search the Internet for an organization that focuses on this health issue and summarize your findings for the class.

MEDICAL RECORD ACTIVITIES

1. A patient complains of a red, flat rash with intense itching. What types of questions should you ask this patient? Use the correct medical terminology to chart your findings. Use appropriate abbreviations. Be sure to include the date and your signature.

_____

_____

2. A patient comes to the office with a red, raised rash with small blisters. What type of questions should you ask this patient? Use the correct medical terminology to chart your findings. Use appropriate abbreviations.

_____

_____

318

3. Constance Oliver, a 23-year-old patient, has repeated herpes simplex infections. She does not understand why she keeps getting the cold sores. Perform patient education about the disorder and include in your discussion the typical medications used for treatment. Document your discussion with the patient.

_____

_____

4. Alonzo Racine calls the office because he is concerned about his 10-year-old son, Jayce. Jayce had been outside sledding and came in complaining of burning, tingling, and numbness in his cheeks, fingers, and toes, which are a grayish color. Dr. Lee believes the child may have a mild to moderate case of frostbite. What would Dr. Lee suggest that the father do? Should the patient be seen today? Document your interaction in the patient's medical record.

_____

_____

39 Assisting in Gastroenterology

VOCABULARY REVIEW

Provide the correct term for each definition.

1. _____ The surgical joining together of two normally distinct organs

2. _____ A hard, impacted mass of feces in the colon

3. _____ Narrow slits or clefts in the abdominal wall

4. _____ Gas expelled through the anus

5. _____ Abnormal enlargement of the liver

6. _____ The valve guarding the opening between the ileum and cecum

7. _____ The surgical formation of an opening of the ileum on the surface of the abdomen through which fecal material is emptied

8. _____ Black, tarry stool containing digested blood; usually caused by bleeding in the upper gastrointestinal tract

9. _____ Tumors on stems frequently found in the mucosal lining of the colon

10. _____ Physicians who specialize in diseases and disorders of the stomach, small intestine, large intestine (colon), and appendix and the accessory organs of the liver, gallbladder, and pancreas

Define the following terms.

11. Peritoneum

   _____

12. Mesentery

   _____

13. Omentum

   _____

14. Adhesions

   _____

15. Ascites

   _____

16. Carcinogens

   _____

17. Sclerotherapy

_____

18. Endemic disease

_____

19. Portal hypertension

_____

20. Lithotripsy

_____

21. Esophageal varices

_____

22. Hematemesis

_____

23. Peristalsis

_____

24. Valsalva's maneuver

_____

SKILLS AND CONCEPTS

1. Describe the three primary functions of the digestive system.

   a. _____

   b. _____

   c. _____

2. Label the structures of the gastrointestinal (GI) system in the following figure.

3. Using Figure 39-1 from the text, list the processes that occur in the GI system starting with chewing and swallowing food and finishing with excretion of wastes through the rectum. Make sure you identify the organs involved in digestion, absorption, and excretion.

_____

_____

_____

_____

_____

4. Label the nine regions of the abdomen in the following figure.

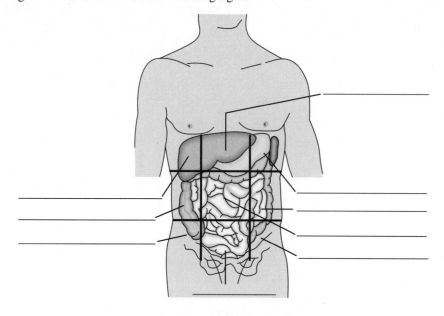

5. Using Table 39-1, complete the characteristics of common GI complaints.

Complaint	Characteristics
Nausea	
Vomiting (emesis)	*Caused by:* *Important characteristics to report and record:*
Diarrhea	*Caused by:* *Important characteristics to report and record:*
Constipation	*Caused by:* *Important characteristics to report and record:*
Abdominal pain	*Caused by:* *Important characteristics to report and record:*

Fill in the blanks.

6. The gallbladder is located in the _____ _____ quadrant of the abdomen.

7. The appendix is located in the _____ _____ quadrant of the abdomen.

8. The stomach is located in the _____ _____ quadrant of the abdomen.

9. The liver is located in the _____ _____ quadrant of the abdomen.

10. The pancreas is located in the _____ _____ quadrant of the abdomen.

11. List the seven parts of the large intestine in order, starting with the proximal end.

    a. _____

    b. _____

    c. _____

    d. _____

    e. _____

    f. _____

    g. _____

Complete the following sentences.

12. The _____ delivers bile from the liver to the duodenum where digestion is completed.

13. The _____ intestine is made up of the duodenum, jejunum, and ileum.

14. The small intestine is lined with transverse folds of tissue called _____.

15. Describe three disorders of the esophagus and stomach.

    a. _____

    _____

    b. _____

    _____

    c. _____

    _____

16. Describe 10 disorders of the intestines.

a. _____

_____

b. _____

_____

c. _____

_____

d. _____

_____

e. _____

_____

f. _____

_____

g. _____

_____

h. _____

_____

i. _____

_____

j. _____

_____

17. Identify and explain two disorders of the liver and gallbladder.

a. _____

_____

b. _____

_____

18. Complete the following table.

Test	Description and Purpose	Patient Preparation
Barium swallow		
UGI		
Barium enema		
HIDA scan		
Ultrasonography of the liver, gallbladder, biliary system, pancreas		
Sigmoidoscopy		
Colonoscopy		
Endoscopy		

19. Complete the following chart.

Hepatitis Type	Mode of Transmission	Individuals at Risk
A (infectious hepatitis)		
B (serum hepatitis)		
C (non-A, non-B)		
D (delta virus)		
E		
G		

20. Explain the causes of the following GI system cancers.

Tumor	Cause or Contributing Factors
Oral tumors	
Esophageal cancer	
Gastric cancer	
Liver cancer	
Pancreatic cancer	
Colorectal cancer	

CASE STUDIES

Read the case studies and answer the questions that follow.

1. Dr. Sahani has ordered a screening hemoccult kit for a patient. Explain the test to the patient and why it is necessary. What collection instructions should Joan, the medical assistant, provide the patient?

_____

_____

_____

Chapter **39** Assisting in Gastroenterology

2. While you are answering the telephone, a patient calls complaining of right lower quadrant pain. She is concerned about her appendix. Using your knowledge of acute appendicitis, what are the common signs? What questions should you ask the patient? What instructions should you provide the patient? Include the documentation for the patient's medical record. What tests can be done to confirm the diagnosis?

_____

_____

_____

3. Charles is scheduled for a barium swallow tomorrow. Explain the purpose of the procedure and any patient preparation involved.

_____

_____

_____

4. Anna will have a colonoscopy next week. She calls the office and asks Joan whether she will be able to drive herself home after the test. How should Joan respond? Anna is also confused about the patient preparation for the test. What preparation procedures should Joan explain to Anna with regard to the test?

_____

_____

_____

5. Shawna is 25 weeks pregnant and is suspected of having cholelithiasis. What test is the physician likely to order for this patient? Why?

_____

_____

_____

WORKPLACE APPLICATION OPTIONS

Complete one or more of these activities and, if appropriate, share your results with the class.

1. Many of Joan's patients are unsure of the risk factors for developing certain types of GI system cancers. List and describe some of the most common risk factors.

_____

_____

_____

2. Dr. Sahani has asked Joan to create a patient education handout describing the definition, cause, signs, symptoms, diagnosis, and treatment options for gastroesophageal reflux disease (GERD). Be sure to use terminology patients will understand.

_____

_____

_____

Chapter **39** Assisting in Gastroenterology

3. Medical assistants are expected to be able to ask questions designed to gather detailed information from patients about a variety of GI system complaints. List three questions you might ask a patient suffering from each of the problems listed.

a. Nausea and vomiting

_____

_____

_____

b. Diarrhea

_____

_____

_____

c. Constipation

_____

_____

_____

d. Abdominal pain

_____

_____

_____

4. Food poisoning is a disorder that results from the ingestion of food containing bacteria or toxic material. Create a chart for Joan to use as a resource when identifying the common sources, signs, and symptoms of different microorganisms.

Microorganism	Source	Signs and Symptoms
Staphylococcus aureus		
Escherichia coli		
Salmonella sp.		
Campylobacter jejuni		
Clostridium botulinum		

INTERNET ACTIVITY OPTIONS

Complete one or more of these activities and, if appropriate, share your results with the class.

1. Compare the adjustable gastric band and Roux-en-Y weight loss surgeries online. What criteria do patients have to meet to qualify for these procedures? What health conditions will improve with the weight loss that occurs after the procedures? How much do they cost? What complications might occur?

2. Investigate nonalcoholic fatty liver disease online and summarize your findings for the class.

3. Use a drug reference book or the Internet to make drug cards for the following medications. Include drug classification, generic name, usual dose for an adult, and drug form.

   a. Imodium

   b. Lomotil

   c. Phenergan

   d. Tigan

   e. Anzemet

   f. Zofran

   g. Biaxin

   h. Bentyl

   i. Levsin

   j. Axid

   k. Prevacid

   l. Prilosec

   m. Tagamet

   n. Zantac

   o. Nexium

   p. Protonix

MEDICAL RECORD ACTIVITIES

1. Joan's first patient of the day complains of pain in the RUQ. What kinds of questions should Joan ask the patient? In what position should the patient be placed? How should the patient be gowned or draped? What type of vital signs should Joan measure? Document the case.

   _____

   _____

   _____

   _____

2. Rita recently was diagnosed with a hiatal hernia. Dr. Sahani has prescribed Prilosec 20 mg once daily for the patient and has asked Joan to provide education on the drug (using the PDR), as well as any dietary modifications. Document the case.

   _____

   _____

   _____

   _____

3. Study the following case. Then rewrite the case using medical terminology and the proper abbreviations.

Ms. Pullman comes to the office today complaining of pain in the upper right area of her abdomen. Her symptoms include a lack of appetite, profuse sweating, and a yellowish hue to her skin. Upon examination, Dr. Sahani finds an abnormal enlargement of the liver. The blood tests reveal a decrease in the volume percentage of red blood cells in the whole blood.

_____

_____

_____

_____

_____

40 Assisting in Urology and Male Reproduction

VOCABULARY REVIEW

Define the following terms.

1. Albuminuria

   _____

2. Azotemia

   _____

3. Casts

   _____

4. Copulation

   _____

5. Erythropoietin

   _____

6. Urgency

   _____

7. Urology

   _____

Supply the terms for the following four types of urinary tract infections.

8. Inflammation of the urethra

   _____

9. Infection of the urinary bladder

   _____

10. Inflammation of the renal pelvis and kidney

    _____

11. Degenerative inflammation of the glomeruli

    _____

Define the following term and acronyms.

12. Creatinine

    _____

13. BUN

_____

14. UA

_____

15. PSA

_____

16. DRE

_____

Match the following terms with their definitions.

_____ 17. A long, coiled tube that rests on the top and lateral side of each testis

_____ 18. Bed wetting

_____ 19. Kidney stones

_____ 20. A condition in which the signs and symptoms include urinary urgency and frequency, difficulty starting urination, hematuria, and repeated urinary tract infections (UTIs)

_____ 21. Undescended testicles

_____ 22. Inflammation of the prostate

_____ 23. Inflammation of the glans penis

_____ 24. A form of erectile dysfunction

_____ 25. A sac of clear fluid in the scrotum

a. Epididymis

b. Balanitis

c. Impotence

d. Prostatitis

e. BPH

f. Cryptorchidism

g. Hydrocele

h. Enuresis

i. Renal calculi

SKILLS AND CONCEPTS

1. Describe the five functions of the renal system.

   a. _____

   b. _____

   c. _____

   d. _____

   e. _____

2. List and describe the three processes of urine formation.

   a. _____

   b. _____

   c. _____

3. Label the following diagrams to outline urine formation from the glomerulus to excretion through the urethra.

NEPHRON

RIGHT KIDNEY

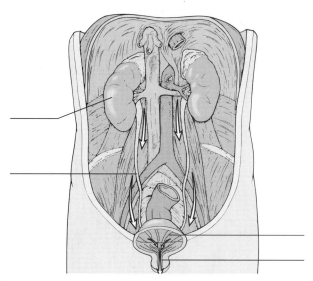

4. Explain stress incontinence in women and the exercise recommended for treatment.

_____

_____

_____

5. List the general signs and symptoms of a urinary tract infection.

   a. _____

   b. _____

   c. _____

   d. _____

   e. _____

6. Explain the difference between acute glomerulonephritis and chronic glomerulonephritis. How is each treated?

   _____

   _____

   _____

7. Explain polycystic kidney disease. What is happening to the kidneys? How can a patient develop it? How is it treated?

   _____

   _____

   _____

8. What is Wilms' tumor? What age group of patients is at risk for this health problem?

   _____

   _____

9. Cryptorchidism can cause serious problems for developing boys. Describe this disorder, summarize the health issues that can occur if it is not corrected, and explain the procedure that is done to correct the problem.

   _____

   _____

   _____

10. Label the structures of the male reproductive system on the following figure.

11. Summarize the important details you learned from your textbook about PSA tests.

_____

_____

_____

_____

12. Describe the treatments for prostate cancer.

    a. _____

    b. _____

    c. _____

13. Summarize the details of the three bacterial sexually transmitted infections (STIs) and their treatment.

_____

_____

_____

_____

14. Explain the difference between the human immunodeficiency virus (HIV) and the acquired immunodeficiency syndrome (AIDS). Describe three tests that can be used to diagnose HIV. Summarize the opportunistic infections that are commonly seen in patients with AIDS.

_____

_____

_____

_____

_____

15. Discuss Health Insurance Portability and Accountability Act (HIPAA) applications for patients with HIV or AIDS.

_____

_____

_____

16. Understanding renal system diagnostic tests and the required patient preparation for each is an important part of the medical assistant's responsibilities. Complete the following table.

Test	Description	Patient Preparation
Kidney-ureter-bladder (KUB) x-ray	Flat plate film of the abdomen; shows the size, shape, location, malformations of kidneys and bladder; used to visualize calculi	
Renal scanning		Patient should void before the procedure; no sedation or fasting is required; patient should drink two or three glasses of water before scanning; contraindicated in pregnancy
Cystography and voiding	X-ray evaluation with contrast dye to study bladder structure or function	
Intravenous pyelography (IVP); may be called intravenous urography (IUG)		Contraindicated in pregnancy and iodine allergies; laxative given the evening before; liquid diet 8 hours before; adequate fluids after; may have enema morning of the study
Arteriography (angiography)	Injection of dye into the renal artery; computerized fluoroscopy permits visualization of the blood flow of the kidneys, and serial x-rays are taken; used to diagnose stenosis of the renal artery and highly vascular renal cancers	
Renal computed tomography (CT)	Can be done with or without contrast dye; transverse views of the kidney are taken by CT to detect tumors, abscesses, cysts, and hydronephrosis	
Renal ultrasonography		No food or fluid restrictions; noninvasive and painless
Cystoscopy	Enemas to clear bowel; force fluids before procedure if local anesthesia is used; for general anesthesia, nothing by mouth (NPO) after midnight; preprocedure sedative to reduce bladder spasms; aftercare: monitor urinary output for 24 hours	
Retrograde pyelography	Dye injected into the bladder, ureters, and kidneys through a cystoscope to detect stones and other obstructions; can replace an IVP for patients with renal failure, obstructions, or allergies to intravenous dye	

Read the case studies and answer the questions that follow.

1. A patient comes to the office today complaining of severe lumbar pain and dysuria. The patient has a history of kidney stones. What diagnostic procedures might the physician order? Why? What type of patient preparation will Sara, the medical assistant, need to provide for the patient? If the patient is allergic to iodine dye, what test would then be recommended?

   _____

   _____

   _____

2. Joe Hackett is a 68-year-old patient recently diagnosed with cancer of the bladder. What are the treatment options for this type of cancer? What might have caused the tumor to form? What diagnostic tool will the physician use to check for recurrences of the tumor?

   _____

   _____

   _____

3. Amir Wood, 7 years old, is being seen today because of chronic enuresis. What are some reasons this problem might occur? What diagnostic studies might the physician order to determine the cause of the problem? How is it treated?

   _____

   _____

   _____

WORKPLACE APPLICATION OPTIONS

Complete one or more of these activities and, if appropriate, share your results with the class.

1. Sara, the medical assistant, deals with many patients with renal failure. She must be proficient in explaining the differences between peritoneal dialysis and hemodialysis. What are the advantages and disadvantages of each?

   _____

   _____

   _____

2. Design a handout explaining the details and instructions for a testicular self-examination.

   a. What is the importance of this exam? How often should it be done? Who performs it?

   b. What different approaches might Sara take to educate her male patients about testicular self-examinations? What resources could she provide?

3. The numbers of patients being seen with genital herpes and genital warts are on the rise. You are responsible for reinforcing patient education, so you need to know the problems these two viral STIs can cause and how they are treated. Summarize the information.

   _____

   _____

   _____

INTERNET ACTIVITY OPTIONS

Complete one or more of these activities and, if appropriate, share your results with the class.

1. Use a drug reference book or the Internet to make drug cards for the following medications. Include the drug classification, generic name, usual dose, and drug form.

   a. Keflex

   b. Bactrim

   c. Viagra

   d. Flomax

   e. Cardura

   f. Detrol

   g. Ditropan

   h. Xylocaine

   i. Cialis

   j. Interferon

   k. Proscar

   l. Zithromax

   m. Combivir

   n. Truvada

   o. Valtrex

   p. Cipro

   q. Uroxatral

   r. Trizivir

2. Use the Internet to search for conferences and training sessions in your area that would aid your continuing education.

   a. Why is it important to attend these conferences?

   b. Do the conferences you found offer continuing education units?

   c. Share your findings with the class.

3. Advances in HIV diagnosis and treatment occur constantly. Search the website for the Centers for Disease Control and Prevention (CDC) (www.cdc.gov) to learn about the most recent diagnostic tests and medications for treatment of HIV.

MEDICAL RECORD ACTIVITIES

1. A 29-year-old male patient comes to the office complaining of discharge of pus, an itching sensation at the opening of the urethra, and burning on urination. What type of questions should Sara, the medical assistant, ask the patient? How should the patient disrobe and be positioned? What tests might the physician order to diagnosis the problem? What type of patient education should Sara provide? Document the case.

_____

_____

_____

2. You collected a clean-catch urine specimen from a male patient. The urine is dark orange but clear. The amount of urine was 460 cc. The patient appeared to be comfortable during the procedure. Document your findings. Use appropriate abbreviations. Be sure to include the date and your signature.

_____

_____

_____

3. Sally Lange, a 23-year-old patient with a history of urinary tract infections (UTIs), is being seen today because of complaints of burning on urination, bladder spasms, urinary urgency, and urine that is dark and foul smelling. She had a Pyridium prescription at home and has already taken several doses. What would you expect her urine to look like? What will the physician order to determine whether Sally has a UTI? Sally is diagnosed with a repeat UTI and is prescribed Bactrim for 14 days. What patient education should she receive? Document the case study in the medical record.

_____

_____

_____

Assisting in Obstetrics and Gynecology

VOCABULARY REVIEW

Define the following terms.

1. Rectocele

   _____

2. Uterine prolapse

   _____

3. Cystocele

   _____

4. PID

   _____

5. Endometriosis

   _____

6. Dilation and curettage

   _____

7. Abruptio placentae

   _____

8. Placenta previa

   _____

9. Hysterectomy

   _____

10. Ultrasonography

    _____

11. Chorionic villus sampling

    _____

12. Amniocentesis

    _____

13. Alpha-fetoprotein (AFP)

    _____

14. Mammography

15. Colposcopy

16. Cryosurgery

17. Bartholin's cyst

18. Neural tube defects

19. Kegel exercises

Fill in the blanks with the correct terms.

20. Term pertaining to women who have had two or more pregnancies

21. Thin, yellow, milky fluid secreted by the mammary glands a few days before and after delivery

22. An x-ray procedure to guide the insertion of a needle into a specific area of the breast

23. Spotting or bleeding between menstrual cycles

24. Excessive menstrual blood loss, such as a menses lasting longer than 7 days

25. Absence of menstruation for a minimum of 6 months

26. Absence of menstruation for 35 days to 6 months

27. A hormone secreted by the placenta that is found in the urine of pregnant females

28. Thinning of the cervix during labor, measured in percentages from 0% to 100%

29. Abnormal cellular development that is diagnosed from a Pap smear

30. Congenital anomalies of the brain and spinal column that occur during embryonic development

_____

31. A disease or condition that has no known cause

_____

32. Toxic substances that cause severe fetal deformities or death

_____

33. A test that uses a combination of fetal monitoring, maternal reports of fetal movement, and the fetal heart rate to determine the health of the baby in utero

_____

SKILLS AND CONCEPTS

1. Label the structures in the following figures.

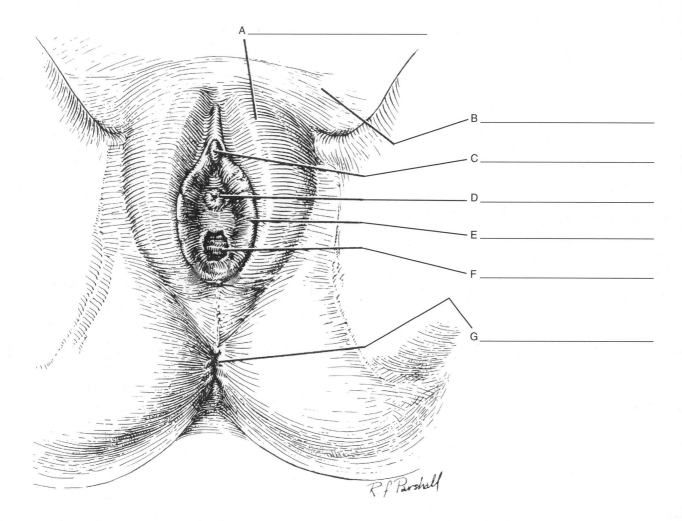

Chapter **41** Assisting in Obstetrics and Gynecology

2. List and describe the three phases of menstruation.

    a. _____

    _____

    b. _____

    _____

    c. _____

    _____

3. Medical assistants should have a basic understanding of sexually transmitted infections (STIs), their typical signs and symptoms, and their treatment. Provide the missing information about STIs in the following table.

Infection (Causative Organism)	Signs and Symptoms	Treatment
Chlamydia (*Chlamydia trachomatis*)		Curable with antibiotic therapy; azithromycin (Zithromax), tetracycline, or Vibramycin
Genital herpes simplex virus (HSV-2)	Painful genital vesicles and ulcers; erythema and pruritus; tingling or shooting pain 1-2 days before outbreak; cycle through episodes. Viral shedding may occur during asymptomatic periods. Newborns can be infected by active lesions in vagina at birth.	
Genital warts (HPV)		Goal of treatment is to remove symptomatic warts; cryotherapy to lesions; podofilox solution or imiquimod cream to lesions

Infection (Causative Organism)	Signs and Symptoms	Treatment
Gonorrhea *(Neisseria gonorrhoeae)*—bacteria	Dysuria; urinary frequency; abdominal pain; increased or decreased vaginal discharge. May cause endometritis, PID, and urethritis.	
Syphilis *(Treponema pallidum)*—spirochete bacteria		Penicillin G (Wycillin); if allergic to penicillin, doxycycline or tetracycline
Trichomoniasis *(T. vaginalis)*—protozoa		Metronidazole (Flagyl); need to treat partner

4. Describe three benign gynecologic tumors.

   a. _____

   b. _____

   c. _____

5. List and describe four gynecologic cancers.

   a. _____
   _____

   b. _____
   _____

   c. _____
   _____

   d. _____
   _____

6. List and define five types of naturally occurring abortions.

   a. _____

   b. _____

   c. _____

   d. _____

   e. _____

7. List and describe two different types of placental abnormalities.

   a. _____
   _____

   b. _____
   _____

8. Labor is the physiologic process by which the uterus expels the fetus and the placenta. It is divided into three stages. Define each stage of labor.

   Stage I _____
   _____

Stage II _____

_____

Stage III _____

_____

9. Explain the difference between perimenopause and menopause. What are the typical discomforts reported by women at this time? How are they treated?

_____

_____

_____

_____

10. Your patient is trying to decide whether to breast-feed or bottle-feed. What are some benefits of breast-feeding you could explain through patient education?

_____

_____

_____

_____

11. Explain the new Pap smear guidelines of the American College of Obstetricians and Gynecologists (ACOG).

_____

_____

_____

_____

12. Describe the American Medical Association's guidelines for recognizing women who are victims of abuse.

_____

_____

_____

_____

CASE STUDIES

1. A 20-year-old patient arrives today for her annual Pap smear. She has questions about the different types of birth control available. What are some of the factors involved in choosing a type of contraception? Using the following chart, create a patient education resource for the different types of contraception.

Type	Failure Rate	Characteristics	Contraindications	Side Effects
Condom (barrier method)				
Diaphragm, cervical cap, cervical sponge (barrier method)				

Type	Failure Rate	Characteristics	Contraindications	Side Effects
Intrauterine device (IUD)				
Implanon				
Depo-Provera (DMPA)				
Oral contraceptives (OCPs), hormonal patch, vaginal ring				

2. You receive a telephone call from a female patient who is experiencing side effects from oral contraceptives. What symptoms will you ask about?

   A _____

   C _____

   H _____

   E _____

   S _____

3. Carly comes to the office today for a prenatal checkup. She states that she has been experiencing some pelvic pain and burning on urination for 5 days. She also has recently stopped taking her prenatal vitamins, which she says make her nauseated. This is her first pregnancy, and she is very nervous about the examination. How can Betsy, the medical assistant, calm her fears? What test results and information should be gathered before the physician's examination? What patient education might be helpful? After Betsy has finished measuring the necessary vital signs and gathering the laboratory specimens, how should Carly be gowned and draped? Once the physician begins the internal examination, how should she be positioned?

   _____

   _____

   _____

   _____

4. Dr. Beck has asked you to prepare a patient for a bimanual examination. How should the patient be gowned and draped? How should you position the patient? What type of supplies will Dr. Beck need to complete the examination?

   _____

   _____

   _____

   _____

5. Mary has been instructed to have a baseline mammogram. What patient education should Betsy provide for Mary before her examination?

   _____

   _____

   _____

   _____

6. Mrs. Alice Carmichael is a 49-year-old patient who is being seen today for an abnormal Pap smear. She asks you to explain to her the different stages of cancer of the cervix. Define Stage 0 to Stage IV of carcinoma of the cervix.

_____

_____

_____

_____

_____

_____

WORKPLACE APPLICATION OPTIONS

Complete one or more of these activities and, if appropriate, share your results with the class.

1. Dr. Beck has asked Betsy to create a patient education handout for patients with fibrocystic breast disease. Include the disease definition, possible causes, and signs and symptoms. Are any dietary restrictions required?

_____

_____

_____

2. One of Betsy's duties includes instructing patients in the performance of breast self-examination. With a partner, explain the steps of this procedure. When should it be performed? For what should the patient be feeling? Why is breast self-examination important?

_____

_____

_____

3. Betsy has been instructed to gather a health history on a patient. What type of questions should she ask? Include both open-ended and closed-ended questions. Practice your interview techniques with a partner. What did you find most difficult about the interview?

_____

_____

_____

4. The mother of two children calls today questioning the use of Gardasil. Her daughter is 10 and her son is 12. Should both children receive the immunization? Explain the recommendation of the Centers for Disease Control and Prevention (CDC) regarding the use of Gardasil in children.

_____

_____

_____

5. Carnisha Johnson is 27 weeks pregnant with her second child and has just been diagnosed with gestational diabetes mellitus (GDM). How is GDM diagnosed and treated? Are there any community resources available that might help Ms. Johnson understand and better manage this health issue?

_____

_____

_____

_____

6. Amanda Angelo, age 37, is 4 weeks pregnant with her first child. The physician you work for recommends that all obstetrical patients over 32 years of age have a series of diagnostic tests performed on the fetus. Explain the four fetal diagnostic tests discussed in your text to Ms. Angelo and answer her questions.

_____

_____

_____

_____

INTERNET ACTIVITY OPTIONS

Complete one or more of these activities and, if appropriate, share your results with the class.

1. Use a drug reference book or the Internet to make drug cards for the following medications. Include the drug classification, generic name, usual dose, and drug form.

   a. Tamoxifen

   b. Premarin

   c. Prempro

   d. Methotrexate (for use in ectopic pregnancies)

   e. Evista

   f. Effexor

   g. Lupron

   h. Diflucan

   i. Flagyl

   j. Rocephin

   k. Boniva

   l. Danazol

   m. Gardasil

   n. ZDV regimen

2. Osteoporosis is a loss of bone tissue and a decrease in bone density. However, osteoporosis may be prevented or controlled with proper calcium intake. Search the Internet for public health programs or patient education programs available in your area that deal with osteoporosis prevention. How are the programs constructed? How do they increase awareness of this disease? How are the programs monitored? Is there a cost? Which program would you most recommend to someone you know? Share your research with your classmates.

3. Search the Internet for resources for pregnant and breast-feeding women. Develop a resource guide for these patients in an obstetric practice.

351

1. Role-play with your partner the following case: Ashley Thomassio, 22 years old, is a new patient in the practice. You are responsible for gathering a gynecologic history, taking vital signs, and preparing the patient for a pelvic examination. Using the gynecologic history guidelines from your textbook, document this information in the medical record.

   _____

   _____

   _____

2. Carla Gomez, 48 years old, is being seen today because she discovered a hard mass on the outside of her left breast. What questions would you ask Mrs. Gomez about this problem? Role-play this case with a partner and document your results. How should the patient be gowned for the physician's examination? What diagnostic tests might the physician order?

   _____

   _____

   _____

   _____

3. Monica Anderson, 17 years old, is being seen today for follow-up of an endometriosis diagnosis. What symptoms would you expect Monica to describe? What are the possible treatments for endometriosis? Document your patient interaction in the medical record.

   _____

   _____

   _____

   _____

42 Assisting in Pediatrics

VOCABULARY REVIEW

Match the following terms with their definitions.

_____ 1. Weakened or changed virulence of a pathogenic microorganism

_____ 2. Enlargement of the cranium caused by abnormal accumulation of cerebrospinal fluid within the cerebral system

_____ 3. Visual examination of the voice box area through an endoscope equipped with a light and mirrors for illumination

_____ 4. Small head size in relation to the rest of the body

_____ 5. A continuous, dry rattling in the throat or bronchial tube caused by partial obstruction

_____ 6. A thin, watery, serum-like drainage

_____ 7. A shrill, harsh respiratory sound heard during inhalation with a laryngeal obstruction

_____ 8. The formation or discharge of pus

_____ 9. A congenital malformation that occurs during fetal development

_____ 10. A space covered by thick membranes between the sutures of an infant's skull

a. Microcephaly

b. Serous

c. Hydrocephaly

d. Stridor

e. Rhonchi

f. Attenuated

g. Suppurative

h. Laryngoscopy

i. Fontanelles

j. Anomaly

SKILLS AND CONCEPTS

The Denver II Developmental Screening Test, a standardized tool, is given to children between 1 month and 6 years of age to screen healthy infants for developmental delays, to validate concerns about an infant's development, or to monitor high-risk children for the development of problems.

1. Explain the difference between growth and development.

_____

_____

_____

_____

2. When should the Denver II Developmental Screening Test (DDST) be administered?

_____

3. DDST focuses on four areas. Describe the types of skills assessed and provide examples of each.

a. Gross motor skills

_____

_____

b. Language skills

_____

_____

c. Fine motor adaptive skills

_____

_____

d. Personal skills

_____

_____

4. The following chart describes different growth and development theories. Fill in the missing information to complete the table.

Age Group	Freud (1856-1939) Psychosexual Theory	Piaget (1896-1980) Cognitive Theory	Erikson (1902-1994) Psychosocial Theory	Kohlberg (1927-1987) Moral Reasoning
Infant	Oral stage; child operates with the pleasure principle, and the id develops.		Building basic trust versus mistrust; learning drive and hope.	
Toddler	Passes through oral aggressive stage to anal stage; elimination is used to control and inhibit.			Avoids punishment and the power of authority figures.
Preschool to early school years		Intuitive-preoperational; preschoolers are egocentric and have magical thinking. Early school-aged children begin to develop understanding of cause and effect. Child functions symbolically using language; develops understanding of life events and relationships.	Preschool processing initiative versus guilt and attempting to develop direction and purpose. Children mimic others and are more purposeful in establishing goals.	

Age Group	Freud (1856-1939) Psychosexual Theory	Piaget (1896-1980) Cognitive Theory	Erikson (1902-1994) Psychosocial Theory	Kohlberg (1927-1987) Moral Reasoning
School age		Concrete operations: uses mental reasoning to solve problems; attempts to reach logical solutions; tests beliefs to establish values.		Conventional morality; doing what is expected is important. Children need to be good in their own eyes as well as doing what they perceive others expect of them; they want to please others.
Adolescence	Genital stage		Identity versus role confusion; developing self-identity that will determine devotion and fidelity in future relationships.	

5. Using the growth charts in the textbook (Figures 42-10 and 42-11), plot the measurements and answer the following questions.

   a. Simon Blackstone, 18 months: head circumference, 14¼ inches; 85 cm long; 14 kg. What are his height and weight percentiles?

   b. Carla Toomis, 9 years old: 50 inches tall and weighs 88 pounds. What are her stature and weight percentiles? What is her body mass index (BMI)?

6. Based on what you have learned about therapeutic approaches for the pediatric patient, what would be the best way to deal with the following patient situations?

   a. A crying 2-month-old scheduled for the first round of vaccinations

   _____

   _____

   b. A 3-year-old who is diagnosed with croup

   _____

   _____

   c. An 8-year-old who has to have his blood glucose checked with a glucometer

   _____

   _____

   d. A 13-year-old who has to receive a penicillin injection in the dorsogluteal site

   _____

   _____

7. Summarize five factors that are important safeguards for keeping vaccines safe during handling and storage.

   a. _____

   b. _____

   c. _____

   d. _____

   e. _____

8. What are three common characteristics of children with autism?

   a. _____

   b. _____

   c. _____

Fill in the blanks in the following statements.

9. Infection or inflammation of the middle ear is called _____.

10. _____ is a viral inflammation of the larynx and the trachea that causes edema and spasm of the vocal cords.

11. During a(n) _____, the bronchial tubes begin to spasm, reducing the amount of air that can pass through them; at the same time, the tissue lining the bronchioles becomes edematous and secretes mucus.

12. _____ is a viral infection of the small bronchi and bronchioles that usually affects children under 3 years of age. The infection varies in severity and is seen in children with a family history of asthma and children exposed to cigarette smoke.

13. Common treatments for _____ include zanamivir (Relenza), which is inhaled every 12 hours, and oseltamivir (Tamiflu), which is available in pill form.

14. _____ can be caused by a bacterial or viral infection that produces a white or yellowish pus that may cause the eyelids to stick shut in the morning.

15. _____, or "slapped cheek disease," is an infection caused by parvovirus B19.

16. _____ is caused by a member of the herpes virus group and is transmitted by direct or indirect droplets from the respiratory tract of an infected person. The incubation period is 14 to 21 days.

17. _____ is an inflammation of the membranes that cover the brain and spinal cord.

18. _____ is the best prevention for Reye's syndrome.

19. _____ is caused by the coxsackievirus. The symptoms include fever; sore throat; painful red blisters on the tongue, mouth, palms of the hands, and soles of the feet; headache; anorexia, and irritability.

20. _____ is an inherited disorder that causes pulmonary obstruction and malabsorption problems.

21. _____ is caused by a faulty gene that is passed from mothers to sons.

22. List eight details that must be documented when a vaccination is given.

a. _____

b. _____

c. _____

d. _____

e. _____

f. _____

g. _____

h. _____

23. Identify the risks as well as the signs and symptoms of postpartum depression.

_____

_____

_____

_____

24. List and discuss the five stages of Reye's syndrome.

a. _____

_____

b. _____

_____

c. _____

_____

d. _____

_____

e. _____

_____

Modified Checklist for Autism in Toddlers (M-CHAT)

The M-CHAT is validated for screening toddlers between 16 and 30 months of age to assess risk for autism spectrum disorders (ASD). The M-CHAT can be administered and scored as part of a well-child checkup and also can be used by specialists or other professionals to assess risk for ASD. Children who fail three or more items total or two or more critical items (particularly if these scores remain elevated after the M-CHAT follow-up interview) should be referred for diagnostic evaluation by a specialist trained to evaluate ASD in very young children. Role-play with your partner the following questions.

Please fill out the following questionnaire about your child's usual behavior, and try to answer every question. If the behavior is rare (you've only seen it once or twice), please answer as if your child does not do it.

1. Does your child enjoy being swung, bounced on your knee, or similar activities?

   Yes   No

2. Does your child take an interest in other children?

   Yes   No

3. Does your child like climbing on things, such as up stairs?

   Yes   No

4. Does your child enjoy playing peek-a-boo/hide-and-seek?

   Yes   No

5. Does your child ever pretend, for example, to talk on the phone or take care of a doll or pretend other things?

   Yes   No

6. Does your child ever use his or her index finger to point, to ask for something?

   Yes   No

7. Does your child ever use his or her index finger to point, to indicate interest in something?

   Yes   No

8. Can your child play properly with small toys (e.g., cars or blocks) without just mouthing, fiddling, or dropping them?

   Yes   No

9. Does your child ever bring objects over to you (parent) to show you something?

   Yes   No

10. Does your child look you in the eye for more than a second or two?

    Yes   No

11. Does your child ever seem oversensitive to noise (e.g., plugging ears)?

    Yes   No

12. Does your child smile in response to your face or your smile?

    Yes   No

13. Does your child imitate you (e.g., if you make a face, will your child imitate it)?

    Yes   No

14. Does your child respond to his or her name when you call?

    Yes   No

15. If you point at a toy across the room, does your child look at it?

    Yes   No

16. Does your child walk?

    Yes   No

17. Does your child look at things you are looking at?

    Yes   No

18. Does your child make unusual finger movements near his or her face?

    Yes   No

19. Does your child try to attract your attention to his or her own activity?

    Yes   No

20. Have you ever wondered if your child is deaf?

    Yes   No

21. Does your child understand what people say?

    Yes   No

22. Does your child sometimes stare at nothing or wander with no purpose?

    Yes   No

23. Does your child look at your face to check your reaction when faced with something unfamiliar?

    Yes   No

1. Explain the diagnosis and treatment of cystic fibrosis.

    _____

    _____

    _____

2. List 10 safety guidelines for parents with small children.

    a. _____

    b. _____

    c. _____

    d. _____

    e. _____

    f. _____

    g. _____

    h. _____

    i. _____

    j. _____

3. Complete the following table.

Vaccine and Disease	Route of Administration	Contraindications (Mild Illness Is Not a Contraindication)	Side Effects
DtaP Diphtheria, tetanus, pertussis (whooping cough)		Moderate or severe acute illness, neurologic problem, complication such as fever or convulsion after previous dose	
HAV Hepatitis A (can use either Havrix or Vaqta brands)			Localized injection site reaction, fever, headache
HBV Hepatitis B (can use either Energix B or Recombivax HB brands)		Moderate or severe acute illness, yeast allergy, severe cardiovascular disease	
Hib *Haemophilus influenzae* serotype B meningitis			Minimal
HPV Human papilloma virus (Gardasil)		Hypersensitivity to the ingredients; pregnancy	Relatively few; mild headache and gastrointestinal (GI) upset
Influenza Either trivalent inactivated influenza vaccine for 6 months; at 2 years use live, attenuated influenza vaccine			Uncommon; fever, local irritation at injection site, general malaise
IPV Inactive poliovirus for polio			Uncommon
MMR Measles, mumps, rubella			Fever
Pneumococcal Pneumococcal pneumonia			
Rotavirus (Rota) RotaTeq for prevention of Rotavirus gastroenteritis			GI upset and blood disorders
Varicella Varicella (chickenpox)			

1. Susie, a medical assistant, is concerned about approaching young children and how and when to involve the parents. Provide tips for approaching children in each of the following age groups.

   a. Infants (birth to 1 year)

   b. Toddlers and preschoolers (2 to 6 years)

   c. School-aged children (7 to 11 years)

   d. Adolescents (12 to 18 years)

   _____

   _____

   _____

   _____

2. A mother comes to the office complaining that her 4-week-old baby has had crying episodes lasting 3 to 4 hours four times during the past week. What type of questions should Susie ask the mother? Role-play this case with a partner and document your findings. The physician diagnoses the baby as having colic. What type of patient education should Susie provide to the mother?

   _____

   _____

   _____

   _____

3. The physician instructs a patient complaining of diarrhea to follow a "BRAT" diet. Define this dietary recommendation.

   _____

   _____

   _____

4. A patient was recently diagnosed with asthma. The physician has asked Susie to educate the patient and parents on the common triggers of asthma attacks. Document the conversation.

   _____

   _____

   _____

   _____

5. Susie is trying to obtain vital signs on a 4-year-old child who refuses to stand on the scale or cooperate while her temperature is taken. What can Susie do to try to obtain the child's cooperation? What is the best way to take this patient's temperature?

   _____

   _____

   _____

   _____

WORKPLACE APPLICATION OPTIONS

Complete one or more of these activities and, if appropriate, share your results with the class.

1. Childhood obesity is becoming an epidemic in the United States. The clinic for which you work is providing an in-service presentation to educate staff members about this growing problem. Susie and the other staff members are asked to create a list of possible reasons for this trend. List the possible causes and describe some solutions to be discussed during the in-service presentation.

   _____

   _____

   _____

   _____

2. At a recent office meeting, the staff concluded that a patient education handout on the common cold would benefit patients in the office. Susie has decided to take on this responsibility.

   a. Creatively design an informative handout for patients.

   b. Be sure to include the definition of the common cold.

   c. How is the infection spread to others? Describe ways to eliminate the spread of infection.

   d. What are the common signs and symptoms? When should the patient be seen in the office?

   e. What common over-the-counter (OTC) medications would the physician recommend?

   f. Include instructions for use of a bulb syringe.

3. Susie is reorganizing the patient waiting room and wants to include some helpful and educational resources for the patients to view. Create a list of possible items Susie could place in the waiting room.

   _____

   _____

   _____

   _____

4. A father calls the office to report that his 4-year-old child is complaining of abdominal pain, occasional diarrhea, and a cough. Summarize five questions Susie should ask to gather more details about the problem.

   a. _____

   b. _____

   c. _____

   d. _____

   e. _____

INTERNET ACTIVITY OPTIONS

Complete one or more of these activities and, if appropriate, share your results with the class.

1. Use a drug reference book or the Internet to make drug cards for the following medications. Include the drug classification, generic name, usual pediatric dose, and drug form.

   a. Amoxicillin

   b. Ceclor

   c. Cipro

   d. Augmentin

   e. EryPed

   f. Septra

   g. Singulair

   h. Albuterol

   i. Tamiflu

   j. Varivax

   k. Relenza

   l. Serevent

   m. Advair Diskus

   n. Zithromax

2. Search the website for the Centers for Disease Control and Prevention (CDC) (www.cdc.gov) for vaccination information sheets (VISs). Print a copy for each of the immunizations recommended in the immunization schedule. Why is using these educational handouts in the office important?

3. Flu vaccinations are recommended for children over 6 months of age. Search the CDC's website (www.cdc.gov) for dosage instructions. Describe dosage instructions for children who have not previously been vaccinated and for those who have. When should a patient *not* receive the flu vaccine?

MEDICAL RECORD ACTIVITIES

1. Drew Cassandra, 3 months old, is being seen today for a well-baby checkup and her first round of immunizations, including her second Hep B immunization. What vaccinations will be given today? What is their route of administration? Explain the criteria for VIS use in this case. Document the visit in the baby's medical record.

   _____

   _____

   _____

   _____

2. Tommy Lango, a 2-year-old patient, is being seen today because of complaints of earache; a harsh, barking cough; and a fever. What are the medical assistant's responsibilities in this case? What questions should be asked to gather more details? Document the information in the patient's medical record.

_____

_____

_____

_____

3. Alisha Johnson, 10 years old, is being seen today for diarrhea that has lasted 3 days, abdominal cramping, and occasional blood in the stool. What are the medical assistant's responsibilities in this case? What questions should be asked to gather more details? Document the information in the patient's medical record.

_____

_____

_____

_____

43 Assisting in Orthopedic Medicine

VOCABULARY REVIEW

Define the following terms.

1. Kyphosis

   _____

2. Lordosis

   _____

3. Luxation

   _____

4. Subluxation

   _____

5. Thoracic

   _____

6. Tendon

   _____

7. Ligament

   _____

8. Atrophy

   _____

9. Bursae

   _____

10. Periosteum

    _____

11. Reduction

    _____

12. Goniometer

    _____

13. Crepitation

    _____

14. Periosteum

_____

15. Epiphyseal plate

_____

16. Medullary cavity

_____

SKILLS AND CONCEPTS

1. List five general functions of the musculoskeletal system.

   a. _____

   b. _____

   c. _____

   d. _____

   e. _____

2. In the following figure, label the bones of the extremities.

3. Label the following drawing with the parts of a long bone.

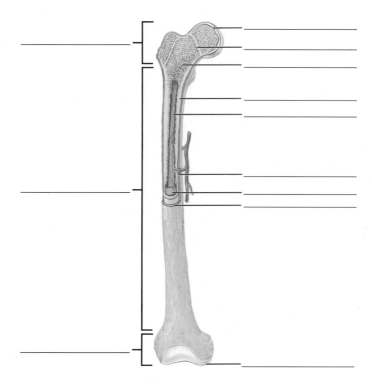

4. Label the three types of muscles shown in the following figure.

Identify the correct types of joints in the following descriptions.

5. _____ permit the skull to grow with the child but have limited flexibility.

6. _____ allow for the greatest range of motion by permitting the joint to rotate in a complete circle.

7. The _____ joints of the elbow and knee allow for movement in one plane, such as bending up and down.

Indicate which statements are true (T) and which are false (F).

_____ 8. The tibia is distal to the femur.

_____ 9. The patella is superior to the metacarpals.

_____ 10. The radius is lateral to the ulna.

_____ 11. The tibia is medial to the fibula.

_____ 12. The metatarsals are inferior to the tarsals.

_____ 13. The biceps are superior to the deltoid.

_____ 14. The trapezius is inferior to the gluteus medius.

_____ 15. The vastus lateralis is a posterior muscle.

_____ 16. The triceps are an anterior muscle group.

17. Label each type of range of motion shown in the following figure.

_____

_____

_____

_____

_____

_____

_____

_____

_____

_____

_____

_____

Chapter **43** **Assisting in Orthopedic Medicine**

Define the following.

18. Gout

_____

19. Osteoarthritis

_____

20. Rheumatoid arthritis

_____

21. Myasthenia gravis

_____

22. Osteomalacia

_____

23. Herniated disk

_____

24. SLE

_____

25. Lyme disease

_____

26. Compare and contrast hot and cold therapeutic modalities.

_____

_____

_____

_____

27. Explain the difference between therapeutic ultrasound and a TENS treatment.

_____

_____

_____

28. Explain why the physician would order paraffin bath treatments and how they are administered.

_____

_____

_____

29. Review and label the fractures shown in the following figure. Match the name of the fracture with the letter corresponding to the illustration of the fracture in the figure in the list.

_____

_____

_____

_____

_____

_____

_____

_____

_____

_____

From Chester GA: *Modern medical assisting,* Philadelphia, 1999, WB Saunders.

_____	1. Transverse	_____	8. Impacted
_____	2. Spiral	_____	9. Greenstick
_____	3. Simple	_____	10. Extracapsular
_____	4. Pathologic	_____	11. Fracture/dislocation
_____	5. Oblique	_____	12. Depressed
_____	6. Longitudinal	_____	13. Compound
_____	7. Intracapsular	_____	14. Comminuted

30. Compare and contrast sprains, strains, and spasms.

_____

_____

_____

_____

_____

_____

Describe the following diagnostic procedures. Indicate when each procedure would be used.

31. ROM testing

_____

_____

_____

32. Muscle strength evaluation

_____

_____

_____

33. X-ray studies

_____

_____

_____

34. CT scans

_____

_____

_____

35. MRI

_____

_____

_____

36. Arthrograms

_____

_____

_____

37. EMG/NCS

_____

_____

_____

38. DEXA scan

_____

_____

_____

CASE STUDIES

1. A patient comes to the office with pain, tenderness, and deformity of the fingers. What questions should you ask? What medications will you ask about? Document the case.

_____

_____

_____

_____

2. A patient calls the office asking about fibromyalgia. She heard about the disease on a TV commercial and would like some information about the disorder. What can you tell her about the signs, symptoms, associated disorders, diagnosis, and treatment of fibromyalgia?

_____

_____

_____

_____

3. A patient on crutches comes to the office for a recheck of an ankle sprain. What questions would be appropriate when interviewing this patient? How should the patient be prepared for the examination?

_____

_____

_____

_____

4. The physician has ordered crutches for a patient with a knee injury. Kaiwan, the medical assistant, is responsible for fitting the patient properly. How should Kaiwan fit the patient? What patient education should Kaiwan provide?

_____

_____

_____

_____

5. A patient is being seen today whose CC is restless leg syndrome. What symptoms might the patient report and how is this syndrome treated?

_____

_____

_____

_____

WORKPLACE APPLICATION OPTIONS

Complete one or more of these activities and, if appropriate, share your results with the class.

1. The office manager has asked you to develop an osteoporosis awareness prevention program for the office staff. Together with a partner, brainstorm ideas for the development of this program.

    a. Many of the staff are young women. Why should they be concerned with osteoporosis?

    b. What are common risk factors for osteoporosis?

    c. What can individuals do to reduce their risk?

    d. What are common treatments?

e. Using your knowledge of the disease, what type of activities can you implement in this program?

_____

_____

_____

_____

_____

2. The office manager asks you to reinforce the correct method for using a walker with an elderly patient in the practice. What guidelines should you include?

_____

_____

_____

3. Tishon Gray, 9 years old, fractured his right tibia and the physician just finished putting a cast on his leg. What patient education should the medical assistant provide for Tishon and his mother?

_____

_____

_____

INTERNET ACTIVITY OPTIONS

Complete one or more of these activities and, if appropriate, share your results with the class.

1. Use a drug reference book or the Internet to make drug cards for the following medications. Include the drug classification, generic name, usual adult dose, and drug form.

   a. Remicade

   b. Ridaura

   c. Enbrel

   d. Zyloprim

   e. Colchicine

   f. Anaprox

   g. Cataflam

   h. Relafen

   i. Toradol

   j. Reclast

   k. Requip

   l. Orudis

   m. Humira

   n. Ultram

   o. Ambien

   p. Lyrica

   q. Fosamax

r. Actonel

s. Evista

t. Miacalcin

u. Soma

v. Boniva

w. Benemid

x. Plaquenil

y. Imuran

z. Cytoxan

2. Search the Internet for information describing proper lifting and patient transfer techniques. Why are proper mechanics important? Make notes on the different techniques and demonstrate your findings to the class.

MEDICAL RECORD ACTIVITIES

1. A patient calls the office and requests the results of her recent magnetic resonance imaging (MRI) study. After finding the patient's medical record, you notice that the physician has not yet reviewed the results. The impression states: HNP of L3 and L4. What should you tell the patient? Why? Document your conversation in the patient's medical record.

_____

_____

_____

2. A patient calls the office explaining that he has just fallen and twisted his ankle. What questions should you ask about the injury? What instructions should you give about applying ice to the ankle? When should the patient be seen? Document the information in the patient's medical record.

_____

_____

_____

3. Mrs. Alonzo Smith is being seen today for possible Lyme disease. How is Lyme disease transmitted? The physician asks you to reinforce teaching on how to prevent Lyme disease. Include in your documentation the patient education criteria for this health issue.

_____

_____

_____

VOCABULARY REVIEW

Define the following terms.

1. Anomalies

   _____

2. Ataxia

   _____

3. Atrophy

   _____

4. Coma

   _____

5. Diplopia

   _____

6. Gait

   _____

7. Aura

   _____

8. Contralateral

   _____

9. Paresthesia

   _____

10. Syncope

    _____

11. Blood-brain barrier

    _____

12. Exacerbation

    _____

13. Ipsilateral

    _____

14. Papilledema

_____

15. Myelin Sheath

_____

16. Benign

_____

17. Cryptogenic

_____

18. Embolus

_____

19. Malignant

_____

20. Occlusion

_____

21. Paroxysmal

_____

22. Proprioception

_____

23. Turbid

_____

Define the following procedures.

24. MRI

_____

_____

25. CT

_____

_____

26. EEG

_____

_____

27. Lumbar puncture

_____

_____

28. PET scan

_____

_____

29. Arteriography

_____

_____

SKILLS AND CONCEPTS

1. Label the parts of the neuron on the following figure.

Describe the functions of each of the following.

2. CSF

_____

_____

3. Brainstem

_____

_____

4. Hypothalamus

_____

_____

5. Cerebrum

_____

_____

6. Spinal nerves

_____

_____

7. Cranial nerves

_____

_____

8. Autonomic nerves

_____

_____

9. Cerebellum

_____

_____

10. Complete the following table, which details the cranial nerves and their functions.

Cranial Nerve	Name	Function
	Olfactory	
II		Vision
III		
	Trochlear	
V		
VI	Abducent	
	Facial	
VIII	Vestibulocochlear	
	Glossopharyngeal	
X		Parasympathetic to thorax and abdomen
XI	Spinal accessory	
	Hypoglossal	

11. Differentiate between a thrombus and an embolus.

_____

_____

_____

12. Compare the afferent and efferent nervous pathways.

_____

_____

_____

13. Label the protective coverings of the brain.

14. Describe the three layers of the meninges and the spaces between each.

_____

_____

_____

_____

_____

15. Explain the three different types of cerebrovascular accidents (CVAs).

_____

_____

_____

_____

_____

Fill in the blanks.

16. A(n) _____ occurs when the blood supply to a particular part of the brain is inadequate for a limited period.

17. CVA is commonly referred to as _____ or brain attack.

18. This _____ often consists of some form of visual disturbance, such as dark lines across or spots within the visual field.

19. Absence or _____ seizures are a less serious form of seizure consisting of momentary clouding of consciousness and loss of contact with reality.

20. The typical presentation of _____ includes muscular rigidity, unilateral pill-rolling tremor of the hand, a high-pitched monotone voice, and a(n) _____-like facial expression. The patient has a bent-forward posture with the head bowed. Muscular tremors and _____ increase.

21. _____ results from progressive inflammation and deterioration of the myelin sheaths, which leaves the nerve fibers uncovered.

22. _____, or Lou Gehrig's disease, is a progressive, destructive neurologic disease that results in muscle atrophy.

23. _____ affects the seventh cranial nerve in the face. It occurs suddenly and usually subsides spontaneously over several weeks to several months.

24. Carpal tunnel syndrome results from a compression or entrapment of the _____ nerve as it courses past the carpal bones of the hand.

25. List nine signs and symptoms that suggest possible neurologic problems.

    a. _____

    b. _____

    c. _____

    d. _____

    e. _____

    f. _____

    g. _____

    h. _____

    i. _____

26. Describe a positive Brudzinski's sign. How is it performed and what does it demonstrate?

    _____

    _____

    _____

    _____

27. Compare and contrast encephalitis and meningitis.

_____

_____

_____

_____

28. Explain the difference between an epidural and a subdural hematoma.

_____

_____

_____

29. Summarize five common signs of a concussion.

_____

_____

_____

30. Explain the difference among spinal transection, paraplegia, and quadriplegia spinal cord injuries.

_____

_____

_____

_____

31. Describe the treatment recommendations for depression and the typical medications prescribed.

_____

_____

_____

_____

32. Summarize four risk factors for suicide.

a. _____

b. _____

c. _____

d. _____

33. Discuss the possible treatments for schizophrenia.

_____

_____

_____

_____

1. A patient comes to the office complaining of numbness in the left side of the face and difficulty walking. The patient is having difficulty with speech and is easily confused. With a partner, role-play this case. Measure vital signs. What questions should you ask the patient? What appears to be the preliminary diagnosis?

_____

_____

_____

_____

2. A mother calls and states that her son suffered a head injury at school today while playing football. She is concerned about the possibility of a concussion. What questions should the medical assistant ask the mother? Explain to the mother the signs and symptoms that might occur immediately after the injury, as well as those that could develop in a few days.

_____

_____

_____

_____

3. A 48-year old diabetic patient is being seen in the office today for peripheral neuropathy. What is this condition? What are the typical signs and symptoms?

_____

_____

_____

_____

4. A patient comes to the office to discuss depression. She is crying and upset while you take her vital signs. What communication skills should you remember to use? What questions should you ask the patient? Describe some of the common signs and symptoms of depression.

_____

_____

_____

_____

WORKPLACE APPLICATION OPTIONS

Complete one or more of these activities and, if appropriate, share your results with the class.

1. The office has been asked to discuss depression at a community health seminar. What can you tell the audience about depression? What are some of the symptoms of depression?

_____

_____

_____

_____

2. Your office manager has asked you to create a patient education guide describing the common risk factors for CVA. What should you include?

_____

_____

_____

_____

3. One of your co-workers was recently diagnosed with carpal tunnel syndrome. Describe the condition and its typical causes. How might this injury be prevented?

_____

_____

_____

_____

INTERNET ACTIVITY OPTIONS

Complete one or more of these activities and, if appropriate, share your results with the class.

1. Use a drug reference book or the Internet to make drug cards for the following medications. Include the drug classification, generic name, usual adult dose, and drug form.

   a. Coumadin

   b. Plavix

   c. Imitrex

   d. Heparin

   e. Maxalt

   f. Sumatriptan succinate

   g. Effexor

   h. Dilantin

   i. Phenobarbital

   j. Valproic acid

   k. Prozac

   l. Zomig

   m. Topamax

   n. Neurontin

   o. Klonopin

   p. Lamictal

   q. Risperdal

   r. Zyprexa

   s. Xanax

   t. BuSpar

u. Zoloft

v. Celexa

w. Rilutek

x. Avonex

y. Mirapex

z. Requip

2. Neurologic diseases and disorders can have an overwhelming impact on family members. Research online the support groups and area resources available for patients with the following conditions:

a. Alzheimer's disease

b. Parkinson's disease

c. Amyotrophic lateral sclerosis (ALS)

d. Schizophrenia

e. Multiple sclerosis (MS)

f. Epilepsy

g. Spinal cord injuries

3. Sports-related head injuries and concussions are a hot topic in the news. Research online articles that relate to this topic and share a summary of one with your class.

4. Investigate online the Health Insurance Portability and Accountability Act (HIPAA) standards for release of patient information for those undergoing psychiatric care. How is this different from a patient diagnosed with a physiological problem?

MEDICAL RECORD ACTIVITIES

1. On discharge from the hospital, a patient is prescribed Neurontin for seizure control. Inform the patient about the drug's actions, side effects, and precautions for taking the medication. Document your patient education session.

_____

_____

_____

_____

2. Mary O'Reilly, age 37, has just been diagnosed with multiple sclerosis. The physician asks you to reinforce patient education about the cause of the disease, recommended treatment, and the remission/relapse cycle that typically occurs. Document your patient interaction.

_____

_____

_____

_____

3. Carl Westover calls today and wants a refill on his Xanax prescription. Carl is an army veteran who suffers from posttraumatic stress disorder. Document your interaction with the patient.

_____

_____

_____

_____

45 Assisting in Endocrinology

VOCABULARY REVIEW

Match the following terms with their definitions.

_____ 1. A hormone produced by the alpha cells of the pancreatic islets that stimu-
        lates the liver to convert glycogen into glucose

_____ 2. The abnormal presence of glucose in the urine

_____ 3. The sugar (starch) formed from glucose and stored mainly in the liver

a. Glycosuria

b. Glycogen

c. Glucagon

Fill in the blanks.

4. Excessive thirst is called _____.

5. _____ is a hormone that stimulates the production and secretion of glucocorticoids; it is released by the
   anterior pituitary gland.

6. _____ is a hormone secreted by the beta cells of the pancreatic islets in response to increased levels of
   glucose in the blood.

7. _____ is the abnormal production of ketone bodies in the blood and tissue as a result of fat catabolism in cells. Ketones accumulate in large quantities when fat instead of glucose is used as fuel for energy
   in cells.

8. _____ is a hormone secreted by the anterior lobe of the pituitary gland that stimulates the secretion
   of hormones produced by the thyroid gland.

9. _____ means increased appetite.

10. _____ is a hormone secreted by the posterior pituitary gland; it encourages fluid resorption in the renal
    tubules of the kidneys and a possible elevation in blood pressure. It is also known as *vasopressin*.

11. _____ is excessive urine production.

12. _____ is an anabolic action in the liver that forms glucose out of proteins and fats.

13. _____, also called *somatotropic hormone,* is responsible for stimulating the epiphyseal plates of the long
    bones to create new tissue.

14. _____ is produced by the anterior pituitary and stimulates the development of breast tissue.

15. _____ is excessive urination during the night.

16. _____ is the state of being satisfied or feeling full after eating.

SKILLS AND CONCEPTS

1. Identify the gland that produces the following hormones and the purpose of each hormone.

   a. Melatonin _____

   _____

   b. Thyroid-stimulating hormone (TSH) _____

   _____

c. Adrenaline _____

_____

d. Insulin _____

_____

e. Glucagon _____

_____

f. Oxytocin _____

_____

2. Explain the difference between an exocrine gland and an endocrine gland.

_____

_____

_____

3. Define negative feedback and give an example of how it works in the body.

_____

_____

_____

4. Describe the hormones released by the anterior pituitary gland.

a. _____

b. _____

c. _____

d. _____

e. _____

f. _____

5. Define the three conditions related to alterations in growth hormone.

a. _____

b. _____

c. _____

6. Define the following.

a. Diabetes insipidus

_____

b. Addison's disease

_____

c. Cushing's syndrome

_____

7. You are interviewing two different patients who have a provisional diagnosis of hypothyroidism and hyperthyroidism. What signs and symptoms would you expect for each condition?

Hypothyroidism _____

_____

Hyperthyroidism _____

_____

8. You are responsible for drawing blood and following through with diagnostic orders for patients suspected of having diabetes mellitus. Identify the diagnostic criteria for DM.

_____

_____

_____

9. Explain prediabetes and how it is diagnosed.

_____

_____

_____

10. Differentiate between diabetes mellitus type 1 and type 2.

_____

_____

_____

11. Differentiate between diabetic coma and insulin shock.

_____

_____

_____

12. Name and define the three "poly" conditions of diabetes mellitus.

a. _____

b. _____

c. _____

13. Medical assistants must be familiar with the different types of insulin that may be prescribed. Complete the following table.

Insulin Type	Onset of Action	Peak Action	Effective Duration	Appearance	Comments
Rapid Acting					
		1-2 hours	2-5 hours	Clear	
Short Acting					
Regular (Novolin R, Humulin R)		2-4 hours	3-5 hours	Clear	Take 30 minutes before meal
Intermediate Acting					
	2-4 hours	4-10 hours			Take at bedtime to minimize nighttime hypoglycemia
Lente		4-12 hours	12-18 hours	Clear	
Long Acting					
	6-10 hours	Minimal Peak		Clear	
Glargine	4-6 hours	Peakless	24 hours	Clear	
Premixed					
	30-60 minutes	2-10 hours	10-16 hours		

14. Describe two alternative methods of insulin administration.

_____

_____

_____

15. Treatment for diabetes mellitus type 2 can involve a complicated combination of oral hypoglycemics, diet, and exercise. Provide the missing information about the most prescribed hypoglycemics.

Medication	Action
Micronase, Glucotrol, Amaryl	
Prandin	
Metformin (Fortamet, Glucophage)	
Avandia	
Precose, Glyset	
Glucovance (Micronase and Glucophage)	
Avandamet (Avandia and Glucophage)	

16. Describe each of the following laboratory tests.

a. TSH

_____

_____

_____

b. OGGT

_____

_____

_____

c. FBS

_____

_____

_____

d. NFBS

_____

_____

_____

e. Glycohemoglobin or hemoglobin A_{1c}

_____

_____

_____

17. Complete the following table that compares average plasma glucose and A_{1c} levels.

A_{1c} (%)	Average Plasma Glucose (mg/dL)
6	
	170
	205
9	
10	

CASE STUDIES

1. A patient at the clinic was recently diagnosed with diabetes insipidus. The physician asks you to educate the patient on the common signs and symptoms. What information do you want to include?

_____

_____

_____

2. A patient comes to the office today complaining of fatigue, hair loss, muscle cramps, menorrhagia, and thick, dry, puffy skin. Her vital signs show a pulse of 56/minute, a temperature of 97.7⌐∫ F, and a weight gain of 25 pounds over the past 3 months. What condition do these signs and symptoms suggest? What laboratory work will the physician most likely order?

_____

_____

_____

Chapter **45 Assisting in Endocrinology**

3. A patient calls the office today stating that she is 20 weeks pregnant and is concerned about her risk for gestational diabetes. What questions would you ask her? How would you educate the patient on the risk factors of gestational diabetes? What community resources might be helpful for this patient?

_____

_____

_____

4. Miguel has been assisting with diabetes nutritional education for Jerry for more than 6 months now. Unfortunately, the effort seems to be unsuccessful. Jerry explains that he feels good and does not see why he should change his eating habits. How could Miguel explain to Jerry the long-term complications related to poorly controlled diabetes? Should Miguel provide any additional patient education? Why or why not? Are any community resources available that might prove useful for this patient?

_____

_____

_____

WORKPLACE APPLICATION OPTIONS

Complete one or more of these activities and, if appropriate, share your results with the class.

1. Medical assistants must have knowledge of the different medications prescribed for patients with endocrine abnormalities. Use the PDR to identify the indications for the following drugs:

   a. Synthroid

   b. Prednisone

   c. Byetta

   d. DiaBeta

   e. Glucophage

   f. Prandin

   g. Micronase

   h. Glucovance

   i. Avandia

   j. Actos

   k. Symlin

   l. Florinef

   m. Levoxyl

   n. Desmopressin

   o. Humulin

   p. Novolin

   q. Avandamet

2. Create a handout that explains the difference between hypoglycemic and hyperglycemic episodes.

_____

_____

_____

_____

3. Carrie has been using her Glucometer for the past 4 months and states that she does not feel the routine controls need to be done. How would you explain to Carrie the importance of the routine controls and when they should be performed?

_____

_____

_____

_____

4. Mr. Carlos Mantea has long-term diabetes type 2 and is complaining about numbness and tingling in his toes. This is the first time he has complained of the symptoms associated with diabetic neuropathy. What types of questions could you ask Mr. Mantea to gather comprehensive information about his condition for documentation?

_____

_____

_____

_____

INTERNET ACTIVITY OPTIONS

Complete one or more of these activities and, if appropriate, share your results with the class.

1. Go to the website www.diabetes.org. Locate the diabetes risk assessment tool and take the test. Are you surprised at the results? What lifestyle changes can you make to reduce your risk for diabetes?

_____

_____

_____

_____

2. Patients on a diabetic meal plan often feel that they are limited in the foods they are allowed to eat. Search the Internet for different recipes and their nutritional exchanges for diabetics. Create a small collection of recipes you can share with your patients. Be sure your selections include a variety of foods so that your list appeals to a large population.

_____

_____

_____

_____

MEDICAL RECORD ACTIVITIES

1. Samantha Carson, a 16-year-old patient with diabetes type 1, is experiencing frequent episodes of hypoglycemia. The physician asks you to reinforce with her the Rule of 15 that she can use if she experiences hypoglycemic symptoms. Summarize the guidelines and document your interaction with the patient.

   _____

   _____

   _____

   _____

2. Scott Anderson has been newly diagnosed with diabetes type 2. Scott does not understand the complexities of his care, and you are responsible for reinforcing the physician's patient education. Summarize a patient education approach for a patient newly diagnosed with type 2 diabetes and document your interaction in the patient's medical record.

   _____

   _____

   _____

   _____

3. A patient with diabetes has come to your office because of a sore on his right great toe. He states that he was trimming a corn a week ago, and the area has become red and painful. You notice that the area is inflamed and warm to the touch. The patient is wearing beach sandals. The patient's fasting blood sugar (FBS) is 348 mg/dL. His oral temperature is 100.9° F, blood pressure is 182/110 mm Hg, and pulse is 88/minute. Should you provide patient education on diabetic foot care? What should you include? Document the case.

   _____

   _____

   _____

   _____

46 Assisting in Pulmonary Medicine

VOCABULARY REVIEW

Define the following terms.

1. Apnea

2. Atelectasis

3. Dyspnea

4. Empyema

5. Hemoptysis

6. Hemothorax

7. Hypercapnia

8. Hyperpnea

9. Hypoxemia

10. Orthopnea

11. Pleurisy

12. Pneumothorax

13. Pyothorax

14. Rhinoplasty

_____

15. Rhinorrhea

_____

16. Tachypnea

_____

17. Thoracotomy

_____

18. Tubercle

_____

19. Bifurcates

_____

20. Chronic bronchitis

_____

21. Pulmonary consolidation

_____

22. Tracheostomy

_____

23. Virulent

_____

SKILLS AND CONCEPTS

1. _____ is the abnormal dilation of the bronchi and bronchioles that may lead to COPD.

2. The _____ are tiny hairlike projections lining the respiratory tract that trap particles and move these unwanted substances up and out of the system.

3. Chronic tissue hypoxia can lead to an abnormal enlargement of the ends of the fingers called _____.

4. Explain the process of ventilation. Include the action of the diaphragm and the intercostal muscles.

_____

_____

_____

5. Label the following drawing with these anatomic landmarks: anterior, posterior, and midaxillary lines.

_____ 1

2 _____

3 _____

6. On the following figure, label the structures of the respiratory system, head, and chest.

1 _____

2 _____

3 _____

4 _____

5 _____

6 _____

7 _____

8 _____

9 _____

10 _____

11 _____

12 _____

13 _____

14 _____

15 _____

16 _____

7. Label the lobes of the lungs on the following figure.

8. List the signs and symptoms of sinusitis.

_____

_____

9. Identify the medications that are used to treat allergic rhinitis:

_____

_____

Fill in the blanks.

10. _____ cancer is the leading cause of cancer-related deaths for both men and women in the United States.

11. A positive _____ reaction indicates the possibility of active or dormant tuberculosis or exposure to the disease.

12. _____ is a noninvasive method of evaluating the oxygen saturation of hemoglobin in arterial blood, as well as the pulse rate.

Match the following occupations with the associated lung diseases.

_____ 13. Stonecutting or sandblasting   a. Anthracosis

_____ 14. Insulation and shipbuilding   b. Silicosis

_____ 15. Coal mining   c. Asbestosis

16. Define the four tests used to diagnose TB.

a. _____

b. _____

c. _____

d. _____

17. Discuss the difference between latent and active tuberculosis.

_____

_____

_____

_____

18. Discuss how tuberculosis is treated.

_____

_____

_____

_____

19. Explain what happens during an asthma attack and how the patient should be treated.

_____

_____

_____

20. You are responsible for teaching a patient how to use an inhaler. Explain the procedure.

_____

_____

_____

_____

21. List six signs and symptoms of obstructive sleep apnea.

a. _____

b. _____

c. _____

d. _____

e. _____

f. _____

22. Carcinoma of the _____ is pathologically linked to smoking and chronic alcohol consumption.

Chapter **46** **Assisting in Pulmonary Medicine**

1. Dr. Samuelson orders a nebulizer treatment for a patient having an acute asthma attack. How should Michael, the medical assistant, prepare for this procedure? Describe the steps for administering a nebulizer treatment to a patient. What information should you provide for the patient? What should Michael watch for while the patient is undergoing the treatment?

_____

_____

_____

_____

2. A patient calls the office and requests an antibiotic for chest congestion. The patient is busy working today and refuses an appointment. What should the medical assistant do in this situation? Why?

_____

_____

_____

_____

3. A patient arrives today complaining of high fever, chills, dyspnea, chest pain during inspiration, and general malaise. The patient is a smoker. Dr. Samuelson suspects pneumonia. What tests are done to confirm the diagnosis? How may the physician determine whether the pneumonia is viral or bacterial? What is the treatment for bacterial pneumonia? What is the treatment plan for viral pneumonia?

_____

_____

_____

_____

4. Felicia Kristoff, a 19-year old patient, is being seen today for complaints of a cold. What symptoms would you expect Felicia to display? What recommendations would the physician make regarding treatment?

_____

_____

_____

_____

WORKPLACE APPLICATION OPTIONS

Complete one or more of these activities and, if appropriate, share your results with the class.

1. Create a handout outlining a spirometry procedure including the lung function studies that are assessed during the procedure.

2. Michael is getting ready to obtain a sputum sample. What universal precautions should Michael follow? What equipment will he need to use? Why?

_____

_____

_____

_____

3. What instruction should the medical assistant provide a patient while scheduling a bronchoscopy?

_____

_____

_____

_____

4. Tom Sebastian is a 12-year old patient recently diagnosed with asthma. You are responsible for performing peak flow meter testing and teaching Tom how to do it at home. Explain the procedure and patient education intervention.

_____

_____

_____

_____

INTERNET ACTIVITY OPTIONS

Complete one or more of these activities and, if appropriate, share your results with the class.

1. One of the duties of a medical assistant is to serve as a resource for patients. Search the Internet for pulmonologists and respiratory durable medical equipment providers in your area. Create either a circular file or an address book with the names, addresses, phone numbers, fax numbers, and websites for each resource. Include any additional information your patients may need (e.g., accepted insurance plans, services provided, hospital contacts).

2. The medical assistant must have knowledge of the different medications prescribed for patients with respiratory system abnormalities. Use the PDR to identify the indications for the following drugs:

   a. Allegra

   b. Flonase

   c. Singulair

   d. Alupent

   e. Advair

   f. Nasalcrom

   g. Isoniazid (INH)

   h. Rifampin

   i. Accolate

   j. Flovent Diskus

   k. Prednisone

MEDICAL RECORD ACTIVITIES

1. Maura, a 10-year-old patient, has recently been diagnosed with asthma. To help her better understand how to recognize her symptoms, Dr. Samuelson has asked Michael to teach Maura how to use a peak flow meter. Role-play with a partner and document the case.

   _____

   _____

   _____

   _____

2. Juan Garcia, a 42-year-old patient, has just been diagnosed with active tuberculosis. What symptoms would you expect Mr. Garcia to exhibit? How would you protect yourself from exposure? What patient education will Mr. Garcia need to protect his family and co-workers from the disease? Document the case in the medical record.

   _____

   _____

   _____

   _____

3. Document the following case. Use correct medical terminology for respiratory system terms.

   Mabel Bishop, 73 years old and one of Dr. Samuelson's patients, has been a long-time smoker with a history of a collapsed right lung and difficulty breathing. The only position she finds comfortable for breathing is sitting upright. She has come to the office today complaining of blood when she coughs; stabbing pain when she breathes, especially on the right side; and excessive nasal drainage. Dr. Samuelson listens to her lungs and can hear both a popping and rumbling sound in the right and left lower lobes.

   _____

   _____

   _____

   _____

47 Assisting in Cardiology

VOCABULARY REVIEW

Fill in the blanks.

1. An abnormal sound or murmur heard on auscultation of an organ, vessel, or gland is a(n) _____.

2. Recurring cramping in the calves caused by poor circulation of blood to the muscles of the lower leg is called _____ claudication.

3. _____ is an autoimmune disorder that affects the blood vessels and connective tissue, causing fibrous degeneration of the major organs.

4. The heart is enclosed in a double-membrane sac called the _____.

5. The middle layer of the heart is the _____, which is the muscle layer.

6. The medical term for heart attack is _____.

7. Patients with _____ have an inherited predisposition for the development of aneurysms.

8. The inner layer of the heart is the _____, which includes the valves of the heart.

9. The _____ are tendons that connect the heart valve cusps to the myocardial wall.

10. A decreased supply of oxygenated blood to an area or body part can result in _____.

11. Abnormal growth of tissue surrounding a heart valve that can occur as a complication of endocarditis are called _____.

12. Describe the action of depolarization and repolarization.

_____

_____

_____

13. Define essential and secondary hypertension.

_____

_____

_____

SKILLS AND CONCEPTS

1. Describe the conduction system of the heart.

_____

_____

_____

2. Label the parts of the heart and describe the blood flow through the heart in the following figure.

3. List three risk factors for heart disease that cannot be changed.

   a. _____

   b. _____

   c. _____

4. Summarize six lifestyle factors that put a patient at risk for heart disease.

   a. _____

   b. _____

   c. _____

   d. _____

   e. _____

   f. _____

5. Explain the process of atheroma formation in a patient with hypercholesterolemia.

   _____

   _____

   _____

6. Summarize the signs and symptoms typically seen in male and female patients experiencing an myocardial infarction (MI).

Male

_____

_____

Female

_____

_____

7. Explain the use of blood tests in diagnosing an MI.

Creatine kinase (CK) levels

_____

_____

Troponin levels

_____

_____

8. _____, such as _____, are administered intravenously to dissolve coronary artery blockage and prevent permanent myocardial damage. However, to be most effective, this treatment must be started within _____ of the episode.

9. Explain the difference between a coronary artery bypass graft (CABG) procedure and a coronary angioplasty.

_____

_____

_____

10. Complete the following table, which summarizes the various stages of hypertension and how they are treated.

Blood Pressure	Treatment
Prehypertension	Lifestyle modification Drug therapy in patients with:
Stage 1	Consider coexisting conditions Medication
Stage 2	Consider coexisting conditions Medication

Chapter **47** **Assisting in Cardiology**

11. List five conditions that can result from hypertension.

a. _____

b. _____

c. _____

d. _____

e. _____

12. Summarize the actions of the antihypertensive medications listed in the following table.

Classification/Name	Action	Treatment Protocol
Thiazide Diuretics (Hydrodiuril, Lasix, Lozol, Aldactone)		First drugs of choice for treatment of hypertension; enhance the action of other blood pressure (BP) medications; used in patients with diabetes and chronic kidney disease who have prehypertension
Beta-blockers (Tenormin, Lopressor, Sectral, Ziac, Inderal)		May be used with a diuretic for stage 1 or stage 2 hypertension
Angiotensin-Converting Enzyme (ACE) Inhibitors (Lotensin, Capoten, Vasotec, Monopril, Prinivil, Zestril)		May be used with a diuretic for stage 1 or stage 2 hypertension; also used for hypertension in patients with coronary artery disease, heart failure, or kidney failure
Angiotensin II Receptor Blockers (Cozaar, Atacand, Avapro, Diovan)		May be used with a diuretic for stage 1 or stage 2 hypertension; also used for hypertension in patients with coronary artery disease, heart failure, or kidney failure
Calcium Channel Blockers (Norvasc, Lotrel, Cardizem, Procardia, Vascor)		May be used with a diuretic for stage 1 or stage 2 hypertension; also used to treat angina and some arrhythmias

13. Identify the causes of the various types of shock.

Type of Shock	Causes
Cardiogenic	
Hypovolemic	
Neurogenic	
Anaphylactic	
Septic	

Fill in the blanks.

14. _____ is diagnosed if the patient experiences a drop in blood pressure when standing.

15. Damage and scar formation on the heart's valves are often seen in patients with _____.

16. _____ carries oxygenated blood away from the heart.

17. _____ is an incompetence in the mitral valve resulting from a congenital defect or vegetation from endocarditis.

18. Dilated, tortuous, superficial veins in the legs are called _____.

19. A cardiac pacemaker is most often used for treatment of _____.

20. A(n) _____ is used for patients experiencing frequent episodes of ventricular fibrillation.

CASE STUDIES

1. A patient is prescribed Tenormin 25 mg once daily. Prepare a prescription for the physician's signature on the following form. The physician wants the patient to be able to fill a 3-month supply of the medication with two refills. Explain to the patient the effects of Tenormin on the body.

2. Adam, a medical assistant, is taking vital signs on a patient and records a blood pressure in the right arm of 168/98 mm Hg. What steps should Adam take next?

3. A patient has been diagnosed with prehypertension. Adam should educate the patient to make what type of lifestyle modifications?

4. A patient complains of calf pain and slight swelling in an area of the left leg. The leg is warm to the touch. What questions should the medical assistant ask this patient? If deep vein thrombosis (DVT) is suspected, what tests can be done to confirm the diagnosis? What is the common treatment for DVT? What precautions should the medical assistant take when performing venipuncture on a patient taking warfarin (Coumadin)?

WORKPLACE APPLICATION OPTIONS

Complete one or more of these activities and, if appropriate, share your results with the class.

1. You are updating the policy and procedures manual for the office manager and physician to review. The new version will include telephone screening templates, which will guide other medical assistants in the proper handling of situations. Create a list of circumstances in which the medical assistant should activate emergency medical services for a patient with chest pain.

2. Corina visits the office and states that she would like the results of her neighbor's heart catheterization. Corina states that her neighbor had a difficult time understanding the results when the physician called her, so Corina thought she might be better able to relay any messages. Can Adam give Corina the requested information? What steps should Adam take to make sure the patient correctly understands the physician's message?

3. An elderly patient, Miss Kate Glasgow, is being seen in the office today for complaints of vertigo and syncope when she stands. The physician suspects orthostatic hypotension. Explain how you would check Miss Glasgow's BP for this condition.

4. The physician practice where you work keeps samples of a number of different medications for lowering blood cholesterol levels onsite. As a medical assistant it is your responsibility to understand the actions, side effects, and cautions of prescribed medications. List these factors for the following drugs.

   a. Mevacor

   _____

   _____

   b. Questran

   _____

   _____

   c. Zetia

   _____

   _____

   d. Lopid

   _____

   _____

   e. Advicor

   _____

   _____

INTERNET ACTIVITY OPTIONS

Complete one or more of these activities and, if appropriate, share your results with the class.

1. As discussed in the text, many risk factors can contribute to the development of heart disease. Visit the American Heart Association site at www.heart.org/HEARTORG/Conditions/HeartAttack/HeartAttackToolsResources/Heart-Attack-Risk-Assessment_UCM_303944_Article.jsp and use the risk assessment tool to determine your risk for heart disease. Did any of the results surprise you? What type of modifications can you make to reduce your risk for heart disease?

2. The medical assistant must be knowledgeable about the different medications prescribed for patients with respiratory system abnormalities. Use the PDR to identify the indications for the following drugs:

   a. Activase

   b. Retavase

   c. Lovenox

   d. Lopressor

   e. Inderal

   f. Lipitor

   g. Mevacor

   h. Zocor

   i. Hydrodiuril

   j. Lasix

   k. Lozol

l. Aldactone

m. Lopressor

n. Ziac

o. Inderal

p. Lotensin

q. Capoten

r. Vasotec

s. Monopril

t. Prinivil

u. Zestril

v. Norvasc

w. Lotrel

x. Cardizem

y. Procardia

z. Vascor

MEDICAL RECORD ACTIVITIES

1. Lucille Kring, a 48-year-old patient, has been diagnosed with metabolic syndrome. What signs and symptoms would you expect to see in this patient? The physician has asked you to reinforce her patient education about risk factors for cardiac disease. What would you include in this information? Document the patient education intervention and the vital signs you would expect to gather from this patient.

2. A 52-year-old male patient calls the office complaining of jaw and neck pain that seems to radiate to both arms. For the past 2 hours he has experienced shortness of breath, pressure in his chest, and sweating. What do you suspect the problem may be? What advice would you give this patient? Document the case.

3. Simon Jacobson is scheduled for a transesophageal echocardiogram as a follow-up for a congenital mitral valve prolapse. He has never had this particular procedure before and is quite concerned about how it will be done and whether he will experience any pain. Explain the procedure to Mr. Jacobson and document your teaching intervention in the patient's medical record.

48 Assisting in Geriatrics

VOCABULARY REVIEW

Match the following terms with their definitions.

_____ 1. The secretion or discharge of tears

_____ 2. A sore or ulcer over a bony prominence caused by ischemia from prolonged pressure; a bedsore

_____ 3. Age-related farsightedness that makes focusing on near objects difficult

_____ 4. Protein that forms the inelastic fibers of tendons, ligaments, and fascia

_____ 5. Pertaining to the ribs

_____ 6. A decreased ability to hear high frequencies and to discriminate sounds; age-related hearing loss

_____ 7. An essential part of elastic connective tissue that is flexible and elastic when moist

_____ 8. Waxy, greasy papules on the skin that vary from tan to dark brown; also called *age spots*

a. Collagen

b. Costal

c. Decubitus ulcer

d. Elastin

e. Lacrimation

f. Seborrheic keratoses

g. Presbyopia

h. Presbycusis

SKILLS AND CONCEPTS

1. List five myths and stereotypes about aging.

   a. _____

   b. _____

   c. _____

   d. _____

   e. _____

2. Describe the effects of aging on the cardiovascular system.

   _____

   _____

   _____

   _____

3. What can aging patients do to reduce their risk of cardiovascular disease?

   _____

   _____

   _____

   _____

413

4. List seven risk factors for cognitive decline.

a. _____

b. _____

c. _____

d. _____

e. _____

f. _____

g. _____

5. Explain the purpose of the Mini-Mental Status Examination. What abilities does it assess and how is it performed? Role-play assessing an elderly patient with this tool.

_____

_____

_____

_____

6. Describe the stages of Alzheimer's disease.

First stage _____

_____

Second stage _____

_____

Terminal stage _____

_____

7. List six suggestions for helping elderly individuals prevent and treat dry skin.

a. _____

b. _____

c. _____

d. _____

e. _____

f. _____

8. Explain the changes that occur in the pulmonary system with aging.

_____

_____

_____

_____

9. List six suggestions for helping an older adult with mobility, dexterity, and balance.

a. _____

b. _____

c. _____

d. _____

e. _____

f. _____

10. Summarize the medical assistant's role in caring for elderly patients.

_____

_____

_____

11. Complete the following table with the age-related changes that typically occur in the body systems as well as examples of health promotion measures.

Body System	Age-Related Changes	Health Promotion
Central nervous system		
Endocrine system		
Gastrointestinal system		
Musculoskeletal system		
Sensory organs		
Urinary system		
Sexuality		

12. Explain four age-related changes that occur in the anatomic structures of the eye.

_____

_____

_____

13. Describe the geriatric depression scale. Why is it a helpful tool for assessing the mental health of aging people?

_____

_____

_____

CASE STUDIES

1. A patient is having difficulty staying steady on his feet and must use a walker to remain mobile. How can the medical assistant aid this patient? What approach should the medical assistant take to prepare the patient for the physician's examination?

_____

_____

_____

2. A patient recently stopped complying with her diabetes treatment plan. What factors should Bill, the medical assistant, be aware of that may affect the patient's diabetes management? How can Bill help the patient deal with these factors?

_____

_____

_____

3. Mary is concerned about her risk for osteoporosis. What can Bill tell Mary about common risk factors for the development of osteoporosis? Can she do anything to prevent the decrease in bone density? What tests are done to diagnosis osteoporosis? Describe methods for preventing and treating osteoporosis.

_____

_____

_____

4. Mr. Carlos Rozera, age 82, has both hearing and vision impairments because of age-related changes. What suggestions can you give Bill to help him communicate with Mr. Rozera?

_____

_____

_____

5. Mr. Herbert Sampson's daughter brings him to the office today because of concerns about his increasing difficulty with memory and confusion. A number of conditions can cause cognitive changes in aging individuals. What risk factors may be contributing to Mr. Sampson's memory loss and confusion? What methods might the family use to improve Mr. Sampson's cognitive ability? What are the signs and symptoms of Alzheimer's disease?

_____

_____

_____

WORKPLACE APPLICATION OPTIONS

Complete one or more of these activities and, if appropriate, share your results with the class.

1. You are asked to speak at a local community center about the prevention of injuries in aging people. What suggestions can you make for preventing falls in this age group?

_____

_____

_____

2. Your office sees many geriatric patients daily. What are some common barriers for aging patients when they come into the office? What changes can you make to provide a safe and welcoming environment?

_____

_____

_____

3. One of the duties of the medical assistant is to inform patients about advance directives. What information should the medical assistant provide to the patient? Why is it important for a patient to have an advance directive?

_____

_____

_____

4. Patient education is vital to helping patients understand various disease processes and health maintenance. Describe some guidelines for effective patient education with older adults.

_____

_____

_____

5. You are interviewing an aging patient and begin to suspect that the patient may be suffering from abuse. What are the indications of elder abuse? How are elder abuse cases handled in your state?

_____

_____

_____

6. The medical practice that you work for has a policy that all patients age 60 or older should receive the Zostavax vaccine. Why is this vaccination indicated in an aging population? Explain how the vaccine is administered.

_____

_____

_____

7. You are interviewing a 72-year-old patient who reports having difficulty sleeping. What are some of the common problems older people experience with sleeping? What questions would you ask to gather detailed information on this patient's problem?

_____

_____

_____

INTERNET ACTIVITY OPTIONS

Complete one or more of these activities and, if appropriate, share your results with the class.

1. Aging individuals frequently need assistance to be able to remain in their homes and maintain independence. The medical assistant should be prepared to provide details on community resources that could be useful to older patients and their families. Conduct a search online for resources that could provide assistance to aging people and develop a resource guide that could be used as a referral source in the ambulatory care setting.

2. One reason patients do not comply with medication orders is the lack of prescription coverage. Search the Internet for programs that assist patients who have concerns regarding medication coverage. What are the criteria for enrollment? Be prepared to discuss your findings in class.

3. Conduct online research on advance directives. Explain the concepts of durable power of attorney and do not resuscitate (DNR) orders. Summarize what you have learned and share it with your class.

4. Research is constantly being done on Alzheimer's disease. Several new medications are currently being tested. Conduct an online review of new treatment options and share them with your class.

5. The medical assistant must be knowledgeable about the different medications prescribed for geriatric patients. Use the PDR to identify the indications for the following drugs:

   a. Fosamax

   b. Actonel

   c. Evista

   d. Calcimar

   e. Miacalcin

   f. Aricept

   g. Exelon

   h. Reminyl

   i. Namenda

   j. Ambien

   k. Restoril

   l. Sonata

   m. Lunesta

   n. Reclast

   o. Cognex

   p. Zostavax

MEDICAL RECORD ACTIVITIES

1. A patient comes to the office today for a follow-up appointment because of orthostatic hypotension. What questions should Bill, the medical assistant, ask the patient? How should Bill measure the patient's vital signs? Document the case.

_____

_____

_____

2. While Bill is taking Mrs. Simoni's health history, she complains of chronic constipation. What questions should Bill ask her? What are the possible causes of constipation in elderly individuals? What dietary measures may provide relief? Document the case.

_____

_____

_____

3. Dr. Kennedy is concerned that Mrs. Isabel Carmassi may be suffering from a nutritional deficiency. What factors could be contributing to her poor dietary choices? What questions should the medical assistant ask to obtain detailed information about her dietary habits? Document the case.

_____

_____

_____

Principles of Electrocardiography

VOCABULARY REVIEW

Match the following terms with their definitions.

_____	1. Bradycardia	a. Complete cessation of cardiac contractions
_____	2. Bundle of His	b. Use of electroshock to convert an abnormal cardiac rhythm to a normal one
_____	3. Cardiac arrest	c. An irregular heart rhythm
_____	4. Cardioversion	d. A heart rate of less than 60 beats per minute
_____	5. Defibrillator	e. Fibers that conduct electrical impulses from the atrioventricular node (AV) node to the ventricular myocardium
_____	6. Dyspnea	f. A heart rate greater than 100 beats per minute
_____	7. Hypertension	g. An area of tissue that has died because of lack of blood supply
_____	8. Infarction	h. A temporary interruption in blood supply to a tissue or organ
_____	9. Ischemic	i. Pertaining to the heart muscle
_____	10. Myocardial	j. Difficulty breathing when in the supine position
_____	11. Arrhythmia	k. The pacemaker of the heart, located in the right atrium
_____	12. Orthopnea	l. A machine used to deliver an electroshock to the heart through electrodes placed on the chest wall
_____	13. Sinoatrial (SA) node	m. Difficulty breathing
_____	14. Tachycardia	n. High blood pressure in which the diastolic pressure is greater than 90 mm Hg

Fill in the blanks.

15. The _____ are the two upper chambers of the heart.

16. The _____ are the two lower chambers of the heart.

17. _____ is the medical term for the heart muscle.

18. A(n) _____ beat is one that does not begin in the sinoatrial node (SA) node.

19. A patient complaining of _____ describes a sensation of the heart pounding or racing.

20. The first three leads recorded in an electrocardiogram (ECG) are called the _____ or _____ leads because each lead uses two limb electrodes to record the heart's electrical activity.

21. The electrical activity recorded by the three _____ leads is relatively small so the ECG machine amplifies the electrical activity of each to record them on the strip.

421

1. Describe diastole and systole.

_____

_____

_____

_____

2. Label each structure on the following figure.

3. Describe the electrical conduction system of the heart.

_____

_____

_____

_____

4. Label the precordial leads on the following drawing.

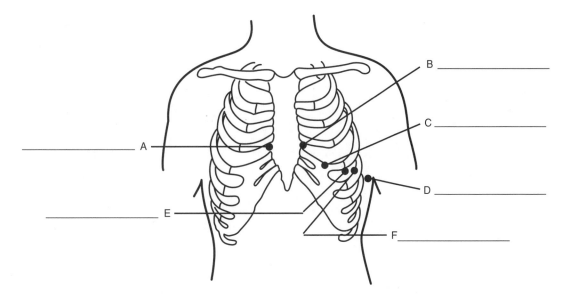

5. Name the rhythm shown in the following illustration.

_____

6. Name the rhythm shown in the following illustration.

_____

7. Name the rhythm shown in the following illustration.

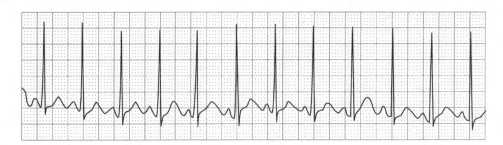

_____

8. Name the rhythm shown in the following illustration.

_____

9. Name the rhythm shown in the following illustration.

_____

10. Name the rhythm shown in the following illustration.

_____

11. Describe the procedure shown in the following illustration.

_____

_____

_____

Fill in the blanks.

12. The _____ wave occurs during the contraction of the atria and shows the beginning of cardiac depolarization.

13. The _____ complex shows the contraction of both ventricles and also reflects the completion of cardiac depolarization.

14. The _____ interval is the time from the beginning of atrial contraction to the beginning of ventricular contraction.

15. The T wave indicates ventricular recovery, or _____ of the ventricles.

16. ECG paper has horizontal and vertical lines at _____-mm intervals.

17. When running at normal speed, one small, 1-mm square passes the stylus every _____ seconds.

18. One large, 5-mm square passes the stylus every _____ seconds.

19. Lead I records the electrical activity between the _____ arm and the _____ arm.

20. Lead _____ records the electrical activity between the right arm and the left leg.

21. Lead III records the electrical activity between the _____ arm and the left leg.

22. _____ records the activity from midway between the left leg and the left arm to the right arm.

23. _____ records the activity from midway between the right arm and the left leg to the left arm.

Chapter **49 Principles of Electrocardiography**

24. _____ records the activity from midway between the right arm and the left arm to the left leg.

25. With the _____ baseline, the stylus gradually shifts away from the center of the paper.

26. _____ shows up on the recording as jagged peaks of irregular height and spacing and a shifting baseline.

27. _____ occurs when the electric connection has been interrupted.

28. _____ interference appears as a series of uniform small spikes on the paper.

29. Cardiac _____ testing is conducted to observe and record the patient's cardiovascular response to measured exercise challenges.

30. A(n) _____ monitor is a portable system for recording the cardiac activity of a patient over a 24-hour period or longer.

31. The stylus should deflect exactly _____ when the standardization button is depressed.

32. The standard speed for an ECG recording is _____.

33. A(n) _____ monitors the heart rhythm and delivers a shock to the heart if it detects a dangerous tachycardia or fibrillation.

34. What information should be analyzed when an ECG strip is read?

   a. _____

   b. _____

   c. _____

   d. _____

   e. _____

35. Summarize the classic changes that occur in the ECG when a patient experiences an myocardial infarction (MI).

   _____

   _____

   _____

36. Complete the following table that describes the ECG changes that occur in a patient with an MI.

Phase	Appearance of ECG Changes	Specific Changes Seen on ECG
I (hyperacute)		
II (fully evolved)		
III (resolution)		
IV (stabilized chronic)		

37. List three reasons cardiac stress tests are performed.

   a. _____

   b. _____

   c. _____

38. _____ is a screening tool that allows physicians to see the amount of plaque in the coronary arteries by showing the presence of calcium deposits.

1. You have been instructed to perform an ECG on a 51-year-old man. As you start to prepare the patient for the examination, you notice a large amount of body hair on his chest. Can the procedure still be performed? What should you do? Why?

   _____

   _____

   _____

2. Martha, the medical assistant, is performing electrocardiography on a patient who complains of orthopnea. In what position can the patient be placed?

   _____

   _____

   _____

3. During the ECG recording, the patient coughs and starts talking. What type of artifacts would you expect to see?

   _____

   _____

   _____

4. The physician has reviewed a patient's ECG and has concluded that the patient has PACs. Explain to the patient what is happening to the heart during this time. What are some common causes of premature atrial contractions (PACs)?

   _____

   _____

   _____

5. The physician has just prescribed digoxin for a patient. What can Martha tell the patient about the effects of the drug? Refer to the PDR for important drug information.

   _____

   _____

   _____

6. You are responsible for recording an ECG on a new patient. Explain how you would prepare both the patient and the room for this procedure.

   _____

   _____

   _____

WORKPLACE APPLICATION OPTIONS

Complete one or more of these activities and, if appropriate, share your results with the class.

1. Martha is showing a new employee around the office during orientation. The office has both a six-channel ECG machine. Describe how the machine works.

_____

_____

_____

2. A new shipment of ECG paper and electrodes has just arrived at the office. What should Martha remember when storing the supplies? Why?

_____

_____

_____

3. Martha is nervous that she will not remember proper lead placement while performing an ECG. Describe the accurate placement for each lead.

RA _____

RL _____

LA _____

LL _____

V_1 _____

V_2 _____

V_3 _____

V_4 _____

V_5 _____

V_6 _____

4. What can the medical assistant do to prevent AC interference on the ECG strip?

_____

_____

_____

5. As you are preparing a patient for Holter monitor testing, he asks why a Holter monitor would be ordered instead of an ECG. How should you respond? The patient states that he is too busy to record his daily activities. Explain to the patient the importance of keeping a diary during Holter monitor testing.

_____

_____

_____

6. You are hired to work in a cardiologist's practice and are concerned about understanding the immediate treatment for a patient who is suffering an MI. Summarize the typical treatment protocol for this cardiac emergency.

_____

_____

_____

INTERNET ACTIVITY OPTION

Complete this activity and, if appropriate, share your results with the class.

The office is considering the purchase of a Holter monitor. You have been asked to research the different types of equipment available. Use the Internet to search for different suppliers of Holter monitors. Consider the usability, cost, and maintenance of the different products. Present your findings to the class. Which product would you recommend and why?

MEDICAL RECORD ACTIVITIES

1. You are responsible for explaining to a patient how to use an event monitor at home. Document your patient education intervention, including an explanation of the purpose of the monitor and directions on how to use it throughout the test period.

_____

_____

_____

2. You have just performed an ECG on a patient. What type of information should be documented about the procedure?

_____

_____

_____

3. You take a telephone call from a patient who reports that one of her Holter monitor leads fell off during the night. She reapplied it when she woke up this morning. What does this mean about her Holter recording? What needs to be done to start an accurate recording again? Document how you managed this problem and your interaction with the patient.

_____

_____

_____

50 Assisting with Diagnostic Imaging

VOCABULARY REVIEW

Match the following terms with their definitions.

_____ 1. Distal

_____ 2. Internal

_____ 3. Plantar

_____ 4. Medial or mesial

_____ 5. Palmar

_____ 6. External

_____ 7. Anterior

_____ 8. Inferior

_____ 9. Lateral

_____ 10. Posterior

_____ 11. Cephalic, cephalad

_____ 12. Caudal, caudad

_____ 13. Superior

_____ 14. Proximal

_____ 15. Radiolucent

a. Forward or the front portion of the body or body part

b. Pertaining to the head; toward the head

c. Away from the head; the opposite of *cephalad*

d. Away from the source or point of origin

e. To the outside, at or near the surface of the body or a body part

f. Below, farther from the head

g. Deep, near the center of the body or a part; the opposite of *external*

h. Referring to the side; away from the center to the left or right

i. Toward the center of the body or of a body part; the opposite of *lateral*

j. Referring to the palm (anterior surface) of the hand

k. Referring to the sole of the foot

l. Backward or the back portion of the body or body part; the opposite of *anterior*

m. Toward the source or point of origin; the opposite of *distal*

n. Above, toward the head; the opposite of *inferior*

o. Pertaining to a substance that is easily penetrated by x-rays; these substances appear dark on radiographs

Fill in the blanks with the correct terms.

1. _____ refers to the making of x-ray images called *radiographs*.

2. X-rays can penetrate most substances to some degree, but some substances, such as metal and bone, are more difficult to penetrate and are said to be _____.

3. _____ is a technique performed with special equipment that allows the radiologist to view x-ray images in motion.

4. The _____ scanner consists of a movable table with remote control, a circular gantry structure that supports the x-ray tube and detectors, an operator console with a monitor, and the supporting computer system.

5. _____ medicine scans do not provide clear images of anatomic structures. They are used to obtain information about the function of organs and tissues.

6. A(n) _____ is the radioactive substance administered to patients for nuclear medicine imaging procedures.

7. The _____ is the moving grid device that prevents scatter radiation from fogging x-ray film.

8. The _____ is the part of the sonography machine in contact with the patient; it sends high-frequency sound waves and receives the sound echoes that return from the patient's body.

9. A(n) _____ is a fluoroscopic examination of the soft tissue components of joints with direct injection of a contrast medium into the joint capsule.

10. Barium sulfate is an example of a(n) _____.

11. The _____ is the part of the CT scan that surrounds the patient and gathers imaging data.

12. A(n) _____ may be created on x-ray film if the patient wears clothing with heavy seams or buttons during an x-ray procedure.

Fill in the blanks by choosing the correct terms from the following list.

Lower gastrointestinal series   Angiography
Recumbent   Supine
Embolization   NPO
Upright   Dorsal recumbent
Prone   Ventral recumbent
Lateral recumbent   Intravenous urogram

13. Lying facedown is known as the _____ position.

14. Lying down is referred to as the _____ position.

15. Lying on the back with the knees bent and the feet flat on the table is called the _____ position.

16. Lying on the side is the _____ position.

17. Lying facedown, prone, is called the _____ position.

18. Lying face up is known as the _____ position.

19. An x-ray examination performed while the patient is standing or seated would be called a(n) _____ view.

20. A(n) _____ is an x ray examination of the urinary tract using intravenous injection of an iodine contrast medium.

21. A(n) _____ is a fluoroscopic examination of the colon, usually using rectal administration of barium sulfate as a contrast medium.

22. _____ is an interventional technique performed by a radiologist in which a catheter is used to block off a blood vessel to prevent hemorrhage.

23. A(n) _____ is performed with an iodine dye to visualize blood vessels.

24. A physician order for the patient to fast before a diagnostic examination is called _____.

1. Name the directions and planes of the body shown in the following figure.

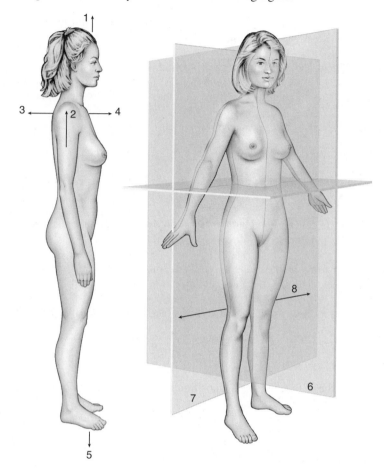

1. _____
2. _____
3. _____
4. _____
5. _____
6. _____
7. _____
8. _____

2. List and describe the four prime factors of exposure.

a. _____

b. _____

c. _____

d. _____

Indicate which statements are true (T) and which are false (F).

_____3. Patients with cardiac pacemakers cannot have magnetic resonance imaging (MRI) examinations.

_____4. Radiation control regulations do not require that female patients of childbearing age be advised of potential radiation hazards before an x-ray examination.

_____5. If the patient is supine facing the x-ray tube, the projection is said to be anteroposterior (AP).

_____6. X-rays do not linger in the room after the exposure, and they are not capable of making the objects in the room radioactive.

Fill in the blanks.

7. The radiographer selects the correct cassette and places a(n) _____ marker on it to identify the patient's right or left side.

8. The _____ (R) is the conventional unit of radiation exposure that represents a measurement of radiation intensity and is determined by the interaction of the x-ray beam with air.

9. The conventional unit for measuring both therapeutic radiation doses and specific tissue doses received in diagnostic applications is the _____, which stands for "radiation absorbed dose."

10. The dose-equivalent unit used to measure the occupational dose or other exposure that may involve more than one type of radiation is the _____, which stands for "roentgen equivalent in man."

11. Identify each type of radiographic projection in the following pictures.

Film

X-ray tube

A _____

B _____

C _____

12. Medical assistants must understand the purpose of diagnostic procedures and must be able to reinforce patient education on how to prepare for them. Complete the following table to demonstrate your knowledge of this topic.

Study	Diagnostic Purpose	Procedure	Patient Preparation
Arteriogram		Catheter is inserted into the femoral or brachial artery and advanced, under fluoroscopy, to the target site. Dye is injected, and x-ray images are taken.	
Arthrogram		Fluoroscopic and radiographic examination of a joint after injection of air or contrast dye.	
Barium enema		Fluoroscopic and radiographic examination of the colon after a barium enema to detect internal structural abnormalities; takes approximately 1 hour.	
Barium swallow		Fluoroscopic and radiographic examination performed as barium is swallowed to detect abnormalities of the pharynx, esophagus, and stomach; takes about 15 minutes.	
Bone scan	To detect bone cancer; bone infection; osteoarthritis; and osteomyelitis		
Computed tomography (CT)	To obtain detailed, cross-sectional views of all types of tissue; one of the best tools for studying the chest and abdomen		
Intravenous urogram (IVU) or intravenous pyelogram (IVP)	To evaluate the structure and function of the kidneys, ureters, bladder		
Magnetic resonance imaging (MRI)	To aid diagnosis of intracranial and spinal lesions, aneurysms, heart defects, multiple sclerosis, and soft tissue abnormalities in the body		
Myelogram		Fluoroscopic and radiographic examination of the spinal column after injection of a contrast medium into the subarachnoid space; takes about 1 hour.	

13. Nuclear medicine studies are difficult for patients to understand and can be frightening because of the potential exposure to radioactive materials. Complete the following table by providing the purpose of several nuclear medicine procedures.

Procedure	Purpose
Bone scan	
Brain scan	
Liver scan	
Lung scan	
PET scan	
Thallium stress test	
Thyroid scan	

CASE STUDIES

1. A patient with irritable bowel syndrome has been ordered to have a barium enema. What can Sara, the medical assistant, tell the patient about the examination? What patient preparation is involved?

2. Sara is providing instructions to a patient for whom a DEXA scan has been ordered to check for evidence of osteoporosis. Describe the procedure and the patient preparation.

3. Sara is assisting a patient during an x-ray examination. The patient asks, "What does the x-ray show? Is anything broken?" How should Sara respond?

WORKPLACE APPLICATION OPTIONS

Complete one or more of these activities and, if appropriate, share your results with the class.

1. Sara occasionally assists the radiology technician in preparing and positioning patients during x-ray procedures. Should she wear a dosimeter? Explain the purpose of a dosimeter and how the employer must manage these devices.

2. Sara is putting away a recent shipment of films. What factors should she remember when handling and storing films?

Chapter **50** Assisting with Diagnostic Imaging

3. Describe the methods Sara can use to minimize unnecessary exposure of her patients to radiation.

4. You are responsible for scheduling a patient for several diagnostic procedures. Summarize the proper sequencing order for scheduling various types of diagnostic studies.

INTERNET ACTIVITY OPTION

Complete this activity and, if appropriate, share your results with the class.

Visit the website of the Radiological Society of North America at www.rsna.org. Investigate the site, especially the patient education section. Is the website something you could find useful in a healthcare setting? What are the different features of the site?

MEDICAL RECORD ACTIVITIES

1. You are responsible for explaining to a patient how to prepare for an LGI. Document your patient teaching intervention.

2. Tara Silverman, a 7-year-old patient, is scheduled for multiple x-ray films the next day. Her mother is quite concerned about Tara and whether she will be able to be with her during the procedures. Summarize the guidelines for pediatric x-ray examinations for Mrs. Silverman and document appropriately.

51 Assisting in the Clinical Laboratory

1. Explain the concept of normal or reference ranges for laboratory specimens.

   _____

   _____

2. Convert the following from Greenwich time to military time or from military time to Greenwich time.

   a. 2:30 a.m. _____

   b. 12 p.m. _____

   c. 4:20 a.m. _____

   d. 1500 hours _____

   e. 1815 hours _____

3. Label the parts of a microscope in the following figure and define each.

4. One blood glucose meter always reads 10% too high. Another meter reads anywhere from 5% to 9% too high. Which one is more precise? Which one is more accurate? How is accuracy different from precision?

   _____

   _____

   _____

   _____

5. List five occasions when it is absolutely necessary to wash your hands in the laboratory area.

    a. _____

    b. _____

    c. _____

    d. _____

    e. _____

6. Describe three types of hazards in the laboratory setting.

    a. _____

    b. _____

    c. _____

7. Summarize methods for preventing physical hazards in the clinical laboratory.

    _____

    _____

    _____

    _____

8. Explain the hazard identification system developed by the National Fire Protection Association to provide information on the potential health, flammability, and chemical reactivity hazards of materials.

    _____

    _____

    _____

    _____

9. Differentiate between qualitative and quantitative results. Give an example of each.

    _____

    _____

    _____

    _____

10. Identify and explain the four major divisions of the clinical laboratory.

    a. _____

       _____

    b. _____

       _____

    c. _____

       _____

    d. _____

       _____

11. Label each of the following according to its clinical laboratory division.

Hemoglobin _____

Urine specific gravity _____

Urine culture _____

Blood glucose _____

Throat culture _____

White blood cell count _____

Cholesterol _____

Complete blood count _____

12. What is an MSDS? What type of information does it include?

_____

_____

_____

13. What is the role of Occupational Safety and Health Administration (OSHA) in the clinical laboratory?

_____

_____

_____

14. Summarize the 16-section MSDS template recommended by OSHA.

_____

_____

_____

_____

_____

_____

15. What is CLIA and what are the three different levels of laboratory testing?

_____

_____

_____

_____

16. Medical assistants are trained to perform CLIA-waived tests in the ambulatory healthcare setting. Complete the following table with the information medical assistants should know about these tests.

CLIA-Waived Test	Function
Dipstick or tablet reagent urinalysis (nonautomated) for bilirubin, glucose, hemoglobin, ketone, leukocytes, nitrite, pH, protein, specific gravity, urobilinogen	
Urine pregnancy tests: visual color comparison tests	
Urine chemistry analyzer; automated urine dipstick analysis	
Urine chemistry analyzer for microalbumin and creatinine	
Ovulation tests: visual color comparison tests for luteinizing hormone	
Fecal occult blood	
Erythrocyte sedimentation rate: nonautomated	
Hemoglobin-copper sulfate: nonautomated	
HemoCue Hemoglobin system	
Blood glucose by glucose monitoring devices cleared by the Food and Drug Administration (FDA) specifically for home use	
HemoCue B	
Spun microhematocrit	
STAT-CRIT hematocrit	
Hemoglobin and hemoglobin A_{1c} by single analyte instruments with self-contained or component features to perform specimen-reagent interaction	
Cholestech LDX	
Blood mononucleosis antibodies	
Helicobacter pylori antibodies	
Borrelia burgdorferi antibodies	
Whole blood OraSure HIV-1 test	
Nasal influenza A and B	
Streptococcus A throat swab	

17. Describe the chain of custody. Why is it important? What steps must be followed?

_____

_____

_____

_____

18. Summarize the label information typically required when specimens are sent to a reference laboratory.

_____

_____

_____

_____

19. Explain the basic units of the metric system used in the clinical laboratory.

_____

_____

20. Which of the following statements is/are true about laboratory beakers?

_____ Beakers are wide, straight-sided cylindric vessels used for mixing or reagent preparation.

_____ Beakers are calibrated to hold an exact volume.

_____ Erlenmeyer flasks are used for reagent preparation and are calibrated for exact measurements.

21. Which of the following statements is/are true about pipets?

_____ A bulb or vacuum pump–type device is required to draw liquid into a pipet.

_____ A TD pipet delivers a specified volume by drawing the liquid up to the calibration mark and then allowing it to drain out vertically, unassisted.

_____ A serologic pipet has a large tip opening that delivers a fast flow of liquid with accuracy.

22. How is a 1:10 dilution prepared in the medical laboratory?

_____

_____

_____

23. Explain the functions of the following clinical laboratory equipment.

Incubator

_____

_____

_____

Autoclave

_____

_____

_____

1. Marsha, the medical assistant, is preparing to draw blood from a patient. What standard precautions should she take when performing the procedure?

2. Marsha has been asked to develop a safety manual for the office. What information should be included?

3. Marsha is in charge of performing quality assurance in the office. Describe when QA testing should be done for the following tests:

   a. Urinalysis

   b. Pregnancy tests

   c. Glucometer test strips

   d. Automated chemistry analyses

   e. Temperature logs

WORKPLACE APPLICATION OPTIONS

Complete one or more of these activities and, if appropriate, share your results with the class.

1. Marsha is preparing a requisition form for a collected specimen. What information must be included?

2. On the thermometer drawings provided, mark the range of common laboratory temperatures for the following items.

   a. Body and incubator temperature

   b. Room temperature

   c. Freezer temperature

   d. Refrigerator temperature

A

B

C

D

3. Your centrifuge starts to vibrate markedly while you are spinning a specimen. What should you check? What precautions should you take while operating a centrifuge?

4. Record the volume in milliliters for the two cylinders pictured.

a. _____

b. _____

   a. How much diluent is added to a 1-mL sample to make a 1:10 dilution?

   _____ mL

   b. How much diluent is added to a 2-mL sample to make a 1:10 dilution?

   _____ mL

   c. How much diluent is added to a 1-mL sample to make a 1:20 dilution?

   _____ mL

   d. How much diluent is added to a 2-mL sample to make a 1:10 dilution?

   _____ mL

5. Marsha is evaluating the laboratory for the risk of fire. What type of equipment should be kept in the laboratory in case of an open flame emergency?

6. Investigate chemicals that are stored in your laboratory at school. Choose one and complete the following MSDS sheet with the required information.

MATERIAL SAFETY DATA SHEET   **FILE NO.:**

NAME OF PRODUCT

<u>**MSDS DATE: / /**</u>_____

PRODUCT NAME: _____

SYNONYMS: _____

PRODUCT CODES: _____

MANUFACTURER: _____

DIVISION: _____

ADDRESS: _____

EMERGENCY PHONE: _____

CHEMTREC PHONE: _____

OTHER CALLS: _____

FAX PHONE: _____

CHEMICAL NAME: _____

CHEMICAL FAMILY: _____

CHEMICAL FORMULA: _____

PRODUCT USE: _____

PREPARED BY: _____

SECTION 1 NOTES:

_____

_____

SECTION 2: COMPOSITION/INFORMATION ON INGREDIENTS

INGREDIENT:

CAS NO.   % WT   % VOL

SARA 313 REPORTABLE   ppm   mg/m3

   OSHA PEL-TWA: _____

   OSHA PEL STEL: _____

   OSHA PEL CEILING: _____

   ACGIH TLV-TWA: _____

   ACGIH TLV STEL: _____

   ACGIH TLV CEILING: _____

Chapter **51** **Assisting in the Clinical Laboratory**

SECTION 2 NOTES:

_____

_____

SECTION 3: HAZARDS IDENTIFICATION

EMERGENCY OVERVIEW:

_____

_____

ROUTES OF ENTRY: _____

POTENTIAL HEALTH EFFECTS

    EYES: _____

    SKIN: _____

    INGESTION: _____

    INHALATION: _____

ACUTE HEALTH HAZARDS: _____

CHRONIC HEALTH HAZARDS: _____

MEDICAL CONDITIONS GENERALLY AGGRAVATED BY EXPOSURE:

_____

_____

CARCINOGENICITY

OSHA: ACGIH: NTP: IARC: OTHER:

SECTION 3 NOTES:

_____

_____

SECTION 4: FIRST AID MEASURES

EYES: _____

SKIN: _____

INGESTION: _____

INHALATION: _____

NOTES TO PHYSICIANS OR FIRST AID PROVIDERS:

_____

_____

SECTION 4 NOTES:

_____

_____

SECTION 5: FIRE-FIGHTING MEASURES

FLAMMABLE LIMITS IN AIR, UPPER: _____

   (% BY VOLUME)   LOWER: _____

FLASH POINT:

   F: _____

   C: _____

METHOD USED: _____

AUTOIGNITION TEMPERATURE:

   F: _____

   C: _____

NFPA HAZARD CLASSIFICATION

   HEALTH: FLAMMABILITY: REACTIVITY:

   OTHER:

HMIS HAZARD CLASSIFICATION

   HEALTH: FLAMMABILITY: REACTIVITY:

   PROTECTION:

EXTINGUISHING MEDIA: _____

SPECIAL FIRE FIGHTING PROCEDURES: _____

UNUSUAL FIRE AND EXPLOSION HAZARDS: _____

HAZARDOUS DECOMPOSITION PRODUCTS: _____

SECTION 5 NOTES:

_____

_____

SECTION 6: ACCIDENTAL RELEASE MEASURES

ACCIDENTAL RELEASE MEASURES:

_____

_____

449

SECTION 6 NOTES:

_____

_____

SECTION 7: HANDLING AND STORAGE

HANDLING AND STORAGE:

_____

OTHER PRECAUTIONS:

_____

SECTION 7 NOTES:

_____

_____

SECTION 8: EXPOSURE CONTROLS/PERSONAL PROTECTION

ENGINEERING CONTROLS: _____

VENTILATION: _____

RESPIRATORY PROTECTION: _____

EYE PROTECTION: _____

SKIN PROTECTION: _____

OTHER PROTECTIVE CLOTHING OR EQUIPMENT: _____

WORK HYGIENIC PRACTICES: _____

EXPOSURE GUIDELINES: _____

SECTION 8 NOTES:

_____

_____

SECTION 9: PHYSICAL AND CHEMICAL PROPERTIES

APPEARANCE: _____

ODOR: _____

PHYSICAL STATE: _____

pH AS SUPPLIED: _____

pH (Other): _____

BOILING POINT:

     F: _____

     C: _____

450

MELTING POINT:

     F: _____

     C: _____

FREEZING POINT:

     F: _____

     C: _____

VAPOR PRESSURE (mmHg):

     F: _____

     C: _____

VAPOR DENSITY (AIR = 1):

     F: _____

     C: _____

SPECIFIC GRAVITY (H_2O = 1):

     F: _____

     C: _____

EVAPORATION RATE: _____

BASIS (=1): _____

SOLUBILITY IN WATER: _____

PERCENT SOLIDS BY WEIGHT: _____

PERCENT VOLATILE:

  BY WT/ BY VOL

     F: _____

     C: _____

VOLATILE ORGANIC COMPOUNDS (VOC):

  WITH WATER: _____ LBS/GAL

  WITHOUT WATER: _____ LBS/GAL

MOLECULAR WEIGHT: _____

VISCOSITY:

     F: _____

     C: _____

SECTION 9 NOTES:

_____

_____

SECTION 10: STABILITY AND REACTIVITY

STABLE   UNSTABLE

STABILITY: _____

CONDITIONS TO AVOID (STABILITY): _____

INCOMPATIBILITY (MATERIAL TO AVOID): _____

HAZARDOUS DECOMPOSITION OR BY-PRODUCTS: _____

HAZARDOUS POLYMERIZATION: _____

CONDITIONS TO AVOID (POLYMERIZATION): _____

SECTION 10 NOTES:

_____

_____

SECTION 11: TOXICOLOGICAL INFORMATION

TOXICOLOGICAL INFORMATION:

_____

SECTION 11 NOTES:

_____

_____

SECTION 12: ECOLOGICAL INFORMATION

ECOLOGICAL INFORMATION:

_____

SECTION 12 NOTES:

_____

_____

SECTION 13: DISPOSAL CONSIDERATIONS

WASTE DISPOSAL METHOD:

_____

_____

RCRA HAZARD CLASS:

_____

SECTION 13 NOTES:

_____

SECTION 14: TRANSPORT INFORMATION

U.S. DEPARTMENT OF TRANSPORTATION

    PROPER SHIPPING NAME: _____

    HAZARD CLASS: _____

    ID NUMBER: _____

    PACKING GROUP: _____

    LABEL STATEMENT: _____

WATER TRANSPORTATION

    PROPER SHIPPING NAME: _____

    HAZARD CLASS: _____

    ID NUMBER: _____

    PACKING GROUP: _____

    LABEL STATEMENTS: _____

AIR TRANSPORTATION

    PROPER SHIPPING NAME: _____

    HAZARD CLASS: _____

    ID NUMBER: _____

    PACKING GROUP: _____

    LABEL STATEMENTS: _____

OTHER AGENCIES:

_____

_____

SECTION 14 NOTES:

_____

_____

SECTION 15: REGULATORY INFORMATION

U.S. FEDERAL REGULATIONS

  TSCA (TOXIC SUBSTANCE CONTROL ACT):

_____

  CERCLA (COMPREHENSIVE RESPONSE COMPENSATION, AND LIABILITY ACT):

_____

453

SARA TITLE III (SUPERFUND AMENDMENTS AND REAUTHORIZATION ACT):

311/312 HAZARD CATEGORIES:

313 REPORTABLE INGREDIENTS:

STATE REGULATIONS:

INTERNATIONAL REGULATIONS:

SECTION 15 NOTES:

SECTION 16: OTHER INFORMATION

OTHER INFORMATION:

PREPARATION INFORMATION:

DISCLAIMER:

INTERNET ACTIVITY OPTION

Complete this activity and, if appropriate, share your results with the class.

Visit the laboratory section of OSHA's website at www.osha.gov/SLTC/laboratories/index.html. Investigate one of the topics under the "What's New" section and summarize what you learn for your class.

MEDICAL RECORD ACTIVITIES

1. You are responsible for collecting a throat specimen and sending it to the reference laboratory for analysis. Document the procedure in the patient's medical record.

2. Marsha is conducting a quality control test on the urinalysis dipsticks used routinely in the clinic. Explain the significance of the QC check and discuss the documentation required for this procedure.

52 Assisting in the Analysis of Urine

Fill in the blanks with the correct vocabulary terms from this chapter.

1. _____ Abnormal presence of a hemoglobin-like chemical of muscle tissue in urine as the result of muscle deterioration.

2. _____ Essential amino acid found in milk, eggs, and other foods.

3. _____ Decreased blood flow to a body part or organ caused by constriction or plugging of the supplying artery.

4. _____ Chemical reaction controlled by an enzyme.

5. _____ White blood cells; leukocytes that have segmented nuclei; also known as *polymorphonuclear neutrophils* (PMNs) or *segmented neutrophils*.

6. _____ Presence of glucose in the urine.

7. _____ White blood cells; leukocytes that have unsegmented nuclei; monocytes and lymphocytes in particular.

8. _____ Causing light to refract, creating a sharp boundary or image.

9. _____ Level above which a substance cannot be reabsorbed by the renal tubules and therefore is excreted in the urine.

10. _____ Fluid that remains after a liquid is passed through a membranous filter.

11. _____ A sealed glass float with a calibrated paper scale in its stem. With a slight spinning motion, it is placed in a cylinder containing a urine sample, and the value is read at the meniscus of the urine.

12. _____ Strips used to test the specific gravity of urine.

13. _____ Device that measures the refraction of light through solids in a liquid.

14. _____ Glucose test on a reagent strip. A tablet is dropped into a test tube of urine, and the color of the tube's contents is compared with a chart.

15. _____ Reagent tablets used to test for fat metabolism by-products.

16. _____ Substance detected in a positive pregnancy test.

17. _____ Increases in the concentration of urine shortly before ovulation.

18. _____ Shape of urates or phosphates that settle out of unrefrigerated urine samples.

19. _____ Procedure performed in the microbiology laboratory in which a specimen is cultured on artificial media to detect bacterial or fungal growth, followed by appropriate screening for antibiotic sensitivity.

20. _____ Medical term for a urine sample with a persistent greenish yellow foam that may indicate the patient has viral hepatitis.

21. _____ Definitive diagnostic test to which all others are compared.

22. _____ Protein that has taken on the size and shape of the renal tubules that is washed into the urine.

23. _____ A visual examination of the urinary bladder using a fiberoptic instrument.

24. _____ A term used when reporting bacteriuria; one unit represents one bacterium present in the urine sample.

25. _____ The product of drug metabolism that is excreted into the urine.

26. _____ Notches or leaflike, scalloped edges that form on an object, such as the changes that occur on the surface of a red blood cell when it is exposed to a hypertonic saline solution.

27. _____ A substance that is capable of staining living cells after their removal from a living or recently dead organism.

SKILLS AND CONCEPTS

1. Identify the structures of the urinary system shown in the following figure.

a. _____

b. _____

c. _____

d. _____

e. _____

f. _____

g. _____

h. _____

i. _____

j. _____

k. _____

l. _____

m. _____

n. _____

o. _____

2. Label the structures of the kidney shown in the following figure.

a. _____

b. _____

c. _____

d. _____

e. _____

f. _____

g. _____

h. _____

i. _____

j. _____

3. Urine is formed after three separate processes occur in the kidney. What are they, and in which anatomic structures of the kidney do they occur?

_____

_____

_____

_____

4. Requesting a urine specimen make create an embarrassing moment for the patient. How can the medical assistant make this request without causing the patient undue discomfort?

_____

_____

_____

5. List and describe six different methods of collecting a urine specimen.

a. _____

_____

b. _____

_____

c. _____

_____

d. _____

_____

e. _____

_____

f. _____

_____

6. Why must a sterile container be used if a urine culture is ordered?

_____

7. Explain the five components of the physical examination of urine.

a. _____

b. _____

c. _____

d. _____

e. _____

8. Explain the eight chemical components of urine.

a. _____

b. _____

c. _____

d. _____

e. _____

f. _____

g. _____

h. _____

9. Microscopic examination of urine sediment includes evaluating casts, cells, crystals, and miscellaneous findings. Summarize each.

_____

_____

_____

_____

_____

10. Summarize the terminology and number system used to report the microscopic examination of a urine sample.

_____

_____

_____

_____

_____

_____

_____

_____

_____

11. Explain how urine samples are used to screen for bladder cancer.

_____

_____

_____

CASE STUDIES

1. A patient brings a urine sample to the office in an old "pill bottle." Should Rosa, the medical assistant, accept the urine sample for testing? Why or why not? What patient education guidelines for collecting a urine sample at home should Rosa provide this patient?

_____

_____

_____

_____

_____

2. One of Rosa's duties is to perform urine drug testing in the office. How may urine be altered to affect the results of the drug test? What can Rosa do to prevent this from happening?

_____

_____

_____

_____

_____

WORKPLACE APPLICATION OPTIONS

Complete one or more of these activities and, if appropriate, share your results with the class.

1. You are performing a microscopic examination of urine, and you notice the blood cells shown in the following figure. What type are they?

a. _____

b. _____

2. You are performing a microscopic examination of urine, and you notice the pathogens shown in the following figure. What type are they?

A

B

C

a. _____

b. _____

c. _____

3. Dr. Hill has ordered both a UA and C&S. Which test should Rosa perform first? Why?

_____

_____

4. You are responsible for collecting urine samples from patients, handling them properly, and preparing them for transport to a reference laboratory. How should you perform these procedures?

_____

_____

_____

5. Explain how to perform a specific gravity determination in the physician's office setting.

_____

_____

_____

_____

6. Rosa is responsible for orienting a new employee to drug testing and chain of custody procedures in Dr. Hill's office. Summarize these guidelines.

_____

_____

_____

_____

_____

_____

_____

_____

_____

INTERNET ACTIVITY OPTIONS

Complete one or more of these activities and, if appropriate, share your results with the class.

1. Search the Internet for different types of home pregnancy tests. How are they similar? How do they differ? How do these tests work, and what hormone are these tests detecting in the body? When should the patient seek a physician's advice when performing these tests? Prepare to discuss your findings in class.

2. Investigate toxicology screening at the National Institutes of Health Medline Plus site at www.nlm.nih.gov/medlineplus/ency/article/003578.htm. Would this be a helpful resource for medical practices that perform urine toxicology screenings? Summarize what you have learned.

MEDICAL RECORD ACTIVITIES

1. Dr. Hill has asked Rosa to obtain a clean-catch urine sample from a patient. What instructions should Rosa provide the patient? Document the case.

_____

_____

_____

_____

_____

2. Dr. Hill has asked Rosa to instruct a patient on the collection of a 24-hour urine sample. What should Rosa include in the patient teaching intervention? Document the case.

_____

_____

_____

_____

_____

53 Assisting in Phlebotomy

VOCABULARY REVIEW

Fill in the blanks with the correct terms.

1. A blood draw that is ordered to be done immediately is a(n) _____ order.

2. A laboratory paper used to collect a blood sample from newborns is a(n) _____.

3. _____ is the liquid portion of whole blood that remains after the blood has clotted.

4. _____ is the liquid portion of whole blood that contains active clotting agents.

5. _____ is a situation in which the concentration of blood cells is increased in proportion to the plasma.

6. _____ refers to fainting.

7. _____ is the destruction or dissolution of red blood cells, with a subsequent release of hemoglobin.

8. _____ is a material that appears to be a solid until subjected to a disturbance, such as centrifugation, at which point it becomes a liquid.

9. _____ is an agent that inhibits bacterial growth and can be used on human tissue.

SKILLS AND CONCEPTS

1. On the following figure, identify the parts of a Vacutainer (evacuated tube) system.

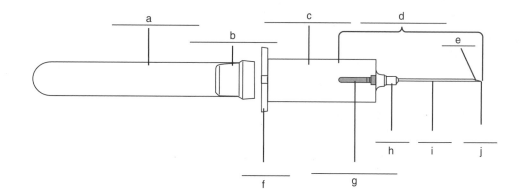

a. _____	f. _____
b. _____	g. _____
c. _____	h. _____
d. _____	i. _____
e. _____	j. _____

2. On the following figure, label the veins used for venipuncture.

3. Capillary puncture may be warranted in:

a. _____

b. _____

c. _____

d. _____

e. _____

f. _____

g. _____

Fill in the blanks.

4. _____ tubes, also known as *microhematocrit tubes,* are small glass or plastic tubes, open at each end, that will hold a volume of 75 L.

5. Microcollection, or _____, tubes hold up to 750 L of blood and are available with a variety of anticoagulants and additives.

6. For children younger than 1 year, dermal puncture is performed on the medial and lateral surfaces of the _____ surface of the heel.

7. The most commonly used skin preparation is _____%, also known as *rubbing alcohol.*

8. If a blood culture is ordered, additional preparation is needed at the venipuncture site to eliminate contaminating bacteria.

9. _____-iodine solution (_____) is commonly used.

Which needle gauge should be used in the following situations?

10. A blood bank typically uses _____-gauge needles to prevent hemolysis.

11. _____-gauge needles are used to collect samples from fragile or small veins.

12. Routine adult venipuncture requires a _____-gauge needle.

464

13. List three causes of a hematoma.

a. _____

b. _____

c. _____

14. Describe the steps involved in performing a venipuncture.

_____

_____

_____

15. Performing phlebotomy procedures on children can be challenging. Complete the following table by providing actions that may make the procedure less traumatic.

Age	Typical Mental State	Suggested Parental Involvement
Newborns (0-12 months)	Trust that adults will respond to their needs	
Infants and toddlers (1-3 years)	Minimal fear of danger but fear of separation; limited language and understanding of procedure	
Preschoolers (3-6 years)	Fearful of injury to body; still dependent on parent	
School-aged children (7-12 years)	Less dependent on parent and more willing to cooperate	
Teenagers (13-18 years)	Fully engaged in the process; embarrassed to show fear and may exhibit hostility to cover emotions	

16. Hemolysis of a blood sample usually requires a repeat blood draw. Complete the following table by explaining how to prevent hemolysis when performing phlebotomy.

Cause of Hemolysis	Explanation	Prevention
Alcohol preparation	Transfer of alcohol into the specimen causes hemolysis.	
Incorrect needle size	A high-gauge needle causes the blood to be forced through a small lumen with great force, shearing the cell membranes; a very low-gauge needle allows a large amount of blood to suddenly enter the tube with great force, causing frothing.	
Loose connections on the vacuum tube assembly	If the connection between the needle holder and the double-pointed needle or the syringe and needle is loose, air can enter the sample and cause frothing.	
Removing the needle from the vein with the tube intact	The remaining vacuum in the tube can cause air to be drawn forcefully into the tube.	
Underfilled tubes	Underfilling tubes leads to an improper blood to additive ratio.	
Syringe collections	Pulling back forcibly on the plunger draws blood too quickly through the needle, shearing cell membranes; transferring blood into a vacuum tube further traumatizes red blood cells.	
Mixing tubes too vigorously	All tubes except the red-stoppered tube must be mixed.	

Continued

465

Cause of Hemolysis	Explanation	Prevention
Temperature and transport problems	Trauma and temperature extremes can damage cells.	
Separation of plasma or serum from red cells	Removing the serum or plasma from the cells minimizes the risk of contaminating the specimen with red cell contents.	
Prolonged tourniquet time	While the tourniquet restricts blood flow, interstitial fluid can leak into the veins and hemolyze red cells.	
Poor collection; blood flowing too slowly into the tube	The lumen of the needle may be blocked.	

17. Complete the following table by providing strategies to prevent or manage possible complications from a phlebotomy procedure.

Possible Complication	Strategies
Burned area	
Convulsions	
Damaged or scarred veins or infected areas	
Edema	
Hematoma	
Intravenous (IV) therapy or blood transfusion sites	
Mastectomy	
Nausea	
No blood	
Petechiae	
Syncope	

18. The medical assistant must know which tube top color to use when drawing blood samples. Complete the following table to identify additives and their functions and the laboratory uses for each type of tube.

Vacutainer Color	Additive and Its Function	Laboratory Use
Yellow		
Red		
Red-gray (marbled)		
Light blue		
Green		
Green-gray (marbled)		
Yellow-gray (marbled)		
Lavender		
Gray		
Royal blue		

CASE STUDIES

1. Leah, the medical assistant, is gathering supplies for venipuncture. Explain to the patient why a tourniquet is necessary. Describe the proper way to apply a tourniquet. List three consequences of improper application.

2. As Leah is demonstrating a capillary puncture, the patient states, "I'm not a good bleeder; it may not be wise to waste the first drop of blood." Explain to the patient why the first drop of blood is wiped away.

3. One of Leah's co-workers has just experienced a needle stick. What instruction should Leah provide about care of the exposure site?

4. Leah is preparing a requisition for a patient's laboratory work. What information should be included on the requisition?

5. While Leah is performing venipuncture, she notices that the patient is becoming pale, is sweating, and is not conversing. What steps should be taken for patients who faint during venipuncture?

Complete one or more of these activities and, if appropriate, share your results with the class.

1. The medical assistant must be able to recognize equipment and supplies used for phlebotomy. Identify the venipuncture supplies shown in the figure.

a. _____

b. _____

c. _____

d. _____

e. _____

f. _____

g. _____

Chapter **53** **Assisting in Phlebotomy**

h. _____

i. _____

j. _____

k. _____

l. _____

m. _____

n. _____

2. List seven reasons the laboratory may reject a specimen.

a. _____

b. _____

c. _____

d. _____

e. _____

f. _____

g. _____

3. The National Committee for Clinical Laboratory Standards has developed a set of standards outlining the order of draw for a multitube draw. The same order applies to the filling of tubes when the blood is collected in a syringe. A mnemonic device that is useful for remembering the order of the draw is STOP, RED LIGHT, GREEN LIGHT, READY, GO. Use the mnemonic device and fill in the blanks.

a. _____ tubes are collected first, because they are sterile.

b. _____-topped tubes are collected second, because they have no additive and therefore nothing to transfer to another tube.

c. _____ blue-topped tubes are next, because other anticoagulants might contaminate the sample collected for coagulation studies.

d. _____-topped tubes are next, because heparin is less likely to interfere with EDTA than vice versa.

e. _____-topped tubes follow. EDTA binds with calcium, so this tube is drawn near the end.

f. _____-_____ marble-topped tubes are next. They contain a clot activator that could interfere with specimens if passed into another tube.

g. The _____-topped tube is last because the contents can elevate electrolyte levels or damage cells if passed into another tube.

4. Leah is attending a conference on needle-stick prevention. List some of the ways accidental needle sticks can be prevented.

_____

_____

_____

5. Develop an exposure control plan for the office to follow in case of accidental needle sticks. What should be included?

_____

_____

_____

6. Leah has just received a shipment of winged infusion sets (butterfly needles). When might Leah choose this equipment? When would Leah *not* want to choose a butterfly needle?

_____

_____

_____

7. Leah is responsible for orienting a new employee on the significance of filling collection tubes adequately. Why is this an important part of phlebotomy technique? Complete the following table that describes the effects of underfilling collection tubes.

Stopper Color	Effect
Yellow	
Red	
Red-gray	
Light blue	
Green	
Green-gray	
Lavender	
Yellow-gray	
Gray	
Royal blue	

INTERNET ACTIVITY OPTION

Complete this activity and, if appropriate, share your results with the class.

Leah is in charge of ordering phlebotomy needles with sharps injury protection devices. Search the Internet for the different types of safety needles. Print out some of the various examples and compare them. Which type do you like the best? Why is it so important to implement the use of safety needles?

MEDICAL RECORD ACTIVITIES

1. You are ordered to collect a complete blood count (CBC) and H&H on Viola Mullen because of suspected anemia. Ms. Mullen has a history of being a difficult stick. After you apply the tourniquet, she complains of feeling dizzy. Document the procedure in the patient's medical record.

_____

_____

_____

2. You are ordered to collect a blood sample from Mrs. Antonia Hall, an elderly frail woman 87 years of age. What would be the best method for collecting this blood sample? Document the procedure in the patient's medical record.

_____

_____

_____

3. The physician orders a capillary stick on an 18-year-old patient in the office today for a football physical. The patient tells you he gets sick when he sees needles. How would you manage this procedure? Document the blood draw in the patient's medical record.

_____

_____

_____

VOCABULARY REVIEW

Match the following terms with their definitions.

_____ 1. A condition marked by deficiency of red blood cells (RBCs)

_____ 2. An apparatus consisting essentially of a compartment spun about a central axis to separate contained materials of different specific gravities or to separate colloidal particles suspended in a liquid

_____ 3. Any of several complex proteins produced by cells that act as catalysts in specific biochemical reactions

_____ 4. A substance, usually a peptide or steroid, produced by one tissue and conveyed by the bloodstream to another to effect physiologic activity, such as growth or metabolism

_____ 5. A substance produced by metabolism

_____ 6. An increase in the number of normal white blood cells (WBCs)

_____ 7. A condition marked by an abnormally large number of RBCs in the circulatory system

_____ 8. An abnormal condition of pregnancy characterized by hypertension, edema, and protein in the urine

_____ 9. Tests performed to assess the compatibility of blood to be transfused

_____ 10. The major nitrogenous end product of protein metabolism and the chief nitrogenous component of the urine

_____ 11. An enzyme that catalyzes the hydrolysis of urea to form ammonium carbonate

_____ 12. The layer of white cells or platelets found between the plasma and the packed RBCs after whole blood is centrifuged

_____ 13. Structures or features not normally present but visible as a result of an external agent or action, such as in a microscopic specimen after fixation

a. Anemia

b. Enzyme

c. Urea

d. Hormone

e. Polycythemia vera

f. Toxemia

g. Metabolite

h. Leukocytosis

i. Centrifuge

j. Urease

k. Type and cross-match

l. Buffy coat

m. Artifacts

SKILLS AND CONCEPTS

1. List the main functions of blood.

   a. _____

   b. _____

   c. _____

2. Describe the role of hematology in patient care.

   _____

   _____

   _____

3. Identify the blood cells in the following illustration.

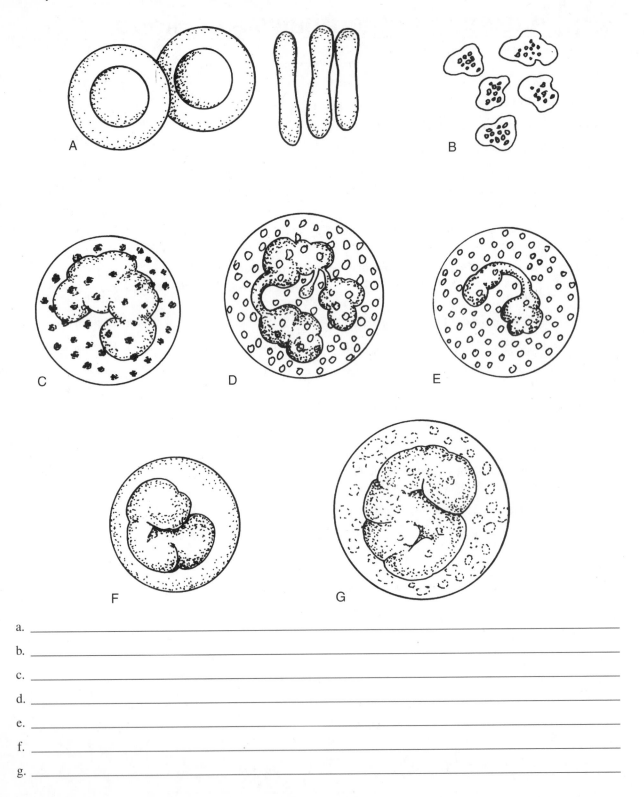

a. _____

b. _____

c. _____

d. _____

e. _____

f. _____

g. _____

Fill in the blanks.

4. Whole blood is composed of formed elements suspended in a clear, yellow liquid portion called _____. It makes up approximately 55% of the blood by volume. The remaining 45% consists of the formed cellular elements, which are the _____ (red blood cells), _____ (white blood cells), and _____ (platelets).

5. _____ on the RBC carries oxygen throughout the body.

6. The life span of an erythrocyte is about _____ days, and once matured an erythrocyte has a _____ shape.

7. The granular leukocytes are called *polymorphonuclear leukocytes* and include the _____, _____, and _____.

8. The agranular leukocytes are the _____ and _____, both of which have clear cytoplasm and a solid nucleus.

9. The purpose of the _____ cell count is to analyze and quantitate the types of WBCs found in a sample of blood.

10. Explain the function of the following WBCs.

   Neutrophils _____

   Bands _____

   Eosinophils _____

   Basophils _____

   Lymphocytes _____

   Monocytes _____

11. Explain the characteristics of a good wedge smear and how it should be dried.

   _____

   _____

   _____

12. What are the normal ranges for an adult differential?

   _____

   _____

   _____

13. Explain the characteristics of red blood cell morphology:

   _____

   _____

   _____

14. What factors might affect an ESR result?

_____

_____

_____

15. _____ are the smallest formed elements of the blood.

16. The platelets produce a substance that combines with _____ ions in the blood, which in turn converts the protein into thrombin in a complex series of reactions. Thrombin, an enzyme, converts fibrinogen, a protein substance, into

_____, an insoluble protein that forms an intricate network of minute threadlike structures called *fibrils* and causes the blood plasma to gel.

17. The _____ test is used to monitor the condition of patients taking warfarin (Coumadin).

18. Explain the relationship between the PT test and INR levels when following a patient on anticoagulant therapy. What is considered a therapeutic INR level?

_____

_____

_____

19. Vacutainer tubes containing _____ are used for hematology testing. Why?

_____

_____

Match the following T cells with their function.

a. Cytotoxic or killer T cells

b. Helper T cells

c. Suppressor T cells

d. Memory T cells

e. Natural killer cells

20. _____ Respond quickly to the presentation of the same antigen at a later date; have a long life span

21. _____ Most numerous type of T cell; stimulate the activity of other T cells

22. _____ Kill foreign, virus-infected, and tumor cells; produce proteins called *perforins* that induce cell death by punching holes in the cell membrane

23. _____ Inhibit the activity of other T cells

24. _____ Cells infected with viruses and tumor cells without prior sensitization

Fill in the blanks.

25. B cells are formed in the _____.

26. When stimulated, B cells differentiate into _____, which produce specific antibodies against an antigen.

27. Antibodies are protein molecules that attach to _____.

28. Destroying pathogens requires three specific steps: _____, _____, and _____.

476

29. List and describe five commonly used blood chemistry tests.

a. _____

_____

b. _____

_____

c. _____

_____

d. _____

_____

e. _____

_____

30. Explain how HbA_{1c} tests are used to manage diabetes mellitus.

_____

_____

_____

31. Complete the following table with the correct reference ranges for a complete blood count (CBC).

Test	Neonates	Infants (6 months)	Children	Men	Women
RBCs	4.8-7.1 million/mm³	3.8-5.5 million/mm³	4.5-4.8 million/mm³		
Hematocrit (Hct)		30%-40%	35%-41%		
Hemoglobin (Hgb)	17-23 g/dL		11-16 g/dL		
WBCs	9,000-30,000/mm³				
WBC Differential					
Neutrophils	≥45% by 1 week of age	32%			
Bands	—	—	—		
Eosinophils	—	—	0-3%		
Basophils	—	—	1-3%		
Monocytes	—	—	4-9%		
Lymphocytes	≥41% by age 1 week	61%	59% for children 2 years or older		
Platelets		200,000-473,000/mm³	150,000-450,000/mm³		

32. What is the corresponding blood glucose level for the HbA$_{1c}$ levels in the following table?

Glycosylated Hemoglobin (percentage)	Blood Glucose (mg/dL)
14	
13	
12	
11	
10	
9	
8	
7	
6	

CASE STUDIES

1. Dana, the medical assistant, is to perform a microhematocrit procedure on a patient. Explain to the patient the purpose of the microhematocrit and how the procedure will be done. What are the normal values for both men and women? What might a low hematocrit level indicate? What might a high hematocrit level indicate?

_____

_____

_____

2. Dana is drawing blood for an ESR determination on a patient. Define the ESR. What type of conditions can the test indicate? As Dana performs the ESR test, what factor should she be aware of as a source of error?

_____

_____

_____

3. One of the patients in the office has just discovered she is pregnant. Because she is Rh negative, she is concerned about the welfare of her baby. How will she be managed to prevent any risk to the fetus?

_____

_____

_____

4. Gus Langton, age 54, is scheduled for cholesterol screening. Mr. Langton has a family history of hypercholesterolemia and is confused about the importance of high-density lipoprotein (HDL) and low-density lipoprotein (LDL) levels. Explain their significance to Mr. Langton.

_____

_____

_____

WORKPLACE APPLICATION OPTIONS

Complete one or more of these activities and, if appropriate, share your results with the class.

1. The hemacytometer in the office recently was replaced by an automated blood cell counting machine. Explain the principle behind automated blood cell counting.

_____

_____

_____

2. Blood chemistry tests are frequently ordered to confirm a diagnosis or to follow up on patient status. The following table lists a number of commonly ordered chemistry tests. Complete the description and list purpose of each.

Test	Abbreviation	Description	Purpose
Alanine aminotransferase	ALT (SGPT)		
Albumin			
Alkaline phosphatase	ALP		
Aspartate aminotransferase	AST (SGOT)		
Blood urea nitrogen	BUN		
Calcium	CA		
Chloride	Cl		
Cholesterol	CH, Chol		
Creatinine	creat		
Gamma glutamyltransferase	GGT		
Glucose fasting blood sugar	FBS		
Glucose tolerance test	GTT		
Iron	Fe		
Lactate dehydrogenase	LDH		
Troponin I and T			
Thyroid-stimulating hormone (thyrotropin)	TSH		
Thyroxine	T_4		
Triglycerides	Trig		

3. Blood grouping is extremely specific to prevent agglutination. Dana must be prepared to explain the different blood types to her patients. Answer the following questions about blood grouping and the Rh factor.

a. The universal donor is _____.

b. The universal recipient is _____.

c. A patient who is type AB+ may receive _____ blood type.

d. A patient who is type B– may receive _____ blood type.

e. A patient who is O+ may receive _____ blood type.

INTERNET ACTIVITY OPTIONS

Complete one or more of these activities and, if appropriate, share your results with the class.

1. Blood donation is extremely important. Search the Internet for locations in your area to donate blood. Are there opportunities to volunteer your services? If so, what types of duties can volunteers provide?

2. Research online the most recent developments in HbA_{1c}. What equipment is available to perform this important test and how is it used?

MEDICAL RECORDS ACTIVITIES

1. You are reporting test results to a patient. The patient's hemoglobin level is 15 g/dL. Explain to the patient the role of hemoglobin in the body and what the level indicates. What factors can cause the level to vary? Document the patient teaching intervention.

   _____

   _____

   _____

2. The physician has ordered a CBC and differential for a patient. Explain to the patient the different tests included in the CBC. Why might the physician have ordered the differential? Document the patient interaction.

   _____

   _____

   _____

55 Assisting in Microbiology and Immunology

Fill in the blanks with the correct terms.

1. _____ Pertaining to or originating in the hospital; said of an infection not present or incubating before admission to the hospital

2. _____ An agent that causes disease, especially a living microorganism such as a bacterium or fungus

3. _____ A bacterial or fungal culture that contains a single organism

4. _____ A differentiated structure within a cell, such as a mitochondrion, vacuole, or chloroplast, which performs a specific function

5. _____ One billionth ($1/10^{-9}$) of a meter

6. _____ An organism of microscopic or submicroscopic size

7. _____ A single-celled or multicellular organism in which each cell contains a distinct, membrane-bound nucleus

8. _____ Requiring specialized media or growth factors to grow

9. _____ A small capsulelike sac that encloses certain organisms in their dormant or larval stage

10. _____ A sample, as of tissue, blood, or urine, used for analysis and diagnosis

11. _____ A unicellular organism that lacks a membrane-bound nucleus

12. _____ A drug used to treat a broad range of infections

13. _____ Refers to conditions outside a living body

14. _____ The process of removing pathogenic microorganisms or protecting against infection by such organisms

15. _____ The molecules needed for metabolism: carbohydrates, lipids, proteins, and nucleic acids

16. _____ The technique or process of keeping tissue alive and growing in a culture medium

17. _____ A drug used to treat infection

18. _____ A group of like or different atoms held together by chemical forces

19. _____ A medium used to keep an organism alive during transport to the laboratory

20. _____ Capable of living, developing, or germinating under favorable conditions

21. _____ A slide preparation in which a drop of liquid specimen or the like is covered with a coverslip and examined with a microscope

22. _____ A chemical released from cells that causes smooth muscle contraction and pain

23. _____ Glycoproteins produced by cells infected with a virus or another intracellular parasite that can be used medically as antiviral or anticancer therapeutics

24. _____ A protein produced by certain white blood cells that regulates immune responses by activating lymphocytes and initiating fever

25. _____ Cloudiness of a liquid, caused by the presence of suspended particles, which increases with the concentration of particles

26. _____ A category of microorganisms below genus in rank; a genetically distinct group

27. _____ Microbes that live on or in the body that perform vital functions and protect the body against infection

28. _____ A breakdown of a family of microorganisms

SKILLS AND CONCEPTS

1. Identify the three shapes of bacteria shown in the figure.

a. _____

b. _____

c. _____

2. Describe the four different classifications of media.

   a. All-purpose or nutritive _____

   b. Selective _____

   c. Differential _____

   d. Enriched _____

3. Draw the pattern you should make when you prepare a *Streptococcus pyogenes* culture on an agar plate.

4. Compare and contrast the throat culture for *Streptococcus pyogenes* with the rapid strep test.

   _____

   _____

   _____

5. Each colony that grows on a urine culture plate represents _____.

6. Explain how to inoculate a plate for a urine culture.

   _____

   _____

   _____

7. How is a screening urine culture test performed in the physician office laboratory?

   _____

   _____

   _____

8. The acid-fast stain is used in the identification protocol for _____.

9. Explain the methods for performing HIV screening.

_____

_____

_____

10. Describe the characteristics of each of the following:

a. Viruses:_____

_____

b. Bacteria: _____

_____

c. Rickettsiae: _____

_____

d. Chlamydiae: _____

_____

e. Mycoplasma: _____

_____

f. Fungi: _____

_____

g. Helminths: _____

_____

h. Protozoa: _____

_____

11. The medical assistant is responsible for collecting specimens from patients and preparing them properly for transport. Complete the following table with the missing information.

Specimen	Container	Patient Preparation	Storage Before Processing
Blood		Disinfect venipuncture site with alcohol swab and Betadine	
Stool	Clean, leakproof container		
Sputum	Sterile, screw-cap container		
Throat	Transport swab		
Ova and parasite (O&P)	O&P transport device (with formalin and PVA)		
Urine	Sterile, screw-cap container		
Superficial wound			Transport and plate within 24 hours; room temperature storage
Deep wound or abscess		Wipe area with sterile saline or alcohol prep pad before collection	

12. Provide the missing information in the following tables.

Common diseases caused by viruses

Disease	Virus	Transmission	Symptoms	Prevention
Infectious mononucleosis				Avoid direct contact with affected individuals
Influenza	Myxovirus (influenza A and B)		Fever, body aches, cough	
Rabies	Rhabdovirus			Vaccine available; have pets vaccinated
Common cold			Headache, fever, runny nose, congestion	Good hygiene (hand washing)

Common diseases caused by bacilli

Disease	Organism	Transmission	Symptoms	Tests and Specimens
Tuberculosis		**Inhalation**		
Urinary tract infections	*Escherichia coli, Proteus* sp. *Klebsiella* sp., *Pseudomonas aeruginosa*		*Cystitis:* Frequency, burning bloody urine *Pyelonephritis:* Flank pain, fever	
Legionnaires' disease	*Legionella pneumophila*			Sputum; blood
Tetanus (lockjaw)			Toxin affects motor nerves; muscle spasms, convulsions, rigidity	
Botulism	*Clostridium botulinum*		Neurotoxin affects speech, swallowing, vision; paralysis of respiratory muscles, death	
Whooping cough	*Bordetella pertussis*			Swabs for culture
Plague	*Yersinia pestis*		Fever, chills, delirium; enlarged, painful lymph nodes	

Common diseases caused by cocci

Disease	Organism	Transmission	Symptoms	Tests and Specimens
Pneumonia	*Streptococcus pneumoniae*		Productive cough, fever, chest pain	
Strep throat		Direct contact, droplets, fomites		
Wound infection, abscesses, boils		Direct contact, fomites, carriers; poor hand washing		
Staphylococcal food poisoning		Poor hygiene and improper refrigeration of food	Vomiting, abdominal cramps, diarrhea	
Meningococcal meningitis		Respiratory tract secretions		

Common diseases caused by spirilla

Disease	Organism	Transmission	Symptoms	Tests and Specimens
Syphilis		Sexually; congenitally	*Primary:* Painless sore (chancre) *Secondary:* Generalized rash involving palms and soles of feet *Congenital:* Birth defects	
Lyme disease		Tick bite	Fever, joint pain, red bull's-eye rash	
Pyloric ulcers			Burning pain in stomach, especially between meals	

Diseases caused by rickettsiae, chlamydiae, and mycoplasmas

Disease	Organism	Transmission	Symptoms	Tests and Specimens
Rocky Mountain spotted fever	*Rickettsia rickettsii*		Headache, chills, fever, characteristic rash on extremities and trunk	
Typhus	*Rickettsia prowazekii*		Fever, rash, confusion	
Nongonococcal urethritis and vaginitis	*Chlamydia trachomatis*		May be asymptomatic	

Common diseases caused by fungi

Disease	Organism	Predisposing Conditions and Transmission	Symptoms	Tests and Specimens
Thrush (oral yeast), vulvovaginal candidiasis, or monilia (vaginal yeast)		*Oral:* During birth		
Other: After antibiotic therapy; with oral birth control, severe diabetes				
Athlete's foot, jock itch, ringworm (tinea)	*Trichophyton* sp., *Microsporum* sp., and others (skin fungi)		Hair loss; thickening of skin and nails; itching; red, scaly patches	
Histoplasmosis	*Histoplasma capsulatum*		Mild, flulike or systemic	
Pneumocystis pneumonia			Pneumonia-like	

Common protozoal and parasitic diseases

Disease	Organism	Transmission	Symptoms	Tests and Specimens
Malaria	*Plasmodium* species (protozoa)		Chills, fever (cyclic)	
Toxoplasmosis	*Toxoplasma gondii* (protozoa)		Febrile illness, rash;	
Congenital: Jaundice, enlarged liver and spleen, brain abnormalities				
Amebic dysentery	*Entamoeba histolytica* (protozoa)		Bloody diarrhea, cramping, fever	
Giardiasis			Asymptomatic to severe diarrhea and abdominal discomfort	
Trichinosis	*Trichinella spiralis* (roundworm)		Nausea, fever, diarrhea, muscle pain and swelling, edema of the face	
Tapeworm	*Taenia* species		Abdominal discomfort, diarrhea, weight loss	
Pinworm	*Enterobius vermicularis* (roundworm)		Severe rectal itching, restlessness, insomnia	
Scabies			Nocturnal itching, skin burrows	
Lice			Intense itching, skin lesions	

1. A patient has been instructed to provide a stool sample. What type of patient education should be included to ensure proper collection?

_____

_____

_____

2. Anna, the medical assistant, works in an office in which some rapid testing is performed. Describe three microbiology tests that use a rapid identification technique.

   a. _____

   b. _____

   c. _____

3. A 5-year-old patient is brought to the office with pinworms. How do people usually become infested with pinworms? Provide the patient education for specimen collection.

_____

_____

_____

4. Anna is educating a patient on the importance of infection control. What factors should Anna be sure to cover?

_____

_____

_____

WORKPLACE APPLICATION OPTIONS

Complete one or more of these activities and, if appropriate, share your results with the class.

1. Anna is preparing to obtain a sample for testing. What should she keep in mind as she is collecting the specimen? The specimen is an anaerobe. What elements are required for growth?

_____

_____

_____

2. Describe the equipment you would find in the physician microbiology laboratory.

_____

_____

_____

3. What steps should Anna follow while performing a rapid strep test?

_____

_____

_____

4. List and describe the three CLIA-waived immunology tests that Anna may perform in the POL.

_____

_____

_____

5. You are responsible for making sure that a new employee is performing a mono-test correctly. Explain how the procedure should be performed.

_____

_____

_____

INTERNET ACTIVITY OPTION

Complete this activity and, if appropriate, share your results with the class.

Go to the American Biological Safety Association site at www.absa.org. Become familiar with the site. What tools does the site have to help you maintain a safe laboratory environment?

56 Surgical Supplies and Instruments

VOCABULARY REVIEW

Fill in the blanks with the appropriate terms.

1. _____ The act of scraping a body cavity with a surgical instrument, such as a curette.

2. _____ Opening or widening the circumference of a body orifice with a dilating instrument.

3. _____ A sheet or band of fibrous tissue deep in the skin that covers muscles and body organs.

4. _____ An abnormal, tubelike passage between internal organs or from an internal organ to the body surface.

5. _____ Open space, such as within a blood vessel, the intestine, a needle, or an examining instrument.

6. _____ A rigid tube that surrounds a blunt trocar or a sharp, pointed trocar inserted into the body; when withdrawn, fluid may escape from the body through it, depending on where it is inserted.

7. _____ A metal rod with a smooth, rounded tip that is placed into hollow instruments to minimize the damage to body tissues during insertion.

8. _____ A localized collection of pus, under the skin or deep within the body, that causes tissue destruction.

9. _____ Open condition of a body cavity or canal.

10. _____ Tumors with stems, frequently found on mucous membranes.

11. _____ A metal probe that is inserted into or passed through a catheter, needle, or tube to clear it or to facilitate passage into a body orifice.

12. _____ To cut or separate tissue with a cutting instrument or scissors.

13. The Schroeder uterine vulsellum forceps are used to lift the cervix to view the _____.

14. _____ are self-adhesive tapes that are placed over the wound, pulling the wound edges together.

SKILLS AND CONCEPTS

1. List two medications that help control bleeding.

   a. _____

   b. _____

2. What is the purpose of combining epinephrine in a local anesthetic?

   _____

   _____

3. List four groups of surgical instruments and give an example of each.

a. _____

b. _____

c. _____

d. _____

Name the instruments pictured in the following figures.

4.

_____

5.

_____

6.

7.

8.

9.

10.

11.

12.

13.

14.

_____

15.

_____

Indicate which statements are true (T) and which are false (F).

16. _____ An instrument should always be unlocked before immersion in a chemical decontaminate to permit cleansing of the entire surface area.

17. _____ Instruments are always named after the person who designed them.

18. _____ Scissors have ratchets.

19. _____ "Mosquito" and "Kelly" are names of hemostats.

20. _____ All tissues removed from the patient are sent to the pathology laboratory for analysis.

21. _____ Topical silver nitrate solution is used to control epistaxis.

22. _____ Ratchets are located just below the ring handles and are used to lock an instrument into position.

497

Match the following descriptions and instruments.

a. Bayonet forceps

b. Towel forceps (towel clamp)

c. Littauer stitch or suture scissors

d. Needle holders

e. Splinter forceps

f. Nasal specula

g. Bandage scissors

h. Ear curette

23. _____ Have a beak or hook to slide under sutures

24. _____ Jaws are shorter and look stronger than hemostat jaws

25. _____ Design and construction vary; have a fine tip for foreign object retrieval

26. _____ Have very sharp hooks

27. _____ Valves can be spread to facilitate viewing

28. _____ Probe tip is blunt

29. _____ Smooth tipped, manufactured in different lengths, and used to insert packing into or remove objects from the nose and ear

30. _____ Stainless steel loop at the end; used to remove foreign matter from ear canals

31. Describe the characteristics of ideal suture material.

    a. _____

    b. _____

    c. _____

    d. _____

32. Explain the difference between absorbable and nonabsorbable sutures. When would each type of suture be used?

_____

_____

_____

33. Explain the purpose of four different types of additional surgical supplies that may be used in minor surgical procedures in the physician's office.

_____

_____

_____

34. Describe the method of identifying the gauge of suture material.

_____

_____

_____

35. Explain how surgical instruments are handled after a surgical procedure has been completed.

_____

_____

_____

36. Complete the following table, which describes the diameter of individual suture sizes.

Suture Size	Diameter
6-0	
5-0	
4-0	
3-0	
2-0	
0	
1	
2	

CASE STUDIES

1. You are assisting Dr. Samanski during a procedure. The physician has asked you to ensure three local anesthetics are available in the room. List them.

   a. _____

   b. _____

   c. _____

2. Tom, the medical assistant, is preparing an instrument and supply pack for a cervical biopsy. What instruments should be included for autoclaving?

   _____

   _____

   _____

WORKPLACE APPLICATION OPTIONS

Complete one or more of these activities and, if appropriate, share your results with the class.

1. Tom is in charge of establishing a room in the office for minor surgery. What features should be included in this room?

   _____

   _____

   _____

2. Tom is stocking the supplies in the surgery room. List four types of surgical solutions commonly used.

   _____

   _____

   _____

3. Tom is showing a new employee the various instruments in the office. What should Tom tell the new employee about the care and inspection of the instruments?

_____

_____

_____

INTERNET ACTIVITY OPTIONS

Complete one or more of these activities and, if appropriate, share your results with the class.

1. Search the Internet for surgical instruments. How expensive are they? Print out the descriptions of the instruments and bring them to class. Compare your findings with those of a classmate.

2. Research the use of surgical staples. What types of surgeries use staples to close a wound? How are they applied? How are they removed?

57 Surgical Asepsis and Assisting with Surgical Procedures

VOCABULARY REVIEW

Match the following terms with their definitions.

_____ 1. Invasion of body tissues by microorganisms, which proliferate and damage tissues   a. Permeable

_____ 2. Living organisms that can be seen only with a light microscope   b. Contamination

_____ 3. Disease-causing microorganisms   c. Disease

_____ 4. Allowing a substance to pass or soak through   d. Infection

_____ 5. Reducing the number of microorganisms to a relatively safe level   e. Antiseptic

_____ 6. A thick-walled, dormant form of bacteria resistant to disinfection measures   f. Edema

_____ 7. Complete destruction of all forms of microbial life   g. Spores

_____ 8. A substance that kills microorganisms   h. Pathogens

_____ 9. Becoming nonsterile by contact with any nonsterile material   i. Sterilization

_____ 10. A pathologic process having a descriptive set of signs and symptoms   j. Disinfection

_____ 11. Destruction of pathogens by physical or chemical means   k. Microorganisms

_____ 12. Swelling between layers of tissue   l. Sanitization

SKILLS AND CONCEPTS

1. Describe the differences among sanitization, disinfection, and sterilization and how each is performed.

_____

_____

_____

_____

_____

2. Describe the following types of sterilization indicators. Which is considered the best method for checking whether instrument packs are being sterilized when autoclaved?

    a. Chemical

_____

_____

    b. Biologic

_____

_____

3. The medical assistant is responsible for making sure no problems occur with autoclave procedures. Complete the following table, which outlines methods for improving autoclave techniques.

Problem	Causes	Corrective Measures
Damp linens		
Stained linens		
Corroded instruments		
Spotted or stained instruments		
Instruments that have soft hinges or joints		
Ebullition, or caps that blow off solutions		
Steam leakage		
Chamber door does not open		

4. Describe the following common surgical procedures done in the physician's office.

a. Cryosurgery

_____

_____

b. Microsurgery

_____

_____

c. Endoscopic procedures

_____

_____

d. Electrosurgery

_____

_____

e. Laser

_____

_____

5. Explain the importance of skin preparation and describe how it is done.

_____

_____

_____

Indicate which statements are true (T) and which are false (F).

6. _____ Air currents carry bacteria, so body motions over a sterile field and talking should be kept to a minimum.

7. _____ Infection can cause death in some circumstances.

8. _____ A sterile field can get wet but remain microorganism free.

9. _____ Sterile team members should always face each other.

10. _____ You should always keep the sterile field in your view.

11. _____ You should never turn your back on a sterile field or wander away from it.

12. _____ When autoclaving, you should place a gauze sponge around the tips of sharp instruments to prevent them from piercing the wrapping material.

13. _____ Nonsterile individuals should never reach over a sterile field.

14. _____ All hinged instruments are wrapped in the closed position to allow full steam penetration of the joint.

15. _____ When using sterilizing bags, you should insert the grasping end of the instruments first.

16. _____ The medical term for a permanent scar formation is called a cicatrix.

17. _____ When a surgical incision separates or ruptures at the wound edges it is called dehiscence.

Answer the following questions.

18. Describe the three phases of wound healing

    a. _____

    b. _____

    c. _____

19. Describe first and second intention healing and give an example of each.

_____

_____

_____

_____

20. What are the reasons for applying a sterile dressing?

    a. _____

    b. _____

    c. _____

    d. _____

21. What is the purpose of a bandage? Does it have to be sterile?

_____

_____

_____

22. Explain the difference between surgical and medical asepsis. When is each performed?

_____

_____

_____

_____

23. What is the shelf life of sterilized packs?

_____

_____

24. Summarize the steps that must be taken to prepare a patient for surgery in the physician office setting.

_____

_____

_____

_____

25. Describe how to perform skin prep before surgery.

_____

_____

_____

_____

CASE STUDIES

1. Melissa, the medical assistant, is preparing instruments for the autoclave. What rules must she follow when wrapping the instruments?

_____

_____

_____

_____

2. Minor surgical procedures, such as the removal of moles, are commonly done in Melissa's office. What is Melissa's role in these procedures?

_____

_____

_____

_____

3. Melissa is preparing a patient for a procedure, and the patient seems anxious and worried. What can Melissa do to support the patient?

_____

_____

_____

_____

WORKPLACE APPLICATION OPTIONS

Complete one or more of these activities and, if appropriate, share your results with the class.

1. One of Melissa's duties is maintaining the autoclave. What types of PPE should she wear when loading, operating, and unloading the autoclave? Why?

_____

_____

_____

_____

2. What guidelines should be followed when the autoclave is unloaded?

_____

_____

_____

_____

3. A patient is scheduled for a surgical procedure in the office. What details should Melissa attend to before the appointment?

_____

_____

_____

_____

4. The physician has ordered open wound healing for a patient with a traumatic injury. What does this mean? How does healing occur? What are some of the advantages of this type of healing process?

_____

_____

_____

_____

5. The office manager asks Melissa to observe a new employee while she performs a surgical hand scrub. Summarize the important steps to this procedure.

_____

_____

_____

_____

Complete this activity and, if appropriate, share your results with the class.

One of your duties is to purchase supplies for minor office procedures. Search the Internet for equipment and supplies typically needed to perform such procedures. Print a list of materials and prices. Share the information with your classmates. Did you find anything surprising?

MEDICAL RECORDS ACTIVITIES

1. After a surgical procedure, the medical assistant should provide the patient with postoperative instructions. Give five reasons a patient should call the office after a procedure, and document the patient instructions.

   a. _____

   b. _____

   c. _____

   d. _____

   e. _____

2. A patient comes to the office for suture removal. The area, the left forearm, is covered with bandages. How should the patient be prepared for the procedure? What setup is required for this procedure? Document the case, including the patient's vital signs.

   _____

   _____

   _____

   _____

3. Ms. Maria Idione was seen today for removal of a cyst from her left forearm. The physician asks you to reinforce patient education about the healing process. Document your interaction with Ms. Idione, including the factors that may affect healing and indicators of wound infection.

   _____

   _____

   _____

   _____

58 Career Development and Life Skills

VOCABULARY REVIEW

Fill in the blanks with the correct vocabulary terms from this chapter.

1. Jerri wrote a(n) _____ of the facts that she knew related to the theft of petty cash.

2. June found Daniel's attitude to be _____ and finally made a complaint to the office manager.

3. Because Allen was continuing his studies at night and was taking 12 credit hours, he was able to place his student loan in _____.

4. Medical assisting is one of the most versatile _____ a person can enter.

5. The physician asked Merri to _____ the documents for grammar and spelling.

6. Andrea found that _____ provided her with many more job leads than simply looking in the newspaper.

7. Ms. Moore, the office manager, attempted to get the employees to bring up only the _____ facts related to the conflict.

8. Joel tried to _____ his error by placing an amendment in the medical record.

9. Dr. McDonald gave the information to Selinda to rewrite, because she could take the regulations and convert them into a(n) _____, clear document.

10. Mack called his lender to report that he had returned to school full-time so that he would not _____ on his loan.

SKILLS AND CONCEPTS

Part I: Short Answers

1. List three ways job search training helps the newly graduated medical assistant.

   a. _____

   b. _____

   c. _____

2. What are employers' three basic desires when looking for a new employee?

   a. _____

   b. _____

   c. _____

3. Define *job skills* and give two examples.

   _____

   _____

4. Define *self-management skills* and give two examples.

_____

_____

5. Define *transferable skills* and give two examples.

_____

_____

6. What is meant when it is said that a medical assistant knows his or her personal needs?

_____

_____

7. List and define the two best job search methods.

   a. _____

   b. _____

8. Explain at least three ways the Internet can be helpful in a job search.

   a. _____

   b. _____

   c. _____

9. List five items that should be included on a résumé.

   a. _____

   b. _____

   c. _____

   d. _____

   e. _____

10. List two items that should never be included on a résumé.

   a. _____

   b. _____

Part II: Cover Letters

Write a professional cover letter, following the suggestions in the textbook. Turn in the cover letter to the instructor, along with the assignment in Part III.

Part III: Job Applications

Complete the job application found on the following pages. Make sure it is legible, accurate, and complete.

DIAMONTE HOSPITAL

APPLICATION FOR EMPLOYMENT

This application is not a contract. It is intended to provide information for evaluating your suitability for employment. Please read each question carefully and give an honest and complete answer. Qualified applicants receive consideration for employment without unlawful discrimination because of sex, religion, race, color, national origin, age, disability, or other classification protected by law. Applications will remain active for three months.

PLEASE TYPE OR PRINT ALL INFORMATION

Date: _____

Position(s) applying for: _____

How did you learn about us? ☐ Walk-in ☐ Friend ☐ Relative ☐ Job hotline ☐ Employee ☐ Other
☐ Advertisement (Please state name of publication) _____ Referred by: _____

Name: _____
        Last   *First*   *Middle initial*

Mailing address: _____
         City   *State*   *Zip code*

Phone: (____) _____ (____) _____ Social Security #: _____
       Home   *Message*

If related to anyone in our employ, state name and department: _____

If you have been employed under another name, please list here: _____

Are you under 18 years of age? .... ☐ Yes ☐ No

Are you currently employed? .... ☐ Yes ☐ No

May we contact your present employer? .... ☐ Yes ☐ No

Do you have legal rights to work in this country?
(Proof of legal rights to work in this country will be required upon employment) ..... ☐ Yes ☐ No

Have you ever been employed with us before? .... ☐ Yes ☐ No *If "yes," give date(s):* _____

Are you available to work: .... ☐ Full-time ☐ Part-time ☐ Shift work ☐ Temporary

Are you available to work overtime if required? .... ☐ Yes ☐ No

How flexible are you in accepting varying scheduled hours? .... ☐ Very flexible ☐ Somewhat flexible
☐ Need set schedule

Minimum salary desired: _____

Have you ever been discharged from a job or forced to resign? .... ☐ Yes ☐ No
Explain: _____

Have you ever been convicted of a felony?
If "yes," please explain: .... ☐ Yes ☐ No
Criminal convictions are not an absolute bar to _____
employment but will be considered with respect _____
to the specific requirements of the job for which _____
you are applying. _____

EDUCATION

High school: _____ High school graduate/GED: ☐ Yes ☐ No
_____ Date: _____

College: _____ Graduated: ☐ Yes ☐ No

Major/field(s) of study: _____ Degree: _____

Date: _____

College: _____ Graduated: ☐ Yes ☐ No

Major/field(s) of study: _____ Degree: _____

Date: _____

Technical, business, or
correspondence school: _____ Graduated: ☐ Yes ☐ No

Major/field(s) of study: _____ Degree: _____

Date: _____

*Describe any specialized training, apprenticeship, and skills such as computer,
office equipment, etc.* _____
_____
_____
_____
_____

LICENSES AND CERTIFICATIONS

Type of license(s)/certification(s): _____ Expiration date: _____

Type of license(s)/certification(s): _____ Expiration date: _____

Type of license(s)/certification(s): _____ Expiration date: _____

Verified by: _____

Date: _____

REFERENCES

*(Give name, address, and telephone number of three references that you have known for at least one year who are not
related to you.)*

Name: _____ Phone: _____ Years acquainted: _____

Address: _____ Business: _____

Name: _____ Phone: _____ Years acquainted: _____

Address: _____ Business: _____

Name: _____ Phone: _____ Years acquainted: _____

Address: _____ Business: _____

EMPLOYMENT EXPERIENCE

(Please list all employment experience, with most recent employment first. If more space is needed, please use the Additional Employment form.)

Employer: _____   Duties and skills performed:_____

Address: _____   _____

Phone number(s) _____   _____

Job title: _____   _____

Supervisor's name/title: _____   _____

Reason for leaving: _____   _____

Salary received: _____ *hourly / weekly / monthly*   _____

Employed from: _____ to _____   _____
        month / year   *month / year*

Employer: _____   Duties and skills performed:_____

Address: _____   _____

Phone number(s) _____   _____

Job title: _____   _____

Supervisor's name/title: _____   _____

Reason for leaving: _____   _____

Salary received: _____ *hourly / weekly / monthly*   _____

Employed from: _____ to _____   _____
        month / year   *month / year*

Employer: _____   Duties and skills performed:_____

Address: _____   _____

Phone number(s) _____   _____

Job title: _____   _____

Supervisor's name/title: _____   _____

Reason for leaving: _____   _____

Salary received: _____ *hourly / weekly / monthly*   _____

Employed from: _____ to _____   _____
        month / year   *month / year*

Do you expect any of the employers listed above to give you a poor reference? ☐ Yes ☐ No

If yes, explain: _____

511

APPLICANT'S STATEMENT

I hereby certify that the statements and information provided are true, and I understand that any false statements or omissions are cause for termination. I agree to submit to a drug test and physical following any conditional offer of employment, and I grant permission to Diamonte Hospital to investigate my criminal history, education, prior employment history, and references, and hereby release all persons or agencies from all liability or any damage for issuing this information.

I understand that this application is current for only **three months**. At the end of that time, if I do not hear from Diamonte Hospital and still wish to be considered for employment, it will be necessary to update my application.

_____   _____
Signature of Applicant   *Date*

_____
Print Name

DIAMONTE
HOSPITAL

Chapter **58 Career Development and Life Skills**

Part IV: Résumés

Write a professional résumé, following the suggestions in the textbook. Turn in the résumé and cover letter to your instructor.

Part V: Interviews

1. Set up an interview with a physician's office. Perhaps the interview can lead to an externship or a position after graduation. Use the *Record of a Job Lead* form and the *Record of an Interview Form* to record pertinent information.

2. Set up mock interviews with classmates and instructors. Use a variety of instructors so that students are exposed to different individuals during the process. Videotape the interviews if possible, and review them in class, discussing positive and negative aspects of each student's interviewing technique. Suggest ways to improve the interviews. If time allows, repeat the activity and look for improvements.

Part VI: Follow-up Activities

Write a thank-you card to the person with whom you interviewed. If a job opportunity exists, continue follow-up activities with the clinic.

Part VII: Goals

1. Set some realistic goals for your career in medical assisting by answering the following questions.

    a. Where am I today?

    _____

    _____

    _____

    b. Where will I be in 5 years?

    _____

    _____

    _____

    c. Where will I be in 10 years?

    _____

    _____

    _____

    d. What additional skills do I need to get to where I want to be?

    _____

    _____

    _____

    _____

Part VIII: Budgeting

Plan a budget for yourself using your actual living expenses.

Part IX: Figuring Paychecks

Determine the final paycheck given the following information.

1. Robert makes a gross salary of $42,000 a year; $3,500 per month, and is paid once monthly. The following deductions come from his check each month:

    a. Medical/dental deduction: $254.32 per month

    b. Long/short-term disability: $25.75 per month

    c. Dependent life insurance: $9.34 per month

    d. Do not forget to deduct FICA/Medicare for the month.

    Robert's net paycheck amount: _____

2. Angela makes a gross salary of $53,230.00 a year; $4435.83 per month, and is paid twice monthly. The following deductions come from her check each month:

    a. Medical/dental deduction: $334.00 per month

    b. Long/short term disability: $36.00 per month

    c. Life insurance: $40.00 per month

    d. Retirement: $126.00 per month

    e. Do not forget to deduct FICA/Medicare for the month

Part X: E-Mail Address

Open an e-mail account that reflects a professional electronic address using a free service (e.g., Yahoo!, MSN, Hotmail). Make sure the e-mail address you choose is appropriate for professional résumés and job applications.

The Guideline Budget

MONTHLY INCOME	AMOUNT
Net Income	
Spouse Net Income	
Child Support	
Other Income	

MONTHLY EXPENSES	AMOUNT
Rent	
Gas	
Electric	
Home/Renters Insurance	
Water/Sewage	
Trash	
Home Telephone	
Cell Telephone	
Pager	
Cable TV/Satellite	
Internet/DSL	
Child Care	
Lawn Care	
Clothing	
Food-Home	
Food-Work or School	
Food-Eating Out	
Laundry/Dry Cleaning	
Medical Expenses	
Dental Expenses	
Life Insurance	
Medical Insurance	
Dental Insurance	
Eyeglasses	
Prescriptions	
Automobile Payment	
Automobile Insurance	
Repairs	
Gas/Oil	
Furniture	
Beauty/Barber Shop	
Pet Expenses	
Student Loan	
Other Loans	
Credit Cards	
Church/Charities	
Birthdays	
Anniversaries	
Christmas	
Vacation Planning	
Entertainment	

Monica was an exceptional student during school and graduated with a high grade point average. After a successful externship and 1 month looking for employment, she has been unable to secure a job. She calls the placement officer at her school, who sends her on several interviews, which are also unsuccessful. The placement officer asks Monica to come to the school dressed for an interview and to bring her résumé. The placement officer is impressed with Monica's appearance and her communications skills during the interview. However, when she looks down at Monica's résumé, she realizes why Monica has not been hired. What problem did the placement officer probably discover? What can Monica do to be more likely to secure employment?

WORKPLACE ACTIVITY OPTION

Complete this activity and, if appropriate, share your results with the class.

Make a list of 20 potential employers. Use the Internet to obtain information about the facilities. Make a list of five points about each potential employer that could be discussed in an interview. Also, find five ways you qualify for a position in the facility. If appropriate, visit the facilities and make appointments for interviews. Obtain and complete a job application from each facility. Submit the application and a résumé if you are close to the end of your training.

INTERNET ACTIVITIES

Complete one or more of these activities and, if appropriate, share your results with the class.

1. Research potential employers in your geographic area. Find out as much information about the employers as possible. Keep a record of the information using the job lead forms provided in the text.

2. Use the Internet to locate potential job opportunities. Have your résumé in electronic form ready to attach so that you can apply for the jobs that interest you.

3. Look for job search sites other than those in the textbook. Share the sites with your classmates.

4. Form a group on a social networking site, such as Facebook, that includes each classmate. Share e-mails and stay in touch with one another after graduation. Share leads that might result in employment.

5. Perform a job search for medical assisting positions in your area. Look for the 15 most interesting opportunities and print the job descriptions. Compare the job requirements to the skills you have learned. If appropriate, apply for the positions.

6. Investigate budgeting ideas by researching the Internet. Determine what items must be included in the budget and then list all the bills and payments that must be made each month. A budget template may be available on the Microsoft website and can be downloaded for use. Make the estimates as close as possible to your actual income and expenses. Turn the budget in to the instructor.

English-Spanish Terms for the Medical Assistant

abscess A localized collection of pus that causes tissue destruction and may be either under the skin or deep within the body.
absceso Cantidad de pus localizada en un lugar que puede estar bajo la piel o a más profundidad en el interior del cuerpo y causa la destrucción de los tejidos.

academic degree A title conferred by a college, university, or professional school after completion of a program of study.
grado académico Título concedido por una, universidad o escuela profesional, tras completar un programa de estudios.

accommodation Adjustment of the eye for seeing various sizes of objects at different distances.
acomodación Ajuste del ojo para ver distintos tamaños de objetos a distancias diferentes.

account A statement of transactions during a fiscal period and the resulting balance.
cuenta Estado de transacciones durante un periodo fiscal y el saldo resultante.

account balance The amount owed or on hand in an account.
saldo de la cuenta Suma que se debe o que está en una cuenta.

accounts receivable ledger A record of the income and payments due from creditors on an account.
libro mayor de cuentas por cobrar Registro de cargos y pagos asentados en una cuenta.

accreditation The process by which an organization is recognized for adhering to a group of standards that meet or exceed the expectations of the accrediting agency.
acreditación Proceso por el cual se reconoce a una organización por su cumplimiento de ciertos estándares en un grado que cumple o sobrepasa las expectativas de la agencia que la acredita.

act The formal product of a legislative body; a decision or determination by a sovereign, a legislative council, or a court of justice.
ley Producto formal de un cuerpo legislativo; decisión o determinación por un soberano, un consejo legislativo o un tribunal de justicia.

acute Having a rapid onset and severe symptoms.
agudo Que tiene un comienzo rápido y síntomas serios.

adage A saying, often in metaphoric form, that embodies a common observation.
refrán Dicho, con frecuencia metafórico, que refleja una observación común.

adhesions Bands of scar tissue that bind together two anatomic surfaces that normally are separate.
adhesiones Bandas de tejido de una cicatriz que unen dos superficies anatómicas que están normalmente separadas.

adrenocorticotropic hormone (ACTH) A hormone released by the anterior pituitary gland that stimulates the production and secretion of glucocorticoids.
hormona adrenocorticotropina (ACTH) Hormona, liberada por la glándula pituitaria anterior, que estimula la producción y secreción de glucocorticoides.

advent A coming into being or use.
advenimiento Próximo a ser o a usarse.

advocate One who pleads the cause of another; one who defends or maintains a cause or proposal.
abogado Persona que defiende la causa de otro; aqel que defiende o apoya una causa o propuesta.

affable Being pleasant and at ease in talking to others; characterized by ease and friendliness.
afable Que es agradable y tiene un trato fácil con los demás; caracterizado por su trato fácil y amistoso.

agenda A list or outline of things to be considered or done.
agenda Lista o resumen de cosas a considerar o a hacer.

aggression A forceful action or procedure intended to dominate; hostile, injurious, or destructive behavior, especially when caused by frustration.
agresión Acción o procedimiento forzado, con la intención de dominar; comportamiento hostil, injurioso o destructivo, en especial cuando es causado por frustración.

albuminuria Abnormal presence of albumin in the urine.
albuminuria Presencia anómala de albúmina en la orina.

aliquot A portion of a well-mixed sample removed for testing.
alícuota Porción de una muestra bien mezclada, separada para ser analizada.

allegation   A statement of what a party to a legal action undertakes to prove.
alegación   Declaración por una de las partes implicadas en un proceso legal para apoyar lo que dicha parte intenta probar.

allied health fields   Areas of healthcare delivery or related services in which professionals assist physicians with the diagnosis, treatment, and care of patients in many different specialty areas.
campos relacionados con la salud   Áreas del cuidado de la salud y servicios relacionados en los cuales profesionales ayudan a los médicos en el diagnóstico, tratamiento y atención de los pacientes en muchas áreas diferentes.

allocating   Apportioning for a specific purpose or to particular persons or things.
distribuir   Asignar a un fin específico o a personas o cosas en particular.

allopathy   A method of treating a disease by introducing a condition that is intended to cause a pathologic reaction that will be antagonistic to the condition being treated.
alopatía   Método de tratar una enfermedad provocando una afección con el fin de causar una reacción patológica, la cual será opuestaa la enfermedad que se está tratando.

allowed charge   The maximum amount of money that many third-party payors will pay for a specific procedure or service. Often based on the UCR fee.
cargo permitido   Cantidad máxima de dinero que muchos pagadores intermediarios pagan por una práctica o servicio específico; con frecuencia se basa en el cargo UCR.

alopecia   Partial or complete lack of hair.
alopecia   Pérdida de cabello, parcial o total.

alphabetic filing   Any system that arranges names or topics according to the sequence of the letters in the alphabet.
archivo alfabético   Cualquier sistema que ordena los nombres o temas siguiendo la secuencia de las letras del alfabeto.

alphanumeric   Systems made up of combinations of letters and numbers.
alfanumérico   Sistema constituido por combinaciones de letras y números.

ambiguous   Capable of being understood in two or more possible senses or ways; unclear.
ambiguo   Que puede entenderse de dos o más maneras; que no es claro.

amblyopia   Reduction or dimness of vision with no apparent organic cause; often referred to as *lazy eye syndrome*.

ambliopía   Reducción o disminución de la visión sin causa orgánica aparente; con frecuencia se conoce como *síndrome del ojo vago*.

ambulatory   Able to walk about and not be bedridden.
ambulatorio   Capaz de caminar y no tiene que estar postrado en la cama.

amenity   Something conducive to comfort, convenience, or enjoyment.
amenidad   Algo que proporciona confort, comodidad o placer.

amino acids   Organic compounds that form the chief constituents of protein and are used by the body to build and repair tissues.
aminoácidos   Compuestos orgánicos que son los constituyentes principales de la proteína y son usados por el cuerpo para formar y reparar tejidos.

amorphous   Lacking a defined shape.
amorfo   Que carece de forma definida.

analyte   The substance or chemical being analyzed or detected in a specimen.
analito   La sustancia o producto químico que se analiza o que se detecta en una muestra.

anaphylaxis   Exaggerated hypersensitivity reaction that in severe cases leads to vascular collapse, bronchospasm, and shock.
anafilaxia   Reacción de hipersensibilidad exagerada, la cual, en casos graves, conduce a colapso vascular, broncospasmo y choque.

anastomosis   The surgical joining together of two normally distinct organs.
anastomosis   Unión quirúrgica de dos órganos normalmente diferentes.

ancillary   Subordinate; auxiliary.
auxiliar   Subordinado, complementario.

ancillary diagnostic services   Services that support patient diagnoses (e.g., laboratory or x-ray).
servicios de diagnóstico auxiliares   Servicios que apoyan el diagnóstico del paciente (como laboratorio o rayos x).

"and"   In the context of ICD-9-CM, the word "and" should be interpreted as "and/or."
"y"   En el contexto de ICD-9-CM, la palabra "y" debe interpretarse como "y/o."

anemia   A condition marked by deficiency of red blood cells.
anemia   Enfermedad caracterizada por una deficiencia de glóbulos rojos en la sangre.

angiocardiography   Radiography of the heart and great vessels using an iodine contrast medium.

angiocardiografía   Radiografía del corazón y los vasos sanguíneos mayores usando un medio de contraste yodado.

angiography   Radiography of blood vessels using an iodine contrast medium.
angiografía   Radiografía de los vasos sanguíneos usando un medio de contraste yodado.

angioplasty   Interventional technique using a catheter to open or widen a blood vessel to improve circulation.
angioplastia   Técnica quirúrgica que usa un catéter para abrir o hacer más ancho un vaso sanguíneo a fin de mejorar la circulación.

animate   Full of life; to give spirit and support to expressions.
animar   Dar vida; dar ánimo y apoyo a las manifestaciones.

annotating   To furnish with notes, which are usually critical or explanatory.
anotar   Añadir notas, por lo general, críticas o explicatorias.

annotation   A note added by way of comment or explanation.
anotación   Nota añadida a modo de comentario o explicación.

anomalies   Faulty development of the fetus resulting in deformities or deviations from normal.
anomalías   Desarrollo defectuoso del feto que tiene como resultado deformidades o desviaciones de lo normal.

anorexia   Lack or loss of appetite for food.
anorexia   Falta o pérdida del apetito.

anoxia   Absence of oxygen in the tissues.
anoxia   Ausencia de oxígeno en los tejidos.

anteroposterior (AP)   Frontal projection in which the patient is supine or facing the x-ray tube.
anteroposterior (AP)   Proyección frontal en la cual el paciente está en posición supina o frente al tubo de rayos x.

antibody   Immunoglobulin produced by the immune system in response to bacteria, viruses, or other antigenic substances.
anticuerpo   Inmunoglobulina producida por el sistema inmunológico en respuesta a bacterias, virus u otras substancias antigénicas.

anticoagulant   A chemical added to the blood after collection to prevent clotting.
anticoagulante   Producto químico que se añade a la sangre después de extraerla para que no forme coágulos.

antidiuretic hormone (ADH)   A hormone secreted at the posterior pituitary gland that causes water retention in the kidneys and elevates the blood pressure; also known as *vasopressin*.
hormona antidiurética (ADH)   Hormona secretada por la glándula pituitaria posterior y que provoca retención de agua en los riñones y aumento de la presión sanguínea. Es conocida también como *vasopresina*.

antigen   A foreign substance that causes the production of a specific antibody.
antígeno   Substancia extraña que provoca la producción de un anticuerpo específico.

antimicrobial agent   A drug that is used to treat infection.
agente antimicrobiano   Substancia que se usa para tratar infecciones.

antiseptic   Pertaining to substances that inhibit the growth of microorganisms (e.g., alcohol and Betadine).
antiséptico   Perteneciente o relativo a las substancias que inhiben el crecimiento de microorganismos como el alcohol y la Betadina.

antiseptic   A substance that kills microorganisms.
antiséptico   Substancia que mata microorganismos.

antiseptic   An agent that inhibits bacterial growth and can be used on human tissue.
antiséptico   Agente que inhibe el crecimiento bacteriano y que puede usarse en los tejidos humanos.

aortogram   A radiographic image of the aorta made with the use of an iodine contrast medium.
aortograma   Radiografía de la aorta usando un medio de contraste yodado.

apnea   Absence or cessation of breathing.
apnea   Ausencia o cese de la respiración.

appeal   A legal proceeding by which a case is brought before a higher court for review of the decision of a lower court.
apelación   Procedimiento legal por el cual un caso se lleva ante un tribunal superior para obtener una revisión de la decisión de un tribunal inferior.

appellate   Having the power to review the judgment of another tribunal or body of jurisdiction; for example, an appellate court reviews the rulings of a lower court.
de apelación   Que tiene el poder de revisar el veredicto de otro tribunal o cuerpo jurídico, como una corte de apelación.

applications   Software programs designed to perform specific tasks.
aplicaciones   Programas informáticos diseñados para realizar tareas específicas.

appraisal   An expert judgment of the value or merit of something; judging as to quality.

evaluación   Acción de emitir un juicio experto sobre el valor o mérito de algo; juzgar la calidad de algo; evaluar el rendimiento en el trabajo.

arbitration   The hearing and determination of a cause in controversy by a person or persons either chosen by the parties involved or appointed under statutory authority.
arbitraje   Vista y resolución de una causa en conflicto por una persona o personas elegida/s por las partes implicadas o designadas por la autoridad establecida por ley.

arbitrator   A neutral person chosen to settle differences between two parties in a controversy.
árbitro   Persona neutral seleccionada para poner fin a las diferencias entre dos partes involucradas en un conflicto.

archaic   Of, relating to, or characteristic of an earlier or more primitive time.
arcaico   Perteneciente o relativo a una época anterior o más primitiva; que tiene las características de dicha época.

archive   To file or collect records or documents in or as if in an archive.
archivar   Guardar o recoger informes o documentos en un archivo o de manera similar.

arrhythmia   An abnormality or irregularity in the heart rhythm.
arritmia   Anomalía o irregularidad en el ritmo cardiaco.

arteriography   Radiography of the arteries in which an iodine contrast medium is used.
arteriografía   Radiografía de las arterias usando un medio de contraste yodado.

arthritis   Inflammation of a joint.
artritis   Inflamación de una articulación.

arthrogram   A fluoroscopic image of the soft tissue components of a joint for which a contrast medium is injected directly into the joint capsule.
artrografía   Examen fluoroscópico de los componentes de los tejidos blandos de las articulaciones con una inyección directa de un medio de contraste en la cápsula de la articulación.

articular   Pertaining to a joint.
articulatorio   Perteneciente o relativo a una articulación.

artificial intelligence   The aspect of computer science that deals with computers taking on the attributes of humans. An example is an expert system, which is capable of making decisions; this might be software designed to help a physician diagnose an illness when given a set of symptoms. Game-playing programming and programs designed to recognize human language are other examples of artificial intelligence.

inteligencia artificial   Parte de la informática que se ocupa de la incorporación de atributos humanos a las computadoras. Un ejemplo de esto es un sistema práctico capaz de tomar decisiones, como los programas informáticos diseñados para ayudar a los médicos a diagnosticar a un paciente dado un conjunto de síntomas. Los programas de juegos y otros programas diseñados para reconocer el lenguaje humano son otros ejemplos.

ASCII (American Standard Code for Information Interchange)   A code representing English characters as numbers, with each given a number from 0 to 127.
ASCII (Estándar Americano de Codificación para el-Intercambio de Información)   Un código que representa carácteres ingleses como números, en el cual a cada uno se le asigna un número de 0 a-127.

asepsis   The process or state of making or keeping something free of infection or infectious materials; the state of being free of pathogens.
asepsia   Que está libre del infecciones.

assault   An intentional, unlawful attempt to do bodily injury to another by force.
asalto   Intento ilícito de causar daño físico a otro usando la fuerza.

assent   To agree to something, especially after thoughtful consideration.
asentir   Aceptar algo, especialmente cuando se hace tras una detenida reflexión.

asystole   Absence of a heartbeat.
asistolia   Ausencia de latidos del corazón.

ataxia   Failure or irregularity of muscle actions and coordination.
ataxia   Fallo o irregularidad del movimiento y coordinación musculare.

atherosclerosis   A form of arteriosclerosis distinguished by fatty deposits within the inner layers of larger arterial walls.
aterosclerosis   Forma de arteriosclerosis que se distingue por la presencia de depósitos de grasa en las capas internas de las paredes de las arterias mayores.

atria   The two upper chambers of the heart.
aurículas   Las dos cavidades superiores del corazón.

atrioventricular (AV) node   A part of the cardiac conduction system located between the atria and the ventricles.
nódulo aurioventricular (AV)   Parte del sistema cardiaco que se encuentra entre las aurículas y los ventríalculos.

atrophy   A decrease in the size of a normally developed organ.

520

atrofia   Disminución del tamaño de un órgano desarrollado de forma normal.

atrophy   To waste away or decrease in size.
atrofia   Desgastado, disminuido en tamaño.

attenuated   Weakening or a change in virulence of a pathogenic microorganism.
atenuado   Cambio o debilitación en la virulencia de un microorganismo.

audiologist   An allied healthcare professional who specializes in the evaluation of hearing function, detection of hearing impairment, and determination of the anatomic site of impairment.
audiólogo   Profesional del cuidado de la salud que se especializa en evaluar la función auditiva, detectar las dificultades auditivas y determinar el-lugar físico en el que se produce el problema auditivo.

audit   A formal examination of an organization's or individual's accounts or financial situation; a methodic examination and review.
auditoría   Análisis formal de las cuentas o estado financiero de una organización o un individuo; examen y revisión sistemáticos.

augment   To make greater, more numerous, larger, or more intense.
aumentar   Hacer mayor, más numeroso, más grande o más intenso.

aura   A peculiar sensation that precedes the appearance of a more definite disturbance.
aura   Sensación peculiar que precede a la aparición de un trastorno definido.

authorization   A term used by managed care for an approved referral.
autorización   Término usado en el cuido administrado para referirse a la aprobación de la referencia de un paciente de un médico a otro profesional del cuidado o de la salud.

autoimmune   Referring to the development of an immune response to one's own tissues; action against one's own cells that causes localized and systemic reactions.
autoinmune   Desarrollo de una respuesta inmunológica a los propios tejidos; actuar contra sus propias células para originar reacciones sistémicas localizadas.

autoimmune disorder   A disturbance in the immune system in which the body reacts against its own tissue. Examples of autoimmune disorders include multiple sclerosis, rheumatoid arthritis, and systemic lupus erythematosus.
trastorno autoinmune   Trastorno del sistema inmunológico en el cual el cuerpo reacciona contra sus propios tejidos. Algunos ejemplos de trastornos autoinmunes incluyen la esclerosis múltiple, la artritis reumatoide y el lupus eritematoso sistémico.

axial projection   A radiograph taken with a longitudinal angulation of the x-ray beam; sometimes referred to as a *semiaxial projection.*
proyección axial   Radiografía que se toma con un ángulo longitudinal del haz de rayos x; a veces se llama *proyección semi-axial.*

azotemia   Retention of excessive amounts of nitrogenous wastes in the blood.
azotemia   Retención en la sangre de cantidades de desperdicios nitrogenados.

backup   Any type of storage of files to prevent their loss in the event of hard disk failure.
copia de seguridad   Cualquier tipo de almacenamiento de archivos para evitar que se pierdan en caso de que ocurrra un fallo en el disco duro.

bailiff   An officer of some U.S. courts who usually serves as a messenger or usher and keeps order at the request of the judge.
alguacil   Funcionario de algunos tribunales estadounidenses que suele servir como mensajero o ujier y que se ocupa de mantener el orden a petición del juez.

bank reconciliation   The process of proving that a bank statement and checkbook balance are in agreement.
reconciliación bancaria   Proceso por el cual se prueba que un estado bancario y un saldo de una libreta de cheques concuerdan.

banners   Also called *banner ads;* advertisements often found on a Web page that can be animated to attract the user's attention in hopes the person will click on the ad, be redirected to the advertiser's home page, and make a purchase from the site or gain information.
viñetas   Viñetas o anuncios de viñetas; anuncios, a veces animados, que se hallan, con frecuencia en las páginas web; su fin es atraer la atención del usuario con la esperanza de que éste haga clic en el anuncio, y así sea llevado a la página principal del anunciante para que compre algo en ese sitio o para que obtenga información sobre el mismo.

battery   Willful, unlawful use of force or violence on the person of another; offensive touching or use of force on a person without that person's consent.
golpiza   Uso de la fuerza o violencia en contra de la persona de otro, de manera intencional e ilegítima. Tocar de manera ofensiva a una persona o usar la fuerza en contra de ella sin su consentimiento.

beneficence   The act of doing or producing good, especially performing acts of charity or kindness.
beneficencia   Acción de hacer o producir el bien, en especial llevando a cabo obras caritativas o bondadosas.

beneficiary   The person who receives the benefits of an insurance policy. The "insured" person on a Medicare claim.
beneficiario   Persona que recibe los beneficios de una póliza de seguro. La persona "asegurada" en una reclamación de Medicare.

benefits   Services or payments provided under a health plan, employee plan, or some other agreement, including programs such as health insurance, pensions, retirement planning, and many other options, that may be offered to employees of a company or organization.
beneficios   Servicio o pago proporcionado bajo un plan de salud, un plan de empleados o algún otro acuerdo, incluyendo programas como seguros de salud, pensiones, planes de retiro y muchas otras opciones que pueden ser ofrecidas a los empleados de una compañía u organización.

benefits   The amount payable by the insurance company for a monetary loss to an individual insured by that company, under each coverage.
beneficios   Suma que ha de pagar la compañía aseguradora por una pérdida monetaria a un individuo asegurado por dicha compañía, bajo cada cobertura.

benign   Not cancerous and not recurring.
benigno   No canceroso y no recurrente.

bevel   The angled tip of a needle.
bisel   Punta de aguja en ángulo.

bifurcate   To divide from one into two branches.
bifurcar   Dividir una unidad en dos ramas.

bifurcation   The point of forking or separation into two branches.
bifurcación   Lugar en el que se separan dos ramas.

bilirubin   An orange pigment in bile; the accumulation of bilirubin leads to jaundice.
bilirrubina   Pigmento de color naranja que se encuentra en la bilis; cuando se acumula produce ictericia.

bilirubinuria   The presence of bilirubin in the urine.
bilirrubinuria   Presencia de bilirrubina en la orina.

biophysical   Pertaining to the science that deals with the application of physical methods and theories to biologic problems.
biofísico   Perteneciente o relativo a la ciencia que trata de la aplicación de métodos y teorías físicas a los problemas biológicos.

birthday rule   An insurance rule that states that when an individual is covered under two insurance policies, the insurance plan of the policyholder whose birthday comes first in the calendar year (month and day—not year) becomes primary.

regla del cumpleaños   Cuando un individuo está cubierto bajo dos pólizas de seguro, el plan de seguro del titular de la póliza cuya fecha de cumpleaños esté antes en el año civil (mes y día, no año) se convierte en el plan primario.

blatant   Completely obvious, conspicuous, or obtrusive, especially in a crass or offensive manner; brazen.
flagrante   Completamente obvio, notorio o inoportuno, en especial de una manera torpe u-ofensiva; desvergonzado.

bond   A durable, formal paper used for documents.
obligación   Papel duradero y formal usado para documentos.

bounding pulse   A pulse that feels full because of increased power of cardiac contractions or increased blood volume.
pulso saltón   Pulso que se siente lleno debido a un aumento de potencia en las contracciones cardiacas o debido a un aumento del volumen de la sangre.

bradycardia   A slow heartbeat; a pulse below 60 beats per minute.
bradicardia   Latido lento; pulso por debajo de 60 pulsaciones por minuto.

bradypnea   Respirations that are regular in rhythm but slower than normal in rate.
bradipnea   Respiración que tiene un ritmo regular pero es más lenta de lo normal.

broad-spectrum antimicrobial agent   A drug used to treat a broad range of infections.
agente antimicrobiano de amplio espectro   Sustancia que se usa para tratar una amplia gama de infecciones.

bronchiectasis   Dilation of the bronchi and bronchioles associated with a secondary infection or ciliary dysfunction.
broncoectasia   Dilatación de los bronquios y bronquiolos asociada con una infección secundaria o disfunción ciliar.

bronchoconstriction   Narrowing of the bronchiole tubes.
broncoconstricción   Estrechamiento de los bronquiolos.

bruit   An abnormal sound or a murmur heard on auscultation of an organ, vessel, or gland.
ruido   Sonido o murmullo anómalo que se oye al auscultar un órgano, vaso sanguíneo o glándula.

bucky   A moving grid device that prevents scatter radiation from fogging the radiographic film.
bucky   Dispositivo de rejilla móvil que evita que la difusión de la radiación empañe la película.

bundle of His   Fibers that conduct electrical impulses from the AV node to the ventricular myocardium.
haz de His   Fibras que conducen impulsos eléctricos del nódulo aurioventricular al miocardio ventricular.

burnout Exhaustion of physical or emotional strength or motivation, usually as a result of prolonged stress or frustration.
agotamiento Llegar al fin de la fortaleza o motivación física o emocional, por lo general como resultado un prolongado estado de estrés o frustración.

bursa A fluid-filled, saclike membrane that provides for cushioning and frictionless motion between two tissues.
bursa Membrana con forma de saco llena de fluido que proporciona amortiguación y movimiento sin fricción entre dos tejidos.

byte A unit of data that contains 8 binary digits.
byte Unidad de información que contiene ocho dígitos binarios.

C&S (culture and sensitivity) A procedure performed in the microbiology laboratory in which a specimen is cultured on artifical media to detect bacterial or fungal growth, followed by appropriate screening for antibiotic sensitivity.
C&S (cultivo y sensibilidad) Procedimiento llevado a cabo en el laboratorio de microbiología en el cual se cultiva un espécimen en un medio artificial para detectar el crecimiento de bacterias u hongos y después investigar su sensibilidad los antibióticos.

cache A special high-speed storage area that can be part of the computer's main memory or a separate storage device. One function of the cache is to store in the computer's memory the Web sites visited; this allows faster recall the next time the Web site is requested.
caché Almacenamiento especial de alta velocidad que puede formar parte de la memoria principal de la computadora o puede ser un dispositivo de almacenamiento separado. Una función del caché es almacenar las páginas Web visitadas en la memoria de la computadora para llegar a ellas con mayor rapidez la próxima vez que desee ver la página.

candidiasis An infection, caused by a yeastlike fungus, that typically affects the vaginal mucosa and skin.
candidiasis Infección causada por una levadura (una especie de hongo) que típicamente afecta la mucosa y la piel vaginal.

cannula A rigid tube that surrounds a blunt or a sharp, pointed trocar that is inserted into the body; when the trocar is withdrawn, fluid may escape from the body through the cannula, depending on the insertion site.
cánula Tubo rígido que envuelve un trocar romo o un trocar de punta afilada que se inserta en el cuerpo; cuando se saca, puede salir fluido corporal a través de la cánula, según en donde haya sido insertada.

caption A heading, title, or subtitle under which records are filed.

leyenda Encabezamiento, título o subtítulo bajo el cual se archivan los informes.

carbohydrates Chemical substances that contain only carbon, oxygen, and hydrogen; they include sugars, glycogen, starches, dextrins, and celluloses.
carbohidratos Sustancias químicas, en las que se incluyen azúcares, glucógenos, almidones, dextrinas y celulosas, y están formadas sólo por carbono, oxígeno e hidrógeno.

carcinogenic A substance that is known to cause cancer.
cancerígeno Sustancia que se sabe que produce cáncer.

carcinogens Substances or agents that cause the development or increase the incidence of cancer.
carcinógeno Sustancia o agente que origina el desarrollo de cáncer o aumenta su incidencia.

cardiac arrest Complete cessation of cardiac contractions.
paro cardiaco Detención completa de las contracciones cardiacas.

cardiac arrhythmia An irregular heartbeat caused by a malfunction in the heart's electrical system.
arritmias cardiacas Pulso irregular que es resultado de un mal funcionamiento del sistema eléctrico del corazón.

cardioversion The use of electroshock to convert an abnormal cardiac rhythm to a normal one.
cardioversión Utilización de un electrochoque para normalizar un ritmo cardiaco anómalo.

cartilage The rubbery, smooth, somewhat elastic connective tissue that covers the ends of bones.
cartílago Tejido de unión similar a la goma, suave y un tanto elástico, que cubre los extremos de los huesos.

case management The process of assessing and planning patient care, including referral and follow up, to ensure continuity of care and quality management.
administración de casos Proceso de evaluación y planificación de la atención al paciente, incluyendo envío de pacientes a especialistas y seguimiento del caso para asegurar la continuidad del tratamiento y la calidad de la administración.

cash on delivery (COD) The method of payment used when an article or item is delivered; payment is expected before the item is released.
contra reembolso (COD) Método de pago usado cuando se entrega un artículo u objeto y el destinatario ha de pagar antes de recibirlo.

casts A fibrous or proteinaceous material, molded to the shape of the part in which it accumulated, that is thrown off into the urine in kidney disease.

cálculos   Materiales fibrosos o proteínicos que han tomado la forma de la parte del cuerpo en la que han sido acumulados y que se expulsan a través de la orina en los casos de enfermedades renales.

categorically   Placed in a specific division of a system of classification.
categorizado   Colocado en un lugar específico dentro de una división de un sistema de clasificación.

caustic   (1) A sarcastic remark or phrase. (2) A substance that burns or destroys tissue by chemical action.
cáustico   (1) Comentario o frase dicha con sarcasmo. (2) Substancia que quema o destruye tejidos por acción química.

CD burner   A CD writer that can write data onto a blank CD or copy data from a CD to a blank CD.
grabador de CD   Dispositivo que puede escribir datos en un CD en blanco o copiar datos de un CD a otro CD en blanco.

centrifuge   An apparatus consisting essentially of a compartment that spins around a central axis to separate contained materials of different specific gravities or to separate colloidal particles suspended in a liquid.
centrifugadora   Aparato que consiste básicamente de un compartimiento que gira alrededor de un eje central para separar materiales con diferentes pesos específicos, o para separar partículas coloidales suspendidas en un líquido.

cerebrospinal fluid   The fluid within the subarachnoid space, the central canal of the spinal cord, and the four ventricles of the brain.
fluido cerebroespinal   Fluido del interior del espacio subaracnoideo, el canal central de la médula espinal y los cuatro ventrículos del cerebro.

certification   Attested as being true as represented or as meeting a standard; to have been tested, usually by a third party, and awarded a certificate based on proven knowledge.
certificación   Atestiguar que algo es verdadero en cuanto a lo que representa, o al cumplimiento de un estándar; que ha sido examinado, por lo general por una tercera parte, y que se le ha concedido un certificado basándose en el conocimiento del que ha dado prueba.

cerumen   A waxy secretion in the ear canal, commonly called *ear wax*.
cerumen   Secreción cerosa del canal del oído, comúnmente se conoce como *cera de los oídos*.

cervical   Referring to the region of the neck that contains the seven cervical vertebrae.
cervical   Región del cuello en la que hay siete vértebras cervicales.

chain of command   A series of executive positions in order of authority.

cadena de mando   Serie de puestos ejecutivos en orden de autoridad.

channels   A means of communication or expression; a way, course, or direction of thought.
canales   Medios de comunicación o de expresión; vía, curso o dirección del pensamiento.

characteristic   A distinguishing trait, quality, or property.
característica   Rasgo, cualidad o propiedad distintiva.

chief complaint   The reason for seeking medical care.
problema principal   Razón por la cual un paciente solicita atención médica.

chiropractic   A medical discipline; the chiropractic physician focuses on the nervous system and manually and painlessly adjusts the vertebral column to affect the nervous system, resulting in healthier patients.
quiropráctica   Disciplina médica en la que los médicos quiroprácticos se centran en el sistema nervioso y ajustan la columna vertebral manualmente y sin dolor, para lograr un efecto sobre el sistema nervioso, dando como resultado pacientes más sanos.

cholesterol   A substance produced by the liver and also found in plant and animal fats that can cause fatty deposits or atherosclerotic plaques in the blood vessels.
colesterol   Ustancia que produce el hígado y que se halla en las grasas animales y vegetales, y que puede producir depósitos grasos o placas ateroscleróticas en los vasos sanguíneos.

chronic   Persisting for a prolonged period.`
crónico   Que persiste por largo tiempo.

chronic bronchitis   Recurrent inflammation of the membranes lining the bronchial tubes.
bronquitis crónica   Inflamación recurrente de-las membranas que recubren los tubos bronquiales.

chronologic order   Of, relating to, or arranged in or according to the order of time.
orden cronológico   Perteneciente o relativo al orden en el tiempo; organizado según el orden en el tiempo.

circumvent   To manage to avoid something, especially by ingenuity or stratagem.
circunvenir   Lograr evitar algo usando ingeniosidad o estratagemas.

cite   To quote by way of example, authority, or proof, or to mention formally in commendation or praise.
cita   Que se nombra para servir de ejemplo, autoridad o prueba o para hacer una mención formal como recomendación o alabanza.

claims clearinghouse   A centralized facility (sometimes called a *third-party administrator,* or TPA) to which

524

insurance claims are transmitted; the clearinghouse checks and redistributes claims electronically to various insurance carriers.

centro de reclamaciones Establecimiento centralizado (algunas veces conocido como *administrador mediador* o TPA) al cual se transmiten las reclamaciones de seguros y que se encarga de verificar y redistribuir las reclamaciones electrónicamente a varias compañías de seguros.

clarity The quality or state of being clear.
claridad Calidad o estado de claro.

clause A group of words containing a subject and a predicate that functions as part of a complex or compound sentence.
cláusulas Conjunto de palabras que incluye un sujeto y un predicado y que funciona como miembro de una oración compuesta.

clean claim An insurance claim form that has been completed correctly (with no errors or omissions) and can be processed and paid promptly.
reclamación limpia Formulario de reclamación de seguro que ha sido llenado correctamente (sin errores ni omisiones) y que puede procesarse y pagarse prontamente.

clearinghouses Networks of banks that exchange checks with one another.
sistema de compensación Redes bancarias que intercambian cheques entres sí.

clinical trials Research studies that test how well new medical treatments or other interventions work in the subjects, usually human beings.
ensayos clínicos Estudio de investigación que prueba cómo actúan los nuevos tratamientos médicos u otras intervenciones en los sujetos, normalmente en los seres humanos.

clitoris The small, elongated, erectile body situated above the urinary meatus at the superior point of the labia minora.
clítoris Órgano eréctil pequeño y alargado situado sobre el meato urinario a la altura de los labios menores.

clubbing Abnormal enlargement of the distal phalanges (fingers and toes) that is associated with cyanotic heart disease or advanced chronic pulmonary disease.
hipocratismo digital (dedos en palillo de tambor) Engrosamiento anómalo de las falanges distales (en los dedos de las manos y de los pies), relacionado con una enfermedad cardiaca cianótica o una enfermedad pulmonar crónica avanzada.

coagulate To form into clots.
coagular Formar coágulos.

"code also" In ICD-9-CM coding, when more than one code is necessary to identify a given condition fully, "code also" or "use additional code" is used.
"código adicional" Cuando se necesita más de un código para identificar por completo una afección (enfermedad) determinado, se usa "código adicional" o "usar código adicional."

Code of Federal Regulations (CFR) The Code of Federal Regulations (CFR) is a coded delineation of the rules and regulations published in the *Federal Register* by the various departments and agencies of the federal government. The CFR is divided into 50 titles, which represent broad subject areas, and further into chapters, which provide specific detail.
Código de Regulaciones Federales (CFR) El Código de Regulaciones Federales (CFR) es un resumen codificado de las normas y regulaciones publicadas en el Registro Federal por los diferentes departamentos y agencias del gobierno federal. El CFR se divide en 50 Títulos que representan amplias áreas temáticas, los cuales, a su vez, se subdividen en capítulos que proporcionan detalles específicos.

cognitive Pertaining to the operation of the mind; the process by which a person becomes aware of perceiving, thinking, and remembering.
cognitivo Perteneciente o relativo a la operación del proceso mental por el cual nos damos cuenta de cómo, percibimos, pensamos y recordamos.

cohesive Sticking together tightly; exhibiting or producing cohesion.
cohesivo El estado de estar estrechamente unidos; mostrar o producir cohesión.

coitus Sexual union between male and female; also known as *intercourse.*
coito Unión sexual entre un macho y una hembra.

collagen The protein that forms the inelastic fibers of tendons, ligaments, and fascia.
colágeno Proteína que forma las fibras no elásticas de los tendones, los ligamentos y la fascia.

collodion A preparation of cellulose nitrate that dries to a strong, thin, protective, transparent film when applied to the skin.
colodión Preparación de nitrato de celulosa que, cuando se aplica a la piel, se seca formando una película fina resistente, protectora y transparente.

colloidal Pertaining to a gluelike substance.
coloidal Perteneciente o relativo a una substancia parecida a la cola.

colostrum The thin, yellow, milky fluid secreted by the mammary glands a few days before and after delivery.
calostro Fluido lácteo poco espeso y amarillo que segregan las glándulas mamarias unos días antes y después del parto.

coma   An unconscious state from which the patient cannot be aroused.
coma   Estado inconsciente del cual el paciente no puede ser despertado.

comfort zone   A mental state in which an individual feels safe and confident.
zona de bienestar   Un lugar en la mente en el que un individuo se siente seguro y confiado.

commensurate   Corresponding in size, amount, extent, or degree; equal in measure.
equiparable   Que es equivalente en tamaño, cantidad o grado; de igual medida.

commercial insurance   Plans (sometimes called *private insurance*) that reimburse the insured (or his or her dependents) for monetary losses resulting from illness or injury according to a specific schedule as outlined in the insurance policy and on a fee-for-service basis. Individuals insured under these plans normally are not limited to any one physician and usually can see the healthcare provider of their choice.
seguro comercial   Planes (a veces llamados *seguros privados*) que reembolsan al asegurado (o a sus dependendientes) por pérdidas monetarias debidas a enfermedad o lesión siguiendo una escala específica que se explica en la póliza de seguro y cobrando un cargo por cada servicio. Los individuos asegurados bajo estos planes, por lo general, no están limitados a un solo médico y suelen poder acudir al proveedor del cuidado de la salud que elijan.

co-morbidities   Pre-existing conditions that, because of their presence with a specific principal diagnosis, increase the length of stay in a healthcare facility by at least 1 day in approximately 75% of cases.
patologías coexistentes   Enfermedades preexistentes que, debido a su presencia junto al diagnóstico principal, causan un aumento en la duración de la estadía de al menos un día en aproximadamente 75% de los casos.

competence   The quality or state of being competent; having adequate or requisite capabilities.
competencia   Capacidad o aptitud de quien es competente en algo; tener las capacidades necesarias o cumplir con los requisitos necesarios para hacer algo.

competent   Having adequate abilities or qualities; having the capacity to function or perform in a certain way.
competente   Que tiene ciertas capacidades o cualidades; que tiene la capacidad de funcionar o actuar de un modo determinado.

complications   Conditions that arise during the hospital stay that prolong the length of stay by at least 1 day in approximately 75% of the cases.
complicaciones   Condiciones que surgen durante la permanencia en el hospital que prolongan el tiempo de la

estadía en al menos un día en aproximadamente 75% de los casos.

compression   The state of being pressed together.
compresión   Condición de estar apretado.

computed tomography (CT)   A computerized x-ray imaging modality that provides axial and three-dimensional scans.
tomografía asistida por computadora (TAC)   Modalidad de formación computarizada de imágenes de rayos x que proporciona imágenes de escáner axiales y tridimensionales.

computer   A machine designed to accept, store, process, and give out information.
computadora (u ordenador)   Máquina diseñada para aceptar, almacenar, procesar y emitir información.

concise   Expressing much in brief form.
conciso   Que expresa mucho en forma breve.

concurrently   Occurring at the same time.
concurrente   Que ocurre al mismo tiempo.

cones   Structures in the retina that make the perception of color possible.
conos   Estructuras que se encuentran en la retina y que hacen posible la percepción del color.

congruence   Consistency between the verbal expression of the message and the sender's nonverbal body language.
congruencia   Expresión verbal del mensaje que corresponde al lenguaje corporal no verbal del emisor.

congruent   Being in agreement, harmony, or correspondence; conforming to the circumstances or requirements of a situation.
congruente   Que está en acuerdo, armonía o correspondencia; conforme a las circunstancias o requisitos de una situación.

connotation   An implication; something suggested by a word or thing.
connotación   Implicación; lo que sugiere una palabra o una cosa.

contaminate   To make impure or unclean; to make unfit for use by the introduction of unwholesome or undesirable elements.
contaminación   Volver impuro o sucio; hacer que algo sea inadecuado para el uso por la introducción de elementos insalubres o indeseables.

contaminated   Soiled with pathogens or infectious material; nonsterile.
contaminado   Manchado con materiales patógenos o infecciosos; no estéril.

contamination Becoming nonsterile through contact with any nonsterile material.
contaminación Pasar al estado de no estéril por contacto con cualquier material no estéril.

continuation pages The second and following pages of a letter.
paginas de continuación En una carta, la segunda página y las siguientes.

continuing education credits (CEUs) Credits for courses, classes, or seminars related to an individual's profession that are designed to promote education and to keep the professional up-to-date on current procedures and trends in the field; CEUs often are required to maintain licensure.
créditos de educación continua (CEU) Créditos por cursos, clases o seminarios relacionados con la profesión de un individuo y que tienen la finalidad de promocionar la educación y mantener al profesional al corriente de los procedimientos y tendencias actuales en su campo; con frecuencia son obligatorios para obtener una licencia.

continuity of care Care that continues smoothly from one provider to another so that care is not interrupted and the patient receives the most benefit.
continuidad de la atención Atención que continúa sin interrupciones de un proveedor a otro, de manera que el paciente recibe los máximos beneficios sin que haya una interrupción de la atención sanitaria.

contralateral Pertaining to the opposite side of the body.
colateral Perteneciente o relativo a la parte opuesta del cuerpo.

contrast media Substances used to enhance visualization of soft tissues in imaging studies.
medios de contraste Substancias usadas para mejorar la visualización de los tejidos blandos en estudios de formación de imágenes.

contributory negligence Statutes in some states that may prevent a party from recovering damages if the person contributed in any way to the injury or condition.
negligencia concurrente Estatutos existentes en algunos estados que impiden que una parte sea recompensada por daños si esta parte ha contribuido en algún modo a provocar la lesión o enfermedad.

cookies Messages sent to the hard drive from the Web server that identify users and allow preparation of custom Web pages for them, possibly displaying their name on return to the site.
cookies Mensaje que se envía al navegador de la red desde el servidor, el cual identifica a los usuarios y puede preparar páginas web especiales para ellos,

posiblemente, mostrando su nombre la próxima vez que visiten el sitio.

coordination of benefits The mechanism used in group health insurance to designate the order in which multiple carriers are to pay benefits to prevent duplicate payments.
coordinación de beneficios Mecanismo usado en seguros de enfermedad de grupo para designar el orden en el que varias compañías de seguros tienen que pagar los beneficios para evitar pagos dobles.

co-payment Also called *co-insurance;* a policy provision frequently found in medical insurance whereby the policyholder and the insurance company share the cost of covered losses in a specified ratio (e.g., 80/20: 80% by the insurer and 20% by the insured).
co-pago Un co-pago (o *co-seguro*) es una provisión frecuente de la póliza en los seguros médicos, por la que el titular de la póliza y la compañía aseguradora comparten el costo de las pérdidas cubiertas en una proporción determinada (ej.: 80/20: 80% por parte del asegurador y 20% por parte del asegurado).

COPD (chronic obstructive pulmonary disease) A progressive, irreversible lung condition that results in diminished lung capacity.
COPD (enfermedad pulmonar obstructiva crónica) Enfermedad pulmonar progresiva e irreversible que conlleva una reducción de la capacidad pulmonar.

copulation Sexual intercourse.
copulación Cópula sexual.

coronal plane The plane that divides the body into anterior and posterior parts.
plano coronal Plano que divide el cuerpo en una anterior y una posterior.

corticosteroids Natural or synthetic antiinflammatory hormones.
corticosteroides Hormonas antiinflamatorias, naturales o sintéticas.

costal Pertaining to the ribs.
costal Perteneciente o relativo a las costillas.

coulombs per kilogram (C/kg) The international unit of radiation exposure.
culombios por kilogramo (C/kg) Unidad internacional de exposición a la radiación.

counteroffer A return offer made by one who has rejected an offer or a job.
contraoferta Oferta-respuesta hecha por quien ha rechazado una oferta o trabajo.

creatinine Nitrogenous waste from muscle metabolism that is excreted in the urine.

creatinina   Residuo nitrogenado del metabolismo muscular que se excreta en la orina.

credentialing   The act of extending professional or medical privileges to an individual; the process of verifying and evaluating that person's credentials.
concesión de credenciales   Acción de conceder privilegios profesionales o médicos a un individuo; proceso de verificar y evaluar los credenciales de esa persona.

credibility   The quality or power of inspiring belief.
credibilidad   Calidad de creíble; facilidad para ser creído.

credit   An entry on an account constituting an addition to a revenue, net worth, or liability account; the balance in a person's favor in an account.
crédito   Dato que se entra en una cuenta y que constituye una adición a los ingresos, ganancia neta o cuenta de pasivo; saldo a favor de una persona en una cuenta.

crenate   Forming notches or leaflike, scalloped edges on an object.
crenar   Formar muescas o bordes en forma de concha o de hoja en un objeto.

crepitation   A dry, crackling sound or sensation.
crepitación   Sonido o sensación seca y crujiente.

critical thinking   The constant practice of considering all aspects of a situation when deciding what to believe or what to do.
razonamiento crítico   Práctica constante de considerar todos los aspectos de una situación al decidir qué creer o qué hacer.

cross-training   Training in more than one area so that a multitude of duties may be performed by one person or so that substitutions of personnel may be made when necessary or in emergencies.
entrenamiento cruzado   Entrenamiento en más de un área, de modo que una persona pueda desempeñar varias labores o que se puedan realizar sustituciones de personal cuando sea necesario o en caso de emergencia.

cryosurgery   The technique of exposing tissue to extreme cold to produce a well-defined area of cell destruction.
criocirugía   Técnica que consiste en exponer los tejidos a un frío extremo para producir una destrucción de células en un área bien definida.

cryptogenic   Hidden origin.
criptogénico   De origen oculto.

cultivate   To foster the growth of; to improve by labor, care, or study.

cultivar   Promover el desarrollo; mejorar algo por medio de trabajo, cuidado o estudio.

curettage   The act of scraping a body cavity with a surgical instrument, such as a curette.
curetaje   Acción de raspar una cavidad corporal con un instrumento quirúrgico, como una cureta o cucharilla cortante.

cursor   A symbol that appears on the computer monitor to show where the next character to be typed will appear.
cursor   Símbolo que aparece en el monitor y que muestra el lugar donde aparecerá el próximo carácter que se escriba.

curt   Marked by rude or peremptory shortness.
cortante   Caracterizado por una interrupción ruda o perentoria.

cyanosis   A blue discoloration of the mucous membranes and body extremities caused by lack of oxygen.
cianosis   Color azul de las membranas mucosas y las extremidades provocado por una falta de oxígeno.

cyberspace   The nonphysical space of the online world of computer networks.
ciberespacio   Palabra que se usa para describir el espacio no-físico del mundo en linea de las redes informáticas.

cyst   A small, capsulelike sac that encloses certain organisms in their dormant or larval stage.
quiste   Pequeño saco en forma de cápsula que encierra ciertos organismos en estado letárgico o larval.

damages   Loss or harm resulting from injury to person, property, or reputation; monetary compensation imposed by law for losses or injuries.
daños   Pérdidas o perjuicios que resultan de injuriar a una persona, atentar contra una propiedad o una reputación; compensación monetaria impuesta por ley en casos de pérdidas o injurias.

database   A collection of related files that serves as a foundation for retrieving information.
base de datos   Conjunto de archivos relacionados que sirven de base para la recuperación de información.

debit   An entry on an account constituting an addition to an expense or asset balance or a deduction from a revenue, net worth, or liability balance.
débito   Dato que se entra en una cuenta y que constituye una adición a los gastos o a una cuenta de activo o una deducción de un ingreso, ganancia neta o cuenta de pasivo.

debit card   A card similar to a credit card with which money may be withdrawn or the cost of purchases paid directly from the holder's bank account without the payment of interest.

tarjeta de débito   Tarjeta similar a la de crédito pero con la cual se puede retirar dinero o pagar compras directamente de la cuenta bancaria del titular sin tener que pagar intereses.

debridement   The removal of foreign material and dead, damaged tissue from a wound.
desbridamiento   Eliminación de materiales extraños y tejidos muertos y deteriorados de una herida.

decedent   A legal term used to represent a deceased person.
difunto   Término legal usado para referirse a una persona muerta.

decode   To convert, as in a message, into intelligible form; to recognize and interpret.
decodificar   Convertir la información, como en un mensaje, de modo que sea inteligible; reconocer e interpretar.

decubitus ulcer   A sore or ulcer over a bony prominence caused by ischemia from prolonged pressure; a bed sore.
úlcera por decúbito   Llaga o úlcera sobre una prominencia ósea debida a una isquemia por presión prolongada; escara.

deductible   A specific amount of money a patient must pay out of pocket, up front, before the insurance carrier begins paying. Often this amount ranges from $100 to $1,000. The deductible amount must be met on a yearly or per incident basis.
deducible   Cantidad de dinero específica que un paciente debe pagar de su bolsillo antes de que la compañía de seguros comience a pagar. Con frecuencia esta suma está entre 100 y 1000 dólares. Esta cantidad deducible ha de satisfacerse—anualmente o por caso.

default   To fail to pay financial debts, especially a student loan.
incumplimiento   Dejar de pagar deudas financieras, especialmente en un préstamo de estudiante.

defense mechanisms   Psychological methods of dealng with stressful situations that are encountered in day-to-day living.
mecanismos de defensa   Métodos psicológicos de hacer frente a situaciones tensas que surgen en la vida diaria.

deferment   A postponement, especially of payment of a student loan.
aplazamiento   Postergación de un pago, especialmente en un préstamo de estudiante.

defibrillator   A machine used to deliver an electrical shock to the heart through electrodes placed on the chest wall.

desfibrilador   Máquina usada para dar un electrochoque al corazón por medio de electrodos colocados en la pared torácica.

deficiencies   Conditions caused by a below-normal intake of a particular substance.
deficiencias   Estados causados por un consumo menor del normal de una sustancia específica.

demeanor   Behavior toward others; outward manner.
conducta   Comportamiento hacia los demás; comportamiento que se exterioriza.

demographic   The statistical characteristics of human populations (as in age or income), used especially to identify markets.
dato demográfico   Característica estadística de la población humana (como edad o ingresos), que se usa sobre todo para identificar mercados.

detrimental   Harmful or damaging.
perjudicial   Que es obvio que causa daño o perjuicio.

device driver   A computer program or set of commands that enables a device connected to the computer to function. For instance, a printer may come equipped with software that must be loaded onto the computer first so that the printer will work.
controlador de dispositivo   Programa que controla un dispositivo conectado a una computadora y que hace que dicho dispositivo pueda funcionar. Por ejemplo, una impresora puede estar equipada con un programa que primero ha de cargarse en la computadora para que ésta funcione.

diabetes mellitus type 2   A condition in which the body is unable to use glucose for energy because of a lack of insulin production in the pancreas or because of resistance to insulin on the cellular level.
diabetes mellitus tipo 2   Incapacidad de utilizar la glucosa para producir energía, debido a una falta de producción de insulina en el páncreas o a una resistencia a la insulina en el nivel celular.

diagnose   To determine the nature of a disease, injury, or congenital defect.
diagnóstico   Determinación del origen de una enfermedad, lesión o defecto congénito.

diagnosis   The concise technical description of the cause, nature, or manifestations of a condition or problem. *Initial diagnosis:* The physician's temporary impression, sometimes called a *working diagnosis. Differential diagnosis:* A comparison of two or more diseases with similar signs and symptoms. *Final diagnosis:* The conclusion reached by the physician after evaluating all findings, including laboratory and other test results.
diagnóstico   Descripción técnica y concisa de la causa, naturaleza o manifestaciones de una enfermedad o problema. *Inicial:* Impresión momentánea del médico,

a veces se llama diagnóstico de trabajo. *Diagnóstico diferenciado:* comparación de dos o más enfermedades con signos y síntomas similares. *Final:* Conclusión médica a la que se llega tras evaluar todos los datos, incluyendo los resultados de análisis de laboratorio y otras pruebas.

diaphoresis   The profuse excretion of sweat.
diaforesis   Excreción profusa de sudor.

diaphysis   The middle portion of a long bone, which contains the medullary cavity.
diafisis   Parte intermedia de un hueso largo en la que está la cavidad medular.

dictation   The act or manner of uttering words to be transcribed.
dictado   Acción de pronunciar palabras para que sean transcritas.

diction   The choice of words, especially with regard to clearness, correctness, and effectiveness.
dicción   Acción de elegir las palabras, especialmente para lograr claridad, corrección y eficacia en el discurso.

digestion   The process of converting food into chemical substances that can be used by the body.
digestión   Proceso de transformar alimentos en sustancias químicas que pueden ser usadas por el cuerpo.

Digital Subscriber Lines (DSL)   High-speed, sophisticated modulation schemes that operate over existing copper telephone wiring systems; often referred to as "last mile technologies" because DSL is used for connections from a telephone switching station to a home or office and not between switching stations.
Línea de Abonado Digital (DSL)   Sofisticado sistema de modulación de alta velocidad que opera en sistemas de cableado telefónicos de cobre ya existentes; con frecuencia se habla del DSL como "tecnología de las últimas millas" porque se utiliza para conexiones entre un centro de conmutación telefónica y un hogar u oficina, y no entre centros de conmutación.

Digital Versatile Disk (DVD)   An optical disk that holds approximately 28 times more information than a CD and is most commonly used to hold full-length movies. A CD holds approximately 600 megabytes, whereas a DVD can hold approximately 4.7 gigabytes.
Disco Digital Versátil (DVD)   El DVD es un disco óptico con capacidad para almacenar unas 28 veces más información que un CD; su uso más común es para guardar películas de larga duración. Mientras que un CD puede almacenar unos 600 megabytes, un DVD tiene una capacidad aproximada de almacenamiento de 4.7 gigabytes.

dilation   (1) Opening or widening the circumference of a body orifice with a dilating instrument. (2) The opening of the cervix through the process of labor, measured as 0 to 10 centimeters dilated.
dilatación   (1) Proceso de abrir o ensanchar un orificio corporal con un instrumento dilatador. (2) Ensanchamiento del cuello del útero durante el proceso del parto, se mide en centímetros, de 0 a 10.

dilation and curettage (D&C)   The procedure in which the cervix is widened and the endometrial wall of the uterus is scraped.
dilatación y curetaje (D&C)   Proceso de hacer más ancho el cuello del útero y raspar su pared endometrial.

diluent   A liquid used to dilute a specimen or reagent.
diluyente   Líquido usado para diluir un espécimen o un reactivo.

dingy claim   A claim that is put on hold because it lacks certain adjunction that allows it to be processed, often because of system changes.
reclamación oscura   Reclamación en espera de ser procesada debido a que se necesita alguna información o elemento adicional, con frecuencia, debido a cambios en el sistema.

diplopia   Double vision.
diplopía   Visión doble.

direct filing system   A filing system in which materials can be located without consulting an intermediary source of reference.
sistema directo de archivo   Sistema de archivo en el cual los materiales pueden ser localizados sin consultar una fuente de referencia intermedia.

dirty claim   Claims that contain errors or omissions and that cannot be processed or must be processed by hand because of OCR scanner rejection.
reclamación sucia   Reclamación con errores u omisiones que no puede procesarse o que debe procesarse manualmente debido a que el escáner OCR la rechaza.

disbursements   Funds paid out.
desembolsos   Dinero o fondos que se pagan.

discretion   The quality of being discrete; having or showing good judgment or conduct, especially in speech.
discreción   Calidad de discreto; tener sensatez o tacto al obrar, especialmente al hablar.

disease   A pathologic process having a descriptive set of signs and symptoms.
enfermedad   Proceso patológico que tiene una serie descriptiva de signos y síntomas.

disinfection   The destruction of pathogens by physical or chemical means.
desinfección   Destrucción de agentes patógenos con medios físicos o químicos.

disk   A magnetic surface capable of storing computer programs.
disco   Superficie magnética capaz de almacenar programas de computadora.

disk drives   Devices that load a program or data stored on a disk into the computer.
unidades de discos   Dispositivos que cargan en la computadora un programa o datos almacenados en un disco.

disorder   Disruption of normal system functions.
trastorno   Interrupción de las funciones normales de un sistema.

disparaging   Speaking slightingly about something or someone, with a negative or degrading tone.
menospreciar   Hablar con desdén de algo o alguien, con un tono negativo o degradante.

disposition   The tendency of something or someone to act in a certain manner under given circumstances.
disposición   Tendencia de algo o alguien a actuar de un modo específico en determinadas circunstancias.

disruption   A breaking down, or throwing into disorder.
disrupción   Interrupción o creación de un estado de trastorno.

dissect   To cut or separate tissue with a cutting instrument or scissors.
diseccionar   Cortar o separar tejidos con tijeras u otro instrumento cortante.

dissection   The cutting or separating of a specimen into pieces and exposing the parts for scientific examination.
disección   Separar en piezas y dejar las partes a la vista para realizar un estudio científico.

disseminate   To disperse throughout.
diseminar   Dispersar, esparcir.

disseminate   To disburse; to spread around.
diseminado   Suelto, esparcido.

diurnal rhythm   Patterns of activity or behavior that follow day-night cycles.
ritmo diurno   Patrones de actividad o comportamiento que siguen a los ciclos nocturnos.

docket   A formal record of judicial proceedings; a list of legal causes to be tried.
orden del día   Registro formal de procesos judiciales; lista de causas legales a juzgar.

domestic mail   Mail sent within the boundaries of the United States and its territories.
correo nacional   Correo que se envía dentro de los límites de Estados Unidos y sus territorios.

dosimeter   A badge for monitoring the exposure of personnel to radiation.
dosímetro   Placa para controlar la exposición a la radiación del personal.

drawee   The bank or facility on which a check is drawn or written.
librado   Banco o entidad contra la que se gira o emite un cheque.

due process   A fundamental, constitutional guarantee that all legal proceedings will be fair and that one will be given notice of the proceedings and an opportunity to be heard before the government acts to take away life, liberty, or property; a constitutional guarantee that a law will not be unreasonable or arbitrary.
proceso debido   Garantía fundamental constitucional de que todos los procesos legales serán justos, que las partes implicadas serán notificadas de los procedimientos y que se les dará la oportunidad de ser escuchados rantes que el gobierno les quite su vida, libertad o propiedad; garantía constitucional de que la ley no irá en contra de la razón ni será arbitraria.

duty   Obligatory tasks, conduct, service, or functions that arise from one's position, as in life or in a group.
deber   Tareas, conducta, servicio o funciones de carácter obligatorio que conlleva el ocupar un puesto, en la vida o como miembro de un grupo.

dyspnea   Difficult or painful breathing.
disnea   Respiración difícil o dolorosa.

e-banking   Electronic banking via computer modem or over the Internet.
banca electrónica   Operaciones bancarias a través del módem de una computadora o en Internet.

ecchymosis   A hemorrhagic skin discoloration, commonly called *bruising*.
equimosis   Descoloramient o hemorrágico de la piel comúnmente conocido como *magulladura*.

e-commerce   A term used to describe the sale and purchase of goods and services over the Internet; doing business over the Internet; an abbreviation for *electronic commerce*.
comercio electrónico   Expresión que se usa para describir la compra y venta de bienes y servicios a través de Internet; hacer negocios a través de Internet. Se conoce también con la abreviatura de *comercio-e*.

edema   An abnormal accumulation of fluid in the interstitial spaces of tissue; swelling between layers of tissue.
edema   Acumulación anómala de fluido en los espacios intersticiales de los tejidos; inflamación entre capas de tejidos.

effacement   The thinning of the cervix during labor, measured in percentages from 0% to 100% effaced.

531

borramiento   Adelgazamiento del cuello del útero durante el parto. Se mide en porcentaje, borrado de 0 a 100 por ciento.

elastic pulse   A pulse with regular alterations of weak and strong beats, without changes in cycle.
pulso elástico   Pulso con alteraciones regulares de latidos fuertes y débiles sin cambios en el ciclo.

elastin   An essential part of elastic connective tissue that is flexible and elastic when moist.
elastina   Parte esencial del tejido conectivo elástico que cuando está húmedo es flexible y elástico.

electrodesiccation   Destructive drying of cells and tissue by means of short, high-frequency electrical sparks.
electrodesecación   Secado destructivo de células y tejidos por medio de cortas descargas eléctricas de alta frecuencia.

electrolytes   Small molecules that conduct an electrical charge. Electrolytes are necessary for proper functioning of muscle and nerve cells.
electrolitos   Pequeñas moléculas que conducen una carga eléctrica. Los electrolitos son necesarios para un funcionamiento correcto de los músculos y las células nerviosas.

electronic claims   Claims submitted to insurance processing facilities using a computerized medium, such as direct data entry, direct wire, dial-in telephone digital fax, or personal computer download and upload.
reclamación electrónica   Reclamaciones enviadas al lugar de procesamiento de la compañía aseguradora usando un sistema computarizado, tales como entrada de datos directa, cable directo, fax digital con marcado telefónico, o a través de una computadora personal.

e-mail   Communications transmitted via computer using a modem.
correo electrónico   Comunicaciones transmitidas a través de una computadora usando un módem.

emancipated minor   A person under legal age who is self-supporting and living apart from parents or a guardian.
menor emancipado   Persona que no ha alcanzado la mayoría de edad legal y que se mantiene a sí misma y vive sin la custodia de padres o tutores.

embezzlement   Stealing from an employer; appropriation without permission of goods, services, or funds for personal use.
desfalco   Robo a un empleador; apropiación sin permiso de bienes, servicios o fondos para uso personal.

embolization   An interventional technique in which a catheter is used to block off a blood vessel, thereby preventing hemorrhage.

embolización   Técnica de intervención usando un catéter para bloquear un vaso sanguíneo y evitar una hemorragia.

embolus   Foreign material that blocks a blood vessel, frequently a blood clot that has broken away from some other part of the body.
émbolo   Material extraño que bloquea un vaso sanguíneo, con frecuencia un coágulo de sangre procedente de otra parte del cuerpo.

emetic   A substance that causes vomiting.
emético   Sustancia que causa vómito.

emisor   The person who writes a check.
emisor   Persona que emite un cheque.

empathy   Sensitivity to the individual needs and reactions of patients.
empatía   Sensibilidad ante las necesidades y reacciones individuales de los pacientes.

emphysema   The pathologic accumulation of air in the tissues or organs; in the lungs, the bronchioles become plugged with mucus and lose elasticity.
enfisema   Acumulación patológica de aire en los tejidos u órganos; en los pulmones, los bronquiolos se obstruyen con mucosidade y pierden elasticidad.

emulsification   Dispersion of ingested fats into small globules by bile.
emulsionamiento   Dispersión (llevada a cabo por la bilis) en pequeños glóbulos de las grasas ingeridas.

encode   To convert from one system of communication to another; to convert a message into code.
codificar   Convertir de un sistema de comunicación a otro; convertir un mensaje en un código.

encounter   Any contact between a healthcare provider and a patient that results in treatment or evaluation of the patient's condition; not limited to in-person contact.
encuentro   Cualquier contacto entre un proveedor de atención sanitaria y un paciente que resulta en un tratamiento o evaluación del estado del paciente; no se limita a un contacto personal.

encroachment   To advance beyond the usual or proper limits.
intrusiones   Ir más allá de los límites habituales o apropiados.

endemic   A disease or microorganism that is specific to a particular geographic area.
endémico   Enfermedad o microorganismo que-es específico de una zona geográfica en particular.

endocervical curettage   The scraping of cells from the wall of the uterus.

English-Spanish Terms for the Medical Assistant

curetaje endocervical   Raspado de células de la pared uterina.

endorser   The person who signs his or her name on the back of a check for the purpose of transferring title to another person.
endosante   Persona que firma en la parte posterior de un cheque a fin de transferir la propiedad del mismo a otra persona.

enteric coated   A term referring to a special compound used to coat some oral medications; the coating resists the effects of stomach juices and does not dissolve, releasing the medication, until the tablet is exposed to the fluids of the small intestine.
cubierta entérica   Capa exterior que se añade a un medicamento que se toma por vía oral, la cual es resistente a los efectos de los jugos gástricos; recubrimiento diseñado para que la medicina sea absorbida en el intestino delgado; formulación usada en medicinas en la cual las tabletas se recubren con un componente especial que no se disuelve hasta que la tableta es expuesta a los fluidos del intestino delgado.

enunciate   To utter articulate sounds; to be very distinct in speech.
articular   Pronunciar los sonidos de manera cuidada; hablar de una forma muy clara.

enunciation   The utterance of articulate, clear sounds; the act of being very distinct in speech.
articulación   Pronunciación cuidada, con sonidos claros.

enzymatic reaction   A chemical reaction controlled by an enzyme.
reacción enzimática   Reacción química controlada por una enzima.

enzyme   Any of several complex proteins that are produced by cells and that act as catalysts in specific biochemical reactions.
enzima   Cualquiera de las varias proteínas complejas que producen las células y que actúan como catalíticos en reacciones bioquímicas específicas.

epiphysis   The end of a long bone.
epífisis   Extremo de un hueso largo.

erythropoietin   A substance released from the kidney and the liver that promotes red blood cell formation.
eritropoyetina   Sustancia liberada por los riñones y el hígado y que promueve la formación de glóbulos rojos.

essential hypertension   Elevated blood pressure of unknown cause that develops for no apparent reason; sometimes called *primary hypertension.*
hipertensión esencial   Presión sanguínea alta de causa desconocida que surge sin razón aparente; a veces se llama *hipertensión primaria.*

established patients   Patients who are returning to the office and who have previously seen the physician.
pacientes establecidos   Pacientes que regresan al consultorio médico que ya han sido atendidos por el médico con anterioridad.

etiology   The cause of a disorder, as determined for the purpose of classifying a claim.
etiología   Clasificación de una reclamación según la causa del trastorno.

eukaryote   A single-cell or multicellular organism in which the cell or cells have a distinct, membrane-bound nucleus.
eucariote   Organismo unicelular o multicelular cuyas células tienen un núcleo diferenciado rodeado por una membrana.

euthanasia   The act or practice of killing or permitting the death of hopelessly sick or injured individuals in a relatively painless way for reasons of mercy.
eutanasia   Acción o práctica de matar o permitir la muerte de enfermos o heridos en estado terminal, de una forma relativamente sin dolor, por razones de piedad.

exacerbation   An increase in the seriousness of a disease marked by greater intensity of the signs and symptoms; worsening of disease symptoms.
exacerbación   Aumento en la gravedad de una enfermedad, caracterizado por una mayor intensidad de los signos y síntomas. Empeoramiento de los síntomas de una enfermedad.

"excludes"   In insurance claims, exclusion terms are always written in italics, and the word "Excludes" is enclosed in a box to draw particular attention to these instructions. Exclusion terms may apply to a chapter, a section, a category, or a subcategory. The applicable code number usually follows the exclusion term.
"excluye"   Las expresiones de exclusión siempre se escriben en cursiva y la palabra "Excluye" se encierra en una casilla para llamar la atención acerca de estas instrucciones. Los términos de exclusión pueden ser aplicables a un capítulo, una sección, una categoría o una subcategoría. El número de código correspondiente por lo general sigue al término de exclusión.

expediency   Haste or caution; a means of achieving a particular end.
prontitud   Situación que requiere actuar con prisa o precaución; un medio de alcanzar un fin específico.

expert witness   A person who provides testimony to a court as an expert in a certain field or subject to verify facts presented by one or both sides in a lawsuit. An expert witness often is compensated and is used to refute or disprove the claims of one party.
testigo perito   Persona que da testimonio ante un tribunal como perito o experto en cierto campo o tema

533

para verificar los hechos presentados por una o ambas partes en litigio, a menudo, cobrando una retribución económica, y cu yo testimonio suele usarse para refutar o impugnar las demandas de una de las partes.

external noise   Noise outside the brain that interferes with the communication process.
ruido externo   Ruido producido fuera del cerebro y que interfiere con el proceso de comunicación.

externalization   Attribution of an event or occurrence to causes outside oneself.
exteriorización   Acción de atribuir a un suceso o acontecimiento causas externas al mismo.

externship/internship   A training program that is part of the course of study of an educational institution and that is taken in the actual business setting in that field of study; the two terms often are used interchangeably with regard to medical assisting.
prácticas internas/externas   Programa de entrenamiento que es parte de un curso de estudio de una institución educativa y se sigue en un lugar real de trabajo en el campo de estudio; estos términos se intercambian cuando se refieren a los asistentes médicos.

exudates   Fluids with a high concentration of protein and cellular debris that has escaped from the blood vessels and has been deposited in tissues or on tissue surfaces.
exudados   Fluidos con una alta concentración de proteínas y restos celulares extravasados de los vasos sanguíneos y depositados en los tejidos o en sus superficies.

familial   Occurring in or affecting members of a family more than would be expected to occur by chance.
familiar   Que sucede o afecta a miembros de una familia más de lo que podría esperarse por azar.

fascia   A sheet or band of fibrous tissue located deep in the skin that covers muscles and body organs.
fascia   Lámina o banda de tejido fibroso localizada bajo la piel y que cubre los músculos y los órganos.

fastidious   With regard to laboratory cultures, an organism that requires specialized media or growth factors to grow.
exigente   Que requiere un medio o factores especiales para crecer.

fat   A substance stored as adipose tissue in the body that serves as a concentrated energy reserve.
grasa   Sustancia que se almacena como tejido adiposo en el cuerpo y sirve como reserva de energía concentrada.

fax   The abbreviation for the term *facsimile;* a document sent using a fax machine.
fax   Abreviatura de facsímile; documento que se envía usando una máquina de fax.

febrile   Pertaining to an elevated body temperature.
febril   Perteneciente o relativo a una temperatura corporal elevada.

fecalith   A hard, impacted mass of feces in the colon.
fecaloma   Masa de heces endurecidas e impactadas en el colon.

fee profile   A compilation or average of physicians' fees over a given period.
perfil de cargos   Recopilación o porcentaje de cargos médicos en un periodo de tiempo dado.

fee schedule   A compilation of pre-established fee allowances for given services or procedures.
escala de cargos   Recopilación de asignaciones de cargos preestablecidos para servicios o procedimientos dados.

feedback   The transmission of evaluative or corrective information about an action, event, or process to the original or controlling source.
reacciones y comentarios   Envío de información de evaluación o corrección a la fuente original o a la que ejerce el control sobre una acción, suceso o proceso.

felony   A major crime, such as murder, rape, or burglary, that is punishable by a more stringent sentence than that given for a misdemeanor, or lesser crime.
crimen   Delito mayor, como asesinato, violación o robo; se penaliza con una sentencia más severa que un delito menor o falta.

fermentation   An enzymatically controlled transformation of an organic compound.
fermentación   Transformación de un compuesto orgánico controlada por enzimas.

fervent   Exhibiting or marked by great intensity of feeling.
ferviente   Que posee sentimientos de gran intensidad o que da muestra de ellos.

fibrillation   Rapid, random, ineffective contractions of the heart.
fibrilación   Contracciones cardiacas rápidas, aleatorias e inefectivas.

fidelity   Faithfulness to something to which one is bound by pledge or duty.
fidelidad   Fe en algo a lo que se está unido por juramento o deber.

filtrate   The fluid that remains after a liquid is passed through a membranous filter.
filtrado   Fluido que queda después de pasar un líquido a través de un filtro membranoso.

fine   A sum imposed as punishment for an offense; a forfeiture or penalty paid to an injured party or the government in a civil or criminal action.

multa Suma impuesta como penalización por un delito menor; suma que se paga a una parte a la que se ha perjudicado o dañado, o al gobierno, en un proceso civil o penal.

fiscal agent An organization or private plan under contract to the government to act as a financial representative in handling insurance claims from providers of health care; also referred to as a *fiscal intermediary*.
agente fiscal Organización o plan privado bajo contrato con el gobierno para actuar como representantes financieros en la administración de reclamaciones de seguros por parte de proveedores de atención sanitaria; también se conoce como *intermediario fiscal*.

fiscal intermediary An organization that contracts with the government and other insuring entities to handle and mediate insurance claims from medical facilities.
intermediario fiscal Organización que establece un contrato con el gobierno y otras entidades aseguradoras para administrar reclamaciones de seguro provenientes de centros médicos y para mediar en ellas.

fissures Narrow slits or clefts in the abdominal wall.
fisuras Grietas o hendiduras estrechas en la pared abdominal.

fistulas Abnormal, tubelike passages within the body tissue, usually between two internal organs or from an internal organ to the body surface.
fístulas Pasajes anómalos en forma de tubos entre los tejidos corporales, por lo general entre dos órganos internos, o de un órgano interno a la superficie del cuerpo.

flagged Marked in some way to serve as a reminder that specific action needs to be taken.
señalado Marcado de alguna forma para recordar que se necesita que se tomen medidas al respeto.

Flash Animation technology often used on the opening page of a Web site to draw the attention of, excite, and impress the user.
Flash Tecnología de imágenes animadas que se usa con frecuencia en la página inicial de un sitio web para llamar la atención del usuario, entusiasmarlo e impresionarlo.

flatus Gas expelled through the anus.
flato Gas expulsado a través del ano.

fluoroscopy Direct observation of an x-ray image in motion.
fluoroscopía Observación directa de una imagen de rayos x en movimiento.

flush Directly abutting or immediately adjacent to, such as set even with the edge of a page or column; having no indention.
alineado Directamente contiguo o inmediatamente adyacente, ordenado de forma regular en relación con un borde de una página o columna; sin sangría o espacios en blanco.

follicle-stimulating hormone (FSH) A hormone secreted by the anterior pituitary that stimulates oogenesis and spermatogenesis.
hormona foliculoestimulante (FSH) Hormona que segrega la pituitaria anterior y que estimula los procesos de formación y desarrollo de óvulos y de espermatozoides.

font A design, as in typesetting, for a set of characters.
fuente tipográfica Diseño similar al de la composición para un conjunto de caracteres.

format To magnetically create tracks on a disk in which information will be stored; formatting usually is done by the manufacturer of the disk.
formatear Crear pistas magnéticas en un disco destinado a almacenar información; por lo general, el fabricante del disco es quien se encarga de hacerlo.

fovea centralis A small pit in the center of the retina that is considered the center of clearest vision.
fóvea central Pequeña concavidad en el centro de la retina que se cree que es el centro de visión más claro.

frontal projection The radiographic view in which the coronal plane of the body or body part is parallel to the film plane; AP or PA.
proyección frontal Vista radiográfica en la cual el plano coronal del cuerpo o de la parte del cuerpo está paralelo al plano de la película; AP o PA.

gait The manner or style of walking.
andares Forma o estilo de caminar.

gamete A mature male or female germ cell, which usually has a haploid chromosome set and can initiate the formation of a new diploid individual.
gameto Célula germinal madura, tanto masculina como femenina, que por lo general tiene un conjunto cromosómico haploide y es capaz de iniciar la formación de un nuevo individuo diploide.

gangrene The death of body tissue, as a result of the loss of nutritive supply, and subsequent bacterial invasion and putrefaction.
gangrena Muerte de tejido corporal debido a la pérdida de suministro de nutrientes por invasión bacteriana y putrefacción.

gantry The doughnut-shaped portion of a scanner than surrounds the patient and functions at least in part to gather imaging data.
gantry Parte de un escáner con forma de rosquilla que rodea al paciente y funciona, al menos en parte, reuniendo datos de formación de imágenes.

generic Not protected by trademark.

535

genéricas   Medicinas que no están protegidas por una marca registrada.

genome   The genetic material of an organism.
genoma   El material genético de un organismo.

genuineness   Expressing sincerity and honest feeling.
autenticidad   Expresión de sentimientos sincera y honrada.

germicides   Agents that destroy pathogenic organisms.
germicidas   Agentes químicos que destruyen o matan organismos patógenos.

gigabyte   Approximately 1 billion bytes.
gigabyte   Aproximadamente, mil millones de bytes.

girth   A measure around a body or item.
contorno   Medida alrededor de un cuerpo o artículo.

glean   To gather information or material bit by bit; to pick over in search of relevant material.
recopilar   Reunir información o material pedazo a pedazo; examinar en busca de material pertinente.

glucagon   A hormone produced by the alpha cells of the pancreatic islets that stimulates the liver to convert glycogen into glucose.
glucagón   Hormona producida por las células alfa de los islotes pancreáticos; estimula al hígado para que convierta el glucógeno en glucosa.

glucosuria   The abnormal presence of glucose in the urine.
glucosuria   Presencia anómala de glucosa en la orina.

glycogen   The sugar (starch) that is formed from glucose and stored mainly in the liver.
glucógeno   Azúcar (almidón) formado a partir de la glucosa y almacenado principalmente en el hígado.

glycohemoglobin (hemoglobinA$_{1c}$)   A type of hemoglobin that is made slowly during the 120-day life span of the red blood cell (RBC). Glycohemoglobin makes up 3% to 6% of hemoglobin in a normal RBC; in individuals with diabetes mellitus, it makes up to 12%.
glucohemoglobina (hemoglobina A$_{1c}$)   Tipo de hemoglobina que se produce lentamente durante el periodo de los 120 días de vida de los glóbulos rojos (RBC). La glucohemoglobina constituye de un 3% a un 6% de la hemoglobina en un RBC normal; en los casos de diabetes mellitus constituye hasta un 12%.

glycosuria   The presence of glucose in the urine.
glucosuria   Presencia de glucosa en la orina.

goniometer   An instrument used to measure the degrees of motion in a joint.
goniómetro   Instrumento para medir los grados de movimiento de una articulación.

government plan   An insurance or healthcare plan sponsored and/or subsidized by the state or federal government, such as Medicaid and Medicare.
plan del gobierno   Seguro o plan de atención sanitaria patrocinado y subvencionado por el gobierno estatal o federal, como Medicaid y Medicare.

grammar   The study of the classes of words, their inflections, and their functions and relations in a sentence; the study of what is preferred and what should be avoided in inflection and syntax.
gramática   Estudio de las clases de palabras, sus desinencias y sus funciones y relaciones en la oración; estudio del uso que se prefiere y de lo que hay que evitar en cuanto a desinencias y sintaxis.

gray (Gy)   The international unit of radiation dose.
gray (Gy)   Unidad internacional de dosis de radiación.

grief   An unfortunate outcome; deep distress caused by bereavement.
pesar   Resultado desafortunado; profunda aflicción causada por la pérdida de un ser querido.

group policy   Insurance written under a policy that covers a number of people under a single master contract, which is issued to their employer or to an association with which they are affiliated.
póliza de grupo   Seguro contratado bajo una póliza que cubre a varias personas bajo un único contrato maestro establecido con su empleador o con una asociación a la que estén afiliados.

growth hormone (GH)   The hormone that stimulates tissue growth and restricts tissue glucose dependence when nutrients are not available; also called *somatotropic hormone.*
hormona del crecimiento (GH)   También llamada *hormona somatotrópica,* estimula el crecimiento de los tejidos y restringe la dependencia de la glucosa de los tejidos cuando no hay nutrientes disponibles.

guarantor   A person who makes or gives a guarantee of payment for a bill.
garante   Persona que paga una factura o que garantiza su pago.

guardian ad litem   The legal representative of a minor.
tutor ad litem   Representante legal de un menor.

hard copy   The readable paper copy or printout of information.
copia impresa   Copia impresa en papel o impresión de la información.

harmonious   Marked by accord in sentiment or action; having the parts agreeably related.
armonioso   Caracterizado por una armonía en los sentimientos o acciones; partes de un todo relacionadas de forma agradable.

536

health insurance Protection, in return for periodic premiums, that provides reimbursement of monetary losses resulting from illness or injury. Included under this heading are various types of insurance, such as accident insurance, disability income insurance, medical expense insurance, and accidental death and dismemberment insurance. Also known as *accident and health insurance* or *disability income insurance*.
seguro de enfermedad Cobertura a cambio del pago de primas periódicas, la cual proporciona el reembolso de las pérdidas monetarias debidas a enfermedad o lesión. Bajo este nombre se incluyen varios tipos de seguros como seguro de accidente, seguro de incapacidad, seguro de gastos médicos y seguro en caso de muerte y pérdida de extremidades. También se conoce como *seguro de accidente y enfermedad* o *seguro de incapacidad*.

hematemesis Vomiting of bright red blood, which indicates rapid upper gastrointestinal bleeding and is associated with esophageal varices or a peptic ulcer.
hematemesis Vómito de sangre roja brillante que indica hemorragia rápida del sistema gastrointestinal superior, relacionado con varices esofágicas o úlcera péptica.

hematocrit The percentage by volume of packed red blood cells in a given sample of blood after centrifugation; the volume percentage of erythrocytes in whole blood.
hematocrito Porcentaje por volumen de glóbulos rojos en una muestra de sangre dada después de ser centrifugada. Porcentaje del volumen de eritrocitos en la sangre completa.

hematoma A sac filled with blood that may be the result of trauma.
hematoma Saco lleno de sangre que puede ser el resultado de una lesión.

hematuria Blood in the urine.
hematuria Sangre en la orina.

hemoconcentration A condition in which the concentration of blood cells is increased in proportion to the plasma.
hemoconcentración Situación en la cual la concentración de glóbulos rojos ha aumentado en proporción al plasma.

hemoglobin A protein in erythrocytes that transports molecular oxygen in the blood.
hemoglobina Proteína que se encuentra en los eritrocitos que transportan el oxígeno en la sangre.

hemolysis The destruction or dissolution of red blood cells, with subsequent release of hemoglobin.
hemolisis Destrucción o disolución de los glóbulos rojos, con la subsiguiente liberación de hemoglobina.

hemolyzed A term used to describe a blood sample in which the red blood cells have ruptured.

hemolizado Término usado para describir una muestra de sangre en la cual los glóbulos rojos se han roto.

hepatomegaly Abnormal enlargement of the liver.
hepatomegalia Agrandamiento anómalo del hígado.

hereditary Pertaining to a characteristic, condition, or disease transmitted from parent to offspring on the DNA chain.
hereditario Perteneciente o relativo a una característica, estado o enfermedad transmitida de padres a hijos en la cadena de ADN.

hermetically sealed Sealed such that no air may enter or escape.
herméticamente sellado Sellado de forma que el aire no pueda entrar o escapar.

HMO An organization that provides a wide range of comprehensive healthcare services for a specified group at a fixed periodic payment. HMOs may be sponsored by the government, medical schools, hospitals, employers, labor unions, consumer groups, insurance companies, and hospital medical plans.
HMO Organización que proporciona una amplia gama de servicios completos de atención sanitaria para un grupo específico por un pago periódico fijado. Las HMO puedes estar patrocinadas por el gobierno, facultades de medicina, hospitales, patronos, sindicatos laborales, grupos de consumidores, compañías aseguradoras y planes médico-hospitalarios.

holder The person who presents a check for payment.
portador Persona que presenta un cheque para cobrarlo.

holistic Related to or concerned with all of the body's systems as a whole, rather than as separate parts.
holístico Relacionado con todos los sistemas corporales y no dividido en partes.

homeostasis The maintenance of constant internal ambient conditions compatible with life.
homeostasis Mantenimiento de unas condiciones ambientales internas constantes compatibles con la vida.

homeostatic Maintaining a constant internal environment.
homeostático Que mantiene un ambiente interno constante.

hormone A substance, usually a peptide or steroid, produced by one tissue and conveyed by the bloodstream to another to effect physiologic activity, such as growth or metabolism; a chemical transmitter produced by the body and transported to a target tissue or organs by the bloodstream.
hormona Sustancia química transmisora, por lo general un péptido o un esteroide, que es producida por un tejido y transportada por la corriente sanguínea hasta el tejido u

537

órgano—objetivo para provocar un efecto en la actividad fisiológica, como el crecimiento o el metabolismo.

HTML Abbreviation for *hypertext markup language,* the language used to create documents for the Internet.
HTML Abreviatura de *lenguaje de marcas de hipertexto,* que es el lenguaje que se emplea para crear documentos destinados a usarse en Internet.

HTTP Abbreviation for *hypertext transfer protocol,* which designates how messages are defined and transmitted over the Internet; when a URL is entered into the computer, an HTTP command tells the Web server to retrieve the requested Web page.
HTTP Abreviatura de *protocolo de transporte de hipertexto,* que define cómo se interpretan y transmiten los mensajes en Internet; cuando un URL entra en la computadora, una orden de HTTP manda la señal al servidor web para que busque la página web que se solicita.

hub A common connection point for devices in a network containing multiple ports; it often is used to connect segments of an LAN.
nodo Punto de conexión común para dispositivos en una red de conexiones de varios puertos; suele usar se para conectar segmentos de una LAN (red de área local).

hydrocephaly Enlargement of the cranium caused by the abnormal accumulation of cerebrospinal fluid in the cerebral system.
hidrocefalia Agrandamiento del cráneo causado por una acumulación anómala de fluido cerebroespinal en el interior del sistema cerebral.

hydrogenated Combined with, treated with, or exposed to hydrogen.
hidrogenado Combinado con hidrógeno, tratado con él o expuesto a él.

hyperlipidemia An excess of fats or lipids in the blood plasma.
hiperlipemia Exceso de grasas o lípidos en el plasma sanguíneo.

hyperplasia An increase in the number of cells.
hiperplasia Aumento del número de células.

hyperpnea An increase in the depth of breathing.
hiperpnea Aumento en la profundidad de la respiración.

hypertension High blood pressure (i.e., a systolic pressure consistently above 140 mm Hg and a diastolic pressure above 90 mm Hg).
hipertensión Presión sanguínea alta (presión sistólica continuamente por encima de 140 mm Hg y presión diastólica por encima de 90 mm Hg).

hyperventilation Abnormally prolonged and deep breathing, usually associated with acute anxiety or emotional tension.

hiperventilación Respiración profunda anómalamente prolongada, que suele estar asociada con una ansiedad aguda o con tensión emocional.

hypotension Blood pressure that is below normal (i.e., a systolic pressure below 90 mm Hg and a diastolic pressure below 50 mm Hg).
hipotensión Presión sanguínea que está por debajo de lo normal (presión sistólica por debajo de 90 mm Hg y presión diastólica por debajo de 50 mm Hg).

icon A picture, often on the desktop of a computer, that represents a program or an object. By clicking on the icon, the user is directed to the program.
icono Dibujo, con frecuencia colocado en el escritorio de la computadora, que representa un programa o un objeto. Al hacer clic sobre el icono, el usuario es llevado a dicho programa.

idealism The practice of forming ideas or living under the influence of ideas.
idealismo Práctica de formarse ideas o vivir bajo la influencia de ideas.

idiopathic Of unknown cause.
idiopático Causa desconocida.

ileocecal valve The valve at the opening between the ileum and the cecum; also called the *ileocolic valve.*
válvula ileocecal Válvula que controla la abertura entre el íleo y el intestino ciego; también se llama *válvula ileocólica.*

ileostomy The surgical formation of an opening of the ileum onto the surface of the abdomen, through which fecal material is emptied.
ileostomía Formación quirúrgica de una abertura del íleo en la superficie del abdomen, a través de la cual se vacían los materiales fecales.

immigrant A person who comes to a country to take up permanent residence.
inmigrante Persona que va a un país para vivir allí de forma permanente.

immunotherapy The administration of repeated injections of diluted extracts of a substance that causes an allergic reaction; also called *desensitization.*
inmunoterapia Administración de repetidas inyecciones de extractos diluidos de la substancia que provoca una alergia; también se conoce como *desensibilización.*

impenetrable Incapable of being penetrated or pierced; not capable of being damaged or harmed.
impenetrable Que no puede ser penetrado o traspasado; que no puede ser dañado o perjudicado.

implied consent Presumed consent, such as when a patient offers an arm for a phlebotomy procedure.

consentimiento tácito   Consentimiento que se supone que ha sido dado, como cuando un paciente presenta el brazo para que se le extraiga sangre.

in vitro   Refers to conditions outside of a living body.
in-vitro   Expresión que se refiere a condiciones exteriores de un ser vivo.

incentive   Something that incites or spurs to action; a reward or reason for performing a task.
incentivo   Algo que incita o impulsa a actuar; recompensa o razón para llevar a cabo una tarea.

"includes"   In insurance claims, when this term appears under a subdivision such as a category (three digit) code or a two-digit procedure code, this indicates that the code and title include these terms. Other terms also classified to that particular code and title are listed in the Alphabetic Index.
"incluye"   La presencia de esta expresión, cuando aparece bajo una subdivisión, como una categoría (código de tres dígitos) o como un código de procedimiento de dos dígitos, indica que el código y el título incluyen estos términos. En los Índices alfabéticos se enumeran otros términos también clasificados para este código específico.

incontinence   The inability to control excretory functions.
incontinencia   Incapacidad de controlar las funciones excretoras.

indemnity plan   The traditional health insurance plan that pays for all or a share of the cost of covered services, regardless of which doctor, hospital, or other licensed healthcare provider is used. Policyholders of indemnity plans and their dependents choose when and where to get healthcare services.
plan de indemnización   Plan de seguro de enfermedad tradicional que paga todo o parte del costo de los servicios que cubre, sin importar a qué médico, hospital u otro proveedor de atención sanitaria licenciado se acuda. Los titulares de pólizas de planes de indemnización y las personas que dependen de estos titulares escogen cuándo y dónde recibir atención médica.

indicators   An important point or group of statistical values that, when evaluated, indicates the quality of care provided in a healthcare institution.
indicadores   Importante punto o grupo de valores estadísticos que al ser evaluados indican la calidad del servicio que se proporciona en una institución de atención sanitaria.

indict   To charge with a crime by the finding or presentment of a jury according to due process of law.
acusado   Que se le imputa con un cargo criminal por conclusión o acusación de un jurado con el proceso legal debido.

indigent   Totally lacking in something necessary.

indigente   Que carece totalmente de algo necesario.

indirect filing system   A filing system in which an intermediary reference, such as a card file, must be consulted to locate specific files.
sistema indirecto de archivo   Sistema de archivo en el cual debe consultarse una fuente de referencia intermedia, como un fichero, para localizar documentos específicos.

individual policy   An insurance policy designed specifically for the use of one person (and his or her dependents); a policy that is not associated with the amenities of a group policy, such as lower premiums. Often referred to as "personal insurance."
póliza individual   Póliza de seguros destinada específicamente a ser usada por una persona (y quienes dependan de ella) y que no conlleva los beneficios de una póliza de grupo y tiene primas más altas. Con frecuencia se le llama "seguro—personal."

induration   An abnormally hard, inflamed area.
induración   Área anómalamente dura, inflamada.

infarction   Area of tissue that has died because of lack of blood supply.
infarto   Área de tejido que ha muerto debido a una falta de suministro de sangre.

infection   Invasion of body tissues by microorganisms, which then proliferate and damage tissues.
infección   Invasión de los tejidos corporales por microorganismos, los cuales entonces proliferan y dañan los tejidos.

infertile   Not fertile or productive; not capable of reproducing.
estéril   Que no es fértil o productivo; que no tiene la capacidad de reproducirse.

inflammation   A tissue reaction to trauma or disease that includes redness, heat, swelling, and pain.
inflamación   Reacción de los tejidos ante una lesión o enfermedad que incluye enrojecimiento, calentamiento, hinchazón y dolor.

inflection   A change in the pitch or loudness of the voice.
inflexión   Cambio en el tono o volumen de la voz.

informed consent   Consent given because the patient understands the proposed treatment and the risks involved, the reasons it should be done, and alternative treatments available (including no treatment) and their attendant risks.
consentimiento informado   Consentimiento que implica la comprensión del tratamiento al que se va a ser sometido y de los riesgos que conlleva, del porqué de dicho tratamiento, así como la comprensión de los tratamientos alternativos disponibles (incluyendo la ausencia de tratamiento) y los riesgos que conllevan.

infraction   A minor offense against rules or regulations.
infracción   Incumplimiento de la ley; delito menor contra las normas establecidas.

initiate   To introduce; to cause or start something.
iniciativa   El causar o facilitar el comienzo de algo; el hacer que algo comience a ocurrir.

innate   Existing in, belonging to, or determined by factors present in an individual since birth.
innato   Que existe en un individuo, que le pertenece o que está determinado por factores existentes en ese individuo desde el momento de su nacimiento.

input   Information entered into a computer and used to produce output.
entrada   Información introducida en una computadora y que la computadora utiliza.

instigate   To goad or urge forward; to provoke.
instigar   Incitar, exhortar, provocar.

insubordination   Disobedience to authority.
insubordinación   Desobediencia a la autoridad.

insulin   A hormone secreted by the beta cells of the pancreatic islets in response to increased levels of glucose in the blood.
insulina   Hormona que segregan las células beta de los islotes pancreáticos en respuesta a la presencia de altos niveles de glucosa en la sangre.

insured   A person or organization covered by an insurance policy, along with any other parties for whom protection is provided under the policy terms.
asegurado   Persona u organización que está cubierta por una póliza de seguro junto con cualquier otro a quien se proporcione cobertura bajo los términos de la póliza.

intangible   Incapable of being perceived, especially by touch; incapable of being precisely identified or realized by the mind.
intangible   Que no se puede percibir, especialmente que no se puede tocar; que no puede ser identificado con precisión ni ser comprendido por la mente.

integral   Essential; an indispensable part of a whole.
integral   Esencial; parte indispensable de un todo.

interaction   A two-way communication; mutual or reciprocal action or influence.
interacción   Comunicación bidireccional; acción o influencia recíproca o mutua.

intercom   A two-way communication system with a microphone and loudspeaker at each station for localized use.
intercomunicador   Sistema de comunicación bidireccional con un micrófono y un altavoz en cada estación para uso local.

intermittent   Coming and going at intervals; not continuous.
intermitente   Que va y viene a intervalos; de forma no continua.

intermittent claudication   Recurring cramping in the calves caused by poor circulation of blood to the muscles of the lower leg.
cojera intermitente   Calambres recurrentes en las pantorrillas causados por una mala circulación de la sangre de los músculos de la parte inferior de la pierna.

intermittent pulse   A pulse in which beats occasionally are skipped.
pulso intermitente   Pulso en el cual de vez en cuando se salta algún latido.

internal noise   Noise inside the brain that interferes with the communication process.
ruido interno   Ruido en el interior del cerebro que interfiere con el proceso de comunicación.

International Classification of Diseases, Ninth Revision, Clinical Modification (ICD-9-CM)   A system for classifying diseases to facilitate the collection of uniform, comparable health information for statistical purposes and for indexing medical records for data storage and retrieval.
Clasificación Internacional de Enfermedades, Novena Revisión, Modificación clínica (ICD-9-CM)   Sistema de clasificación de enfermedades para facilitar la recopilación de información médica uniforme, tanto para fines estadísticos como para indexar informes médicos a fin de almacenar y recuperar datos.

International Classification of Diseases, Tenth Revision (ICD-10)   A system marked by the greatest number of changes in the ICD's history. To allow more specific reporting of diseases and newly recognized conditions, the ICD-10 has approximately 5,500 more codes than the ICD-9.
Clasificación Internacional de Enfermedades, Décima Revisión (ICD-10)   Sistema que contiene el mayor número de cambios en la historia de la ICD. Para permitir elaborar informes más precisos de las enfermedades y de los estados patológicos que se conocen sólo recientemente, la ICD-10 incluye aproximadamente 5,500 códigos más que la ICD-9.

international mail   Mail sent outside the boundaries of the United States and its territories.
correo internacional   Correo que se envía fuera de los límites de Estados Unidos y sus territorios.

interval   The length of time between events.
intervalo   Espacio de tiempo entre dos sucesos.

intolerable   Not tolerable or bearable.
intolerable   Que no se puede tolerar o soportar.

intravenous urogram (IVU)   A radiographic examination of the urinary tract that uses intravenous injection of an iodine contrast medium.
urograma intravenoso (IVU)   Examen radiográfico del tracto urinario usando una inyección intravenosa de un medio de contraste yodado.

intrinsic   Belonging to the essential nature or constitution of a thing; indwelling, inward.
intrínseco   Que pertenece a la naturaleza o constitución básica de una cosa; inherente, interno.

introspection   An inward, reflective examination of one's own thoughts and feelings.
introspección   Examen de nuestros propios pensamientos y sentimientos.

invariably   Consistently; without changing or being capable of change.
invariablemente   De forma constante; que no cambia ni puede cambiar.

invasive   A term that refers to entry into the living body, as by incision or insertion of an instrument.
invasivo   Que entra en un organismo vivo, como por incisión o inserción de un instrumento.

ipsilateral   Pertaining to the same side of the body.
isolateral   Perteneciente a la misma parte del cuerpo.

irregular pulse   A pulse that varies in force and frequency.
pulso irregular   Pulso que varía en fuerza y frecuencia.

ischemia   Decreased blood flow to a body part or organ, caused by constriction or plugging of the supplying artery; a temporary interruption in blood supply to a tissue or organ.
isquemia   Disminución del flujo sanguíneo a una parte del cuerpo u órgano provocada por la constricción o atasco de la arteria suministradora; interrupción temporal del suministro de sangre a un tejido u órgano.

islets (of Langerhans)   Cells of the pancreas that produce insulin (beta cells) and glucagon (alpha cells); also called *pancreatic islets*.
islotes (de Langerhans)   Células del páncreas que producen insulina (células beta) y glucagón (células alfa); también llamados *islotes pancreáticos*.

jargon   The technical terminology or characteristic idiom of a particular group or special activity.
jerga   Terminología técnica o lenguaje característico de un grupo específico o una actividad especial.

jaundice   Yellowness of the skin and mucous membranes caused by deposition of bile pigment. Jaundice is not itself a disease, but rather a sign of a number of diseases, especially liver disorders.

ictericia   Coloración amarilla en la piel y las membranas mucosas causada por deposición del pigmento biliar. No es una enfermedad pero es un síntoma de muchas enfermedades, sobre todo de trastornos hepáticos.

Java   An object-oriented, high-level programming language commonly used and well suited for the Internet.
Java   Lenguaje de programación de alto nivel y orientado a objetos que es usado ampliamente y es muy adecuado para Internet.

judicial   Of or relating to a judgment, the function of judging, the administration of justice, or the judiciary.
judicial   Perteneciente o relativo al juicio, los procesos jurídicos, la administración de justicia o a la judicatura.

jurisdiction   A power constitutionally conferred on a judge or magistrate to decide cases according to law and to carry sentence into execution. Jurisdiction is *original* when it is conferred on the court in the first instance (original jurisdiction); it is *appellate* when an appeal is given from the judgment of another court (appellate jurisdiction).
jurisdicción   Poder constitucional otorgado a un juez o magistrado para resolver casos de acuerdo con la ley y hacer que se cumplan las sentencias. Es jurisdicción *original* cuando se otorga en un tribunal de primera instancia; es jurisdicción en *apelación* cuando existe una apelación al juicio de otro tribunal.

jurisprudence   The science or philosophy of law; a system or body of law or the course of court decisions.
jurisprudencia   Ciencia o filosofía que trata sobre la ley; sistema o cuerpo legal; línea de decisiones de los tribunales.

keratin   A very hard, tough protein found in the hair, nails, and epidermal tissue.
queratina   Proteína muy dura que se encuentra en el pelo, uñas y tejidos epidérmicos.

keratinocytes   Any one of the skin cells that synthesize keratin.
queratinocitos   Cualquiera de las células de la piel que sintetizan queratina.

ketosis   The abnormal production of ketone bodies in the blood and tissues as a result of fat catabolism in cells. Ketones accumulate in large quantities when fat, instead of sugar, is used as fuel for energy in cells.
quetosis   Producción anormal de cuerpos de quetosis en la sangre y tejidos como resultado de un catabolismo graso en las células. Los quetones se acumulan en grandes cantidades cuando se usa grasa, en lugar de azúcar, como combustible para las células.

kyphosis   An abnormal convex curvature of the thoracic spine region.

541

cifosis Curvatura convexa anómala de la región espinal torácica.

lacrimation The secretion or discharge of tears.
lagrimeo Secreción o descarga de lágrimas.

language barrier Any type of interference that inhibits the communication process and is related to the difference in languages spoken by the people attempting to communicate.
barrera del idioma Cualquier tipo de interferencia que inhibe el proceso de comunicación y que está relacionado con la diferencia en los idiomas que hablan las personas que intentan comunicarse.

laryngoscopy Visual examination of the voice box area through an endoscope equipped with a light and mirrors for illumination.
laringoscopia Examen visual de la laringe por medio de un endoscopio equipado con una luz y espejos.

latent image Invisible changes in exposed film that become a visible image when the film is processed.
imagen latente Cambios invisibles en la película que se convertirán en una imagen visible cuando se procese la película.

law A binding custom or practice of a community; a rule of conduct or action prescribed or formally recognized as binding or enforceable by a controlling authority.
ley Costumbre o práctica obligatoria de una comunidad; norma de comportamiento o proceder prescrita o reconocida formalmente como norma obligatoria o que se puede hacer cumplir por una autoridad encargada.

learning style The way a person perceives and processes information to learn new material.
estilo de aprendizaje Forma en la que un individuo percibe y procesa la información para aprender cosas nuevas.

leukoderma White patches on the skin.
leucodermia Manchas blancas en la piel.

liable Obligated according to law or equity; responsible for an act or circumstance.
responsable Que tiene alguna obligación según la ley o el derecho lato; responsable de un acto o circunstancia.

libel A written defamatory statement or representation that conveys an unjustly unfavorable impression.
libelo Escrito difamatorio que produce una impresión desfavorable injusta.

ligament A tough connective tissue band that holds joints together by attaching to the bones on either side of the joint.

ligamento Banda de tejido conectivo resistente que sostiene las articulaciones uniendo los huesos de cada lado de la articulación.

ligation The process of tying off something to close it (e.g., a blood vessel during surgery) with a tie called a *ligature*.
ligado Proceso de atar algo, por ejemplo, un vaso sanguíneo durante una cirugía, con una atadura llamada *ligadura*.

limited radiography A limited-scope radiography practice, usually in an outpatient setting, that does not require the same credentials as those for professional radiologic technology; also called *practical radiography*.
radiografía limitada Práctica radiográfica de alcance limitado que se suele usar con pacientes externos y que no requiere las mismas credenciales que se necesitan para la tecnología radiográfica profesional. También se llama radiografía práctica.

lithotripsy A procedure for eliminating a stone (as in the bladder) by crushing or dissolving it in situ with high-intensity sound waves.
litotripsia Procedimiento para eliminar una piedra rompiéndola o disolviéndola in-situ por medio del uso de ondas sonoras de alta intensidad.

litigious Prone to engage in lawsuits.
litigioso Propenso a iniciar pleitos y litigios.

loading dose A double dose of medication administered as the first dose. Loading doses usually are given in antibiotic therapy to reach therapeutic drug levels in the blood quickly.
dosis de ataque Dosis doble de una medicación ladministrada como primera dosis. Suele hacerse con terapia antibiótica para alcanzar rápidamente los niveles terapéuticos en sangre.

lordosis An abnormal concave curvature of the cervical and lumbar spines.
lordosis Curvatura cóncava anómala de la espina cervical y lumbar.

lower GI series A fluoroscopic examination of the colon that usually involves rectal administration of barium sulfate (also called a *barium enema*) as a contrast medium.
serie GI inferior Examen fluoroscópico del colon, por lo general usando una administración rectal de sulfato de bario (también llamado *enema de bario*) como medio de contraste.

lumbar The area of the lower back containing the five lumbar vertebrae.
lumbar Región posterior inferior en la que hay cinco vértebras lumbares.

lumen   The open space within a hollow tube such as a blood vessel, the intestine, a needle, or an examining instrument.
lumen   Espacio abierto, como en el interior de un vaso sanguíneo, el intestino, una aguja, un tubo o un instrumento para examinar.

luteinizing hormone (LH)   A hormone produced by the pituitary gland that promotes ovulation.
hormona luteinizante (LH)   Hormona que produce la glándula pituitaria y que promueve la ovulación.

luxation   Dislocation of a bone from its normal anatomic location.
luxación   Dislocación de un hueso de su ubicación anatómica normal.

lymphadenopathy   Any disorder of the lymph nodes or lymph vessels.
linfadenopatía   Cualquier trastorno de los nódulos o de los vasos linfáticos.

macromolecules   The molecules needed for metabolism: carbohydrates, lipids, proteins, and nucleic acids.
macromoléculas   Moléculas que se necesitan para el metabolismo: carbohidratos, lípidos, proteínas y ácidos nucleicos.

magnetic resonance imaging (MRI)   An imaging modality that uses a magnetic field and radiofrequency pulses to create computer images of both bones and soft tissues in multiple planes.
formación de imágenes por resonancia magnética (MRI)   Modalidad de formación de imágenes en la que se usa un campo magnético y pulsos de radiofrecuencia para crear imágenes computarizadas, tanto de huesos como de tejidos blandos, en planos múltiples.

major diagnostic categories (MDCs)   Broad clinical categories differentiated from all others on the basis of body system involvement and cause of disease.
categorías de diagnosis principales (MDCs)   Amplias categorías clínicas que se diferencian de todas las demás en base a la inclusión del sistema corporal y la etiología de la enfermedad.

maker (of a check)   Any individual, corporation, or legal party who signs a check or any type of negotiable instrument.
signatario (de un cheque)   Cualquier individuo, corporación o parte legal que firma un cheque o cualquier tipo de instrumento negociable.

malignant   Cancerous.
maligno   Canceroso.

managed care   An umbrella term for all healthcare plans that provide health care in return for preset monthly payments and that offer coordinated care through a defined network of primary care physicians and hospitals.
atención administrada   Término que engloba todos los planes de atención sanitaria que proporcionan atención médica a cambio de pagos mensuales preestablecidos y atención coordinada a través de una red definida de médicos de cabecera y hospitales.

mandated   Required by an authority or law.
obligatorio   Que lo exige una autoridad o la ley.

mandatory   Containing or constituting a command.
obligatorio   Que contiene una orden o que es una orden en sí mismo.

manifestation   Something easily understood or recognized by the mind.
manifestación   Algo que puede ser comprendido o reconocido por la mente con facilidad.

manipulation   Moving or exercising a body part by an externally applied force.
manipulación   Mover o ejercitar una parte del cuerpo por medio de la aplicación de una fuerza externa.

mastectomy   Surgical removal of the breast, usually including the excision of lymph nodes in the axillary region.
mastectomía   Eliminación quirúrgica del seno que por lo general incluye la escisión de los nódulos linfáticos de la región axilar.

matrix   Something in which a thing originates, develops, takes shape, or is contained; a base on which to build.
matriz   Algo donde las cosas se originan, desarrollan, toman forma o están contenidas; base sobre la cual construir.

m-banking   Banking through the use of wireless devices, such as cellular phones and wireless Internet services.
banca-m   Operaciones bancarias a través de dispositivos inalámbricos, como teléfonos celulares y servicios de comunicaciones inalámbricas.

media   The term applied to agencies of mass communication, such as newspapers, magazines, and telecommunications.
medios de comunicación   Término que se aplica a las agencias de noticias o de comunicación de masas, como periódicos, revistas y telecomunicaciones.

mediastinum   The space in the center of the chest, under the sternum.
mediastino   Espacio en el centro del pecho, bajo el esternón.

medical savings account   A tax-deferred bank or savings account combined with a low-premium, high-deductible

543

insurance policy, designed for individuals or families who choose to fund their own healthcare expenses and medical insurance.

cuenta de ahorros para gastos médicos   Cuenta bancaria o de ahorros de impuestos diferidos combinada con una póliza de seguro con primas bajas y deducibles altos destinada a individuos o familias que eligen financiar ellos mismos sus gastos de atención sanitaria y su seguro médico.

medically indigent   An individual who can afford to pay for his or her normal daily living expenses but cannot afford adequate healthcare.

médicamente indigente   Individuo que puede pagar sus gastos normales de la vida cotidiana pero que no puede abordar el pago de un servicio de atención sanitaria adecuado.

medically necessary   Criteria used by third-party payers to decide whether a patient's symptoms and diagnosis justify specific medical services or procedures; also known as *medical necessity*.

médicamente necesario   Criterio usado por pagadores intermediarios para decidir si los síntomas y el diagnóstico de un paciente justifican el uso de procedimientos o servicios médicos específicos; también se conoce como *necesidad médica*.

Medigap   A term sometimes applied to private insurance products that supplement Medicare insurance benefits.

Medigap   Término que se aplica algunas veces a seguros privados que complementan los beneficios del seguro Medicare.

medullary cavity   The inner portion of the diaphysis that contains the bone marrow.

cavidad medular   Porción interna de la diafisis que contiene la médula ósea.

megabyte   Approximately 1 million bytes.
megabyte   Aproximadamente, un millón de bytes.

megahertz (MHz)   A measuring unit for microprocessors. A megahertz is 1 million cycles of electromagnetic current alternation per second; it is used as a unit of measure for the clock speed of computer microprocessors. The hertz is a unit of measure named after Heinrich Hertz, a German physicist.

megahercio (MHz)   Unidad de medida para microprocesadores, abreviada MHz. Un megahercio es un millón de ciclos de alternancia de corriente electromagnética por segundo y se usa como unidad de medida para la velocidad de los—microprocesadores de computadoras. El hercio recibe su nombre de Heinrich Hertz, un físico alemán.

melena   A black, tarry stool containing digested blood; it usually is the result of bleeding in the upper GI tract.

melena   Deposición negra y alquitranada que contiene sangre digerida y por lo general es le resultado de una hemorragia en el tracto gastrointestinal superior.

mentor   A trusted counselor or guide.
mentor   Consejero o guía de confianza.

metabolite   A substance produced by metabolism.
metabolito   Sustancia producida por el metabolismo.

meticulous   Marked by extreme or excessive care in the consideration or treatment of details.
meticuloso   Caracterizado por una atención exagerada o excesiva a los detalles.

microcephaly   Abnormally small head size in relation to the rest of the body.
microcefalia   Tamaño pequeño de la cabeza en relación con el resto del cuerpo.

microfilm   A film bearing a photographic record of printed or other graphic matter on a reduced scale.
microfilm   Película que contiene una fotografía de un documento impreso u otro elemento gráfico a escala reducida.

microorganism   An organism of microscopic or submicroscopic size.
microorganismo   Organismo de tamaño microscópico o sub-microscópico.

MIDI The abbreviation for *musical instrument digital interface*. A MIDI interface allows computers to record and manipulate sound.
MIDI Abreviatura para *interfaz digital para instrumentos musicales*. Una interfaz MIDI permite a las computadoras grabar y manipular sonido.

miotic   Any substance or medication that causes contraction of the pupil.
miótico   Cualquier sustancia o medicamento que produce una contracción de la pupila.

misdemeanor   A minor crime punishable by fine or imprisonment in a city or county jail rather than in a penitentiary.
falta   Delito menor, por oposición a delito mayor, se penaliza con multa o prisión en una cárcel de una ciudad o condado más bien que con prisión en una penitenciaría.

mock   To imitate or practice.
simular   Imitar o practicar.

modem   The acronym for *modulator demodulator;* a device that allows information to be transmitted over phone lines at speeds measured in bits per second (bps).
módem   Abreviatura para modulador desmodulador, un dispositivo que permite transmitir información a

través de las líneas telefónicas a velocidades que se miden en bits por segundos (bps).

molecule   A group of like or different atoms held together by chemical forces.
molécula   Grupo de átomos iguales o diferentes que se mantiene unido por fuerzas químicas.

monochromatic   Having or consisting of one color or hue.
monocromático   Que tiene un solo color o tonalidad.

mononuclear white blood cell   A leukocyte with an unsegmented nucleus, particularly monocytes and lymphocytes.
glóbulo blanco mononuclear   Leucocito que tiene un núcleo sin segmentar; en particular los monocitos y linfocitos.

mons pubis   The fat pad that covers the symphysis pubis.
monte del pubis   Almohadilla de grasa que cubre la sínfisis púbica.

morale   The mental and emotional condition (e.g., enthusiasm, confidence, or loyalty) of an individual or group with regard to the function or tasks at hand.
moral   Estado mental y emocional (como entusiasmo, lealtad o confianza) de un individuo o grupo en cuanto al puesto que desempeña o el trabajo que realiza.

motivation   The process of inciting a person to some action or behavior.
motivación   Proceso de incitar a una persona a hacer algo o a comportarse de una forma determinada.

multimedia   The presentation of graphics, animation, video, sound, and text on a computer in an integrated way or all at once. CD-ROMs are the most effective multimedia devices.
multimedia   Presentación de gráficos, imágenes animadas, video, sonido y texto en una computadora de forma integrada o simultánea. Los CD ROM son los dispositivos de multimedia más eficaces.

multiparous   Pertaining to women who have had two or more pregnancies.
multípara   Perteneciente o relativo a la mujer que ha tenido dos o más embarazos.

multitasking   Performing multiple tasks at one time.
multitarea   Realización de varias tareas diferentes al mismo tiempo.

municipal court   A court that sits in some cities and larger towns and that usually has civil and criminal jurisdiction over cases arising within the municipality.
Municipal corte   Se aplica al juzgado con sede en algunas ciudades y pueblos grandes y que suele tener jurisdicción civil y penal sobre casos que surgen dentro de la municipalidad.

murmur   An abnormal sound heard on auscultation of the heart; it may or may not be pathologic.
murmullo   Sonido anómalo que se escucha al auscultar el corazón y que puede ser patológico o no.

myelography   A fluoroscopic examination of the spinal canal involving spinal injection of an iodine contrast medium.
mielografía   Examen fluoroscópico del canal espinal con una inyección espinal de un medio de contraste yodado.

myelomeningocele   A herniation of part of the spinal cord and its meninges that protrudes through a congenital opening in the vertebral column.
mielomeningocele   Hernia de una parte de la médula espinal y sus meninges que sale hacia fuera a través de una abertura congénita en la columna vertebral.

myocardial   Pertaining to the heart muscle.
miocárdico   Perteneciente o relativo al músculo cardiaco.

myocardium   The heart muscle.
miocardio   Músculo cardiaco.

myoglobinuria   The abnormal presence of a hemoglobin-like chemical of muscle tissue in the urine; it occurs as a result of muscle deterioration.
mioglobinuria   Presencia anómala en la orina de una susbtancia química del tejido muscular parecida a la hemoglobina; es el resultado de una deterioración muscular.

mysticism   The experience of seeming to have direct communication with God or the ultimate reality.
misticismo   Experiencia de parecer tener comunicación directa con Dios o una realidad superior.

nanometer   One billionth ($1/10^9$) of a meter.
nanómetro   Una mil millonésima parte (10^9) de metro.

naturopathy   An alternative to conventional medicine in which holistic methods are used, as well as herbs and natural supplements, in the belief that the body will heal itself. Currently, naturopathic physicians can be licensed in 12 states.
naturopatía   Alternativa a la medicina convencional en la que se usan métodos holísticos, así como hierbas y suplementos naturales, con la creencia de que el cuerpo sanará por sí mismo. En la actualidad, los médicos naturópatas pueden obtener la licencia en doce estados.

necrosis   Pertaining to the death of cells or tissue.
necrosis   Perteneciente o relativo a la muerte de células o tejidos.

negative feedback mechanism   A homeostatic mechanism that responds as a regulator to counteract a change.
mecanismo de respuesta negativa   Mecanismo homeostático que responde como regulador para contrarrestar un cambio.

negligence   Failure to exercise the care that a prudent person usually exercises; implied inattention to one's duty or business; implied want of due or necessary diligence or care.
negligencia   Falta de cuidado en algo que se hace; falta implícita de atención en el deber o trabajo; deseo implícito de una diligencia o cuidado necesario o merecido.

negotiable   Legally transferable to another party.
negociable   Que se puede transferir legalmente a otra parte.

networking   The exchange of information or services among individuals, groups, or institutions; meeting and getting to know individuals in the same or similar career fields and sharing information about available opportunities.
interconexión   Intercambio de información o servicios entre individuos, grupos o instituciones; conocer a individuos del mismo campo profesional o de campos similares y compartir información acerca de oportunidades de empleo.

neural tube defect   Any of a group of congenital anomalies involving the brain and spinal column that are caused by failure of the neural tube to close during embryonic development.
defecto del tubo neural   Cualquiera de las anomalías congénitas que afectan al cerebro y a la médula espinal y que tienen su origen en que el tubo neural no logró cerrarse durante el desarrollo embrionario.

nodule   A small lump, lesion, or swelling that is felt when the skin is palpated.
nódulo   Pequeña protuberancia, herida o hinchazón que se siente al tocar la piel.

nomogram   A graph on which variables are plotted so that a particular value can be read on the appropriate line.
nomograma   Gráfica en la que las variables están presentadas de tal manera que se puede leer un valor específico en la línea adecuada.

nonmaleficence   Refraining from the act of causing harm or doing evil.
ausencia de maleficencia   No hacer el mal.

no-show   A person who fails to keep an appointment without giving advance notice.
no-acudió   Persona que no acude a una cita médica sin dar previo aviso.

nosocomial infection   An infection acquired during hospitalization or in a healthcare setting. These infections often are caused by *Escherichia coli,* hepatitis viruses, *Pseudomonas* organisms, and staphylococci.
infección nosocomial   Infección adquirida en un establecimiento de atención sanitaria o durante una hospitalización. Con frecuencia se debe a *E. coli,* virus de hepatitis, pseudomonas y estafilococos.

nosocomial   Pertaining to or originating in the hospital; a term for an infection that either was not present or was incubating before the patient was admitted to the hospital.
nosocomial   Perteneciente o relativo al hospital, incubado en el hospital, dícese de la infección que no estaba presente ni en estado de incubación antes de ser ingresado al hospital.

"note"   In coding manuals, notes are found in both the Alphabetic Index and the Tabular Index as instructions or guides for classification assignments; they define the category content or the use of subdivision codes.
"nota"   Las notas se encuentran tanto en los Índices alfabéticos como en las instrucciones o guías en las Asignaciones de clasificación, para definir el contenido de la categoría o el uso de los códigos de subdivisión.

NSAIDs   Nonsteroidal antiinflammatory drugs.
NSAIDs   Medicamentos antiinflamatorios no esterioides.

nuclear medicine   An imaging modality that uses radioactive materials injected or ingested into the body to provide information about the function of organs and tissues.
medicina nuclear   Modalidad de la formación de imágenes que usa materiales radioactivos inyectados en el cuerpo o ingeridos para obtener información acerca del funcionamiento de órganos y tejidos.

obesity   An excessive accumulation of body fat (usually defined as a weight more than 20% above the recommended body weight).
obesidad   Acumulación excesiva de grasa en el cuerpo (se suele definir como más del 20% del peso recomendado).

objective information   Information gathered by watching or observing a patient.
información objetiva   Información que se recoge vigilando u observando a un paciente.

oblique projection   The radiographic view in which the body or part is rotated so that the projection is neither frontal nor lateral.
proyección oblicua   Vista radiográfica en la cual que cuerpo o parte del cuerpo se gira de forma que la proyección no es frontal ni lateral.

obliteration   Making something indecipherable or imperceptible by obscuring or wearing away.
obliterar   Hacer algo indescifrable o imperceptible oscureciéndolo o desgastándolo.

obturator   A disk or plate that closes an opening.
obturador   Disco o placa que cierra una abertura.

obturator A metal rod with a smooth, rounded tip that is placed inside hollow instruments to reduce damage to body tissues during insertion of the instrument.
obturador Varilla de metal con un extremo redondeado que se coloca en el interior de instrumentos huecos para disminuir la destrucción de los tejidos corporales durante su inserción.

occlusion The complete blocking off of an opening.
oclusión Cierre completo de una abertura.

"omit code" In insurance claims, a term used primarily in volume 3 of the ICD-9-CM when a procedure is the method of approach for an operation.
"omitir código" Esta expresión se usa sobre todo en el tomo 3 cuando el procedimiento es el método de acercamiento a una operación.

opaque Not translucent or transparent.
opaco Que no es translúcido ni transparente.

OPIM (other potentially infectious material) Substances or material other than blood (e.g., body fluids, such as urine and semen) that have the potential to carry infectious pathogens.
OPIM (otras materias potencialmente peligrosas) Sustancias o materias además de la sangre (como, por ejemplo, los fluidos corporales, la orina, el semen).

opinion A formal expression of judgment or advice by an expert; the formal expression of the legal reasons and principles on which a legal decision is based.
opinión Expresión formal de un juicio o consejo dado por un experto; expresión formal de las razones y principios legales sobre los que se basa una decisión legal.

opportunistic infection An infection caused by a normally nonpathogenic organism in a host whose resistance has been decreased.
infección oportunista Infección en una persona con una resistencia a las enfermedades más baja de lo normal, provocada por un organismo que en condiciones normales no resulta patógeno.

optic disc The region at the back of the eye where the optic nerve meets the retina. It is considered the blind spot of the eye, because it contains only nerve fibers and no rods or cones and therefore is insensitive to light.
papila óptica Región en la parte posterior del ojo donde el nervio óptico se une con la retina. Se considera el punto ciego del ojo, ya que allí sólo hay fibras nerviosas y no bastoncillos ni conos, y por tanto es insensible a la luz.

optic nerve The second cranial nerve, which carries impulses for the sense of sight.
nervio óptico Segundo nervio del cráneo que transporta impulsos para el sentido de la vista.

optical character recognition (OCR) Electronic scanning of printed items as images, followed by the use of special software to recognize these images (or characters) as ASCII text.
reconocimiento óptico de caracteres (OCR) Proceso de escanear electrónicamente documentos impresos como si fueran imágenes y después, usando un programa de computadora especial, reconocer esas imágenes (o caracteres) como texto ASCII.

ordinance An authoritativwe decree or direction; a law set forth by a governmental authority, specifically a municipal regulation.
ordenanza Decreto u orden de la autoridad; ley definida por una autoridad gubernamental, específicamente, una regulación municipal.

organelle A differentiated structure within a cell (e.g., a mitochondrion, vacuole, or chloroplast) that performs a specific function.
organelo Estructura diferenciada dentro de una célula, como un mitocondrio, vacuola o cloroplasto que realiza una función específica.

orthopnea Difficulty breathing in the supine position. The individual must sit or stand to breathe comfortably.
ortopnea Dificultad para respirar estando en posición supina. El individuo debe estar sentado o de pie para respirar con comodidad.

orthostatic (postural) hypotension A temporary fall in blood pressure when a person rapidly changes from a recumbent position to a standing position.
hipotensión ortostática (relacionada con la postura) Baja temporal de la presión sanguínea cuando una persona cambia con rapidez de una posición recostada a una posición en pie.

osteopathy A medical discipline based primarily on the manual diagnosis and holistic treatment of impaired function resulting from loss of movement in all kinds of tissues.
osteopatía Disciplina médica que se basa primordialmente en el diagnóstico manual y el tratamiento holístico de funciones deterioradas como resultado de la pérdida de movilidad en todo tipo de tejidos.

osteoporosis A condition of loss of bone density; lack of calcium intake is a major factor in its development.
osteoporosis Disminución de la densidad de los huesos. La falta de consumo de calcio es uno de los factores principales de su desarrollo.

otitis externa Inflammation or infection of the external auditory canal.
otitis externa Inflamación o infección del canal auditivo externo.

otosclerosis The formation of spongy bone in the labyrinth of the ear, often causing the auditory ossicles

547

to become fixed and unable to vibrate when sound enters the ears.

otosclerosis   Formación de huesos parecidos a esponjas en el laberinto del oído, a menudo causando que los huesecillos auditivos queden fijos y que no puedan vibrar cuando el sonido entra en los oídos.

ototoxic   Pertaining to a substance or medication that damages the eighth cranial nerve or the organs of hearing and balance.

ototóxico   Perteneciente o relativo a una sustancia o medicamento que daña el octavo nervio craneal o los órganos auditivos y del equilibrio.

OUTfolder   A folder used to provide space for the temporary filing of materials.

Carpeta OUT   Carpeta que se usa para proporcionar espacio para archivar materiales de forma temporal.

OUTguide   A heavy guide used to replace a folder that has been temporarily moved from the filing space.

Guía OUT   Guía grande que se usa para reemplazar una carpeta que ha sido retirada temporalmente del archivo.

output   Information processed by the computer and transmitted to a monitor, printer, or other device.

salida   Información procesada por la computadora y enviada a un monitor, impresora u otro dispositivo.

over-the-counter drugs   Medications legally sold without a prescription.

medicinas de venta libre   Medicinas que se venden sin receta legalmente.

oxytocin   A hormone secreted by the posterior pituitary gland that stimulates smooth muscle contractions of the uterus or mammary glands.

oxitocina   Hormona que segrega la glándula pituitaria posterior y que estimula las contracciones del útero o de las glándulas mamarias.

palliative   An agent that relieves or alleviates symptoms without curing the disease; something that alleviates or eases a painful situation without curing it.

paliativo   Agente que calma o alivia los síntomas sin curar la enfermedad; algo que alivia o hace más soportable una situación dolorosa sin curarla.

pandemic   Affecting most of the people in a country or a number of countries.

pandémico   Que afecta a la mayoría de la población de un país o de varios países.

paper claims   Hard copies of insurance claims that have been completed and sent by surface mail.

reclamaciones de papel   Copias impresas de reclamaciones de seguros que han sido completadas y enviadas por correo ordinario.

papilledema   Bulging of the optic disc and dilated retinal veins, which are seen through ophthalmoscopic examination of the retina. Papilledema is a sign of increased intracranial pressure.

edema papilar   Abultamiento de la papila óptica y de las venas retinianas dilatadas que se ven en un examen oftalmoscópico de la retina. La emeda papilar es una señal de un aumento en la presión intracraneal.

paraphrased   Pertaining to a text, passage, or work that has been restated to give the meaning in another form.

parafraseado   Perteneciente o relativo a un texto, selección u obra que ha sido expresado nuevamente para dar su significado de otra forma.

paraphrasing   Expressing an idea in different wording in an effort to enhance communication and clarify meaning.

parafrasear   Expresar una idea con palabras diferentes para mejorar la comunicación y hacer más claro su significado.

parenteral   Referring to injection or introduction of substances into the body through any route other than the digestive tract (e.g., subcutaneous, intravenous, or intramuscular administration).

parenteral   Inyección o introducción de sustancias en el cuerpo a través de cualquier otra vía que no sea el tracto digestivo, como administración subcutánea, intravenosa o intramuscular.

paresthesia   An abnormal sensation of burning, prickling, or stinging.

parestesia   Sensación anómala de ardor, escozor o aguijoneo.

paroxysmal   Pertaining to a sudden, recurrent spasm of symptoms.

paroxístico   Perteneciente o relativo a espasmos repentinos recurrentes o a sus síntomas.

participating provider   A physician or other healthcare provider who enters into a contract with a specific insurance company or program and by doing so agrees to abide by certain rules and regulations set forth by that particular third-party payer.

proveedor participante   Médico u otro proveedor de atención sanitaria que establece un contrato con una compañía o programa de seguro específico, y al hacerlo acepta respetar ciertas normas y regulaciones establecidas por ese pagador intermediario.

parturition   The act or process of giving birth to a child.

parto   Acción o proceso de dar a luz un niño.

patency   The condition of a body cavity or canal that is open or unobstructed.

abertura   Estado abierto de un cuerpo, cavidad o canal.

548

pathogen An agent that causes disease, especially a living microorganism such as a bacterium or fungus; a disease-causing microorganism.
patógeno Agente que causa enfermedades, especialmente microorganismos vivos como bacterias u hongos; microorganismos causantes de enfermedades.

pathogenic Pertaining to disease-causing microorganisms.
patogénico Perteneciente o relativo a los microorganismos causantes de enfermedades.

pathophysiology The study of biologic and physical manifestations of disease as they are related to system abnormalities and physiologic disturbances.
patofisiología Estudio de las manifestaciones biológicas y físicas de las enfermedades y cómo se relacionan con las anomalías del sistema y las alteraciones fisiológicas.

payables The balance due to a creditor on an account.
pendiente de pago Saldo que se le debe al acreedor en una cuenta.

payee The person named on a draft or check as the recipient of the amount shown.
beneficiario Persona que se nombra en una letra de cambio o en un cheque como receptor de la cantidad indicada.

payer The person who writes a check to be cashed by the payee.
pagador Persona que emite el cheque a ser cambiado por el beneficiario.

peer review organization A group of medical reviewers who contract with the Health Care Financing Administration (HCFA) to ensure quality control and the medical necessity of services provided by a facility.
organizacione de revisión colegial Grupo de revisores médicos contrata dos por HCFA para garantizar el control de calidad y la necesidad médica de los servicios ofrecidos por un establecimiento.

pegboard system A method of tracking patient accounts that allows the figures to be proven accurate by using mathematic formulas; also called the "write it once" system.
sistema de tablero perforado Método de controlar las cuentas de los pacientes que permite la demostración de la exactitud de las cifras por medio de fórmulas matemáticas; también conocido como sistema "escríbelo una vez."

perceiving The process by which an individual looks at information and sees it as real.
percibir Proceso en el cual un individuo mira la información y la ve como real.

perception A quick, acute, and intuitive cognition; the capacity for comprehension; an awareness of the elements of the environment.

percepción Conocimiento rápido, agudo e intuitivo; capacidad de comprensión; conocimiento de los elementos del medio ambiente.

pericardium The membranous sac that encloses the heart.
pericardio Saco membranoso que envuelve el corazón.

periosteum The thin, highly innervated, membranous covering of a bone.
periostio Membrana fina y sin nervios que recubre un hueso.

peristalsis The wavelike movement by which the gastrointestinal tract moves food downward.
peristalsis Movimiento ondulatorio por el cual el tracto gastrointestinal mueve la comida hacia abajo.

perjured testimony Testimony involving the voluntary violation of an oath or vow, either by swearing to what is untrue or by failing to do what has been promised under oath; false testimony.
perjuro Testimonio que comprende la violación voluntaria de un juramento o promesa, ya sea jurando algo que es falso o no cumpliendo lo que se ha prometido bajo juramento; falso testimonio.

"perks" Perquisites; extra advantages or benefits from working in a specific job that may or may not be commonplace in that particular profession.
beneficios adicionales Ventajas o beneficios adicionales del trabajar en un puesto de trabajo específico que pueden ser o no comunes a esa profesión en particular.

permeable Allowing a substance to pass or soak through.
permeable Permite el paso o penetración de una sustancia.

persona An individual's social facade or front that reflects the role the individual is playing in life; the personality a person projects in public.
persona Lo que vemos de un individuo, la imagen social que refleja el papel que dicho individuo tiene en la sociedad; la personalidad que una persona proyecta en público.

pertinent Having a clear, decisive relevance to the matter at hand.
pertinente Que tiene una importancia clara y decisiva en el asunto que se está tratando.

petechiae Small, purplish hemorrhagic spots on the skin.
petequia Pequeñas manchas en la piel, hemorrágicas y de color violeta.

phenylalanine An essential amino acid found in milk, eggs, and other foods.

549

fenilalanina Aminoácido esencial que se encuentra en la leche, los huevos y otros alimentos.

philanthropist An individual who makes an active effort to promote human welfare.
filántropo Individuo que se ocupa activamente de promover el bienestar humano.

philosopher A person who seeks wisdom or enlightenment; an expounder of a theory in a certain area of experience.
filósofo Persona que busca la sabiduría o el esclarecimiento; persona que expone una teoría en cierta área de experiencia.

phlebotomy The invasive procedure used to obtain a blood specimen for testing, experimentation, or diagnosis of disease.
flebotomía Procedimiento invasivo que se usa para obtener un espécimen de sangre para analizar, experimentar o diagnosticar una enfermedad.

phonetic Referring to an alteration of ordinary spelling that better represents the spoken language, that uses only characters of the regular alphabet, and that is used in a context of conventional spelling.
escritura fonética Alteración de la escritura normal que representa mejor el lenguaje hablado, emplea sólo caracteres del alfabeto normal y se usa en un contexto de escritura convencional.

phosphors Fluorescent crystals that give off light when exposed to x-rays.
fósforos Cristales fluorescentes que alumbran cuando se exponen a los rayos x.

photometer An instrument for measuring the intensity of light, specifically to compare the relative intensities of different lights or their relative illuminating power.
fotómetro Instrumento para medir la intensidad de la luz, específicamente para comparar las intensidades relativas de luces diferentes o su poder de iluminación relativo.

photophobia Abnormal visual sensitivity to light.
fotofobia Sensibilidad visual anómala a la luz.

physiologic noise Physiologic interference with the communication process.
ruido fisiológico Interferencia fisiológica con el proceso de comunicación.

pipet A cylindric glass or plastic tube used to deliver fluids.
pipeta Tubo cilíndrico de vidrio o plástico que se usa para distribuir fluidos.

pitch The property of a sound, especially a musical tone, that is determined by the frequency of the waves producing it; the highness or lowness of sound; the relative level, intensity, or extent of some quality or state.

tono Propiedad de un sonido, especialmente de un tono musical, que está determinada por la frecuencia de las ondas que lo producen; cualidad alta o baja de un sonido; nivel, intensidad o extensión relativos de alguna cualidad o estado.

plaque An abnormal accumulation of a fatty substance.
placa Acumulación anómala de una sustancia grasa.

plasma The liquid portion of whole blood that contains active clotting agents.
plasma Parte líquida de la sangre completa que contiene agentes coagulantes activos.

policyholder The person who pays a premium to an insurance company (and in whose name the policy is written) in exchange for the protection provided by a policy of insurance.
titular de la póliza Persona que paga una prima a una compañía aseguradora (y a cuyo nombre se contrata la póliza) a cambio de la cobertura que proporciona una póliza de seguro.

polycythemia vera A condition marked by an abnormally large number of red blood cells in the circulatory system.
policitemia vera Afección que se caracteriza por una cantidad anómalamente elevada de glóbulos rojos en el sistema circulatorio.

polydipsia Excessive thirst.
polidipsia Sed excesiva.

polymorphonuclear white blood cells Leukocytes with a segmented nucleus; also known as *polymorphonuclear neutrophils* (PMNs) or *segmented neutrophils*.
glóbulos blancos polimorfonucleares Leucocitos que tienen un núcleo segmentado; también se conocen como *neutrófilos polimorfonucleares* (PMN) o *neutrófilos segmentados*.

polyphagia Excessive appetite.
polifagia Aumento del apetito.

polyps Tumors on stems; they are frequently found in or on mucous membranes and in the mucosal lining of the colon.
pólipos Tumores en racimos que se encuentran con frecuencia en las membranas mucosas y en el recubrimiento mucoso del colon.

polyuria Excessive urine production; excretion of an unusually large amount of urine.
poliuria Producción y excreción de orina excesivas.

portal hypertension Increased venous pressure in the portal circulation caused by cirrhosis or compression of the hepatic vascular system.

550

hipertensión portal   Aumento de la presión venosa en la circulación portal causado por cirrosis o compresión del sistema vascular hepático.

portfolio   A set of pictures, drawings, documents, or photographs either bound in book form or loose in a folder.
portafolio   Conjunto de ilustraciones, dibujos, documentos o fotografías, organizadas ya sea archivadas en forma de libro, o sueltas en una carpeta.

posteroanterior (PA)   A frontal projection in which the patient is prone or facing the x-ray film or image receptor.
posterioanterior (PA)   Proyección frontal en la que el paciente está boca abajo o de frente a la película de rayos x o al receptor de imagen.

post   To transfer or carry from a book of original entry to a ledger; to enter figures in an accounting system.
asentar   Transferir o traer desde un libro de entradas originales a un libro mayor; entrar cifras en un sistema de contabilidad.

postmortem   Done, collected, or occurring after death.
postmortem   Hecho, recogido o sucedido después de la muerte.

power of attorney   A legal instrument authorizing a person to act as the attorney or agent of the grantor. The authority may be limited to the handling of specific procedures. The person authorized to act as the agent is known as the *attorney in fact*.
potestad legal   Instrumento legal que autoriza a una persona a actuar como abogado o agente de la persona que le concede el poder. La autorización puede estar limitada al manejo de procedimientos específicos. La persona autorizada a actuar como agente se conoce como *abogado de hecho*.

precedence   Superiority in rank, dignity, or importance; the condition of being, going, or coming ahead or in front of another.
precedencia   Superioridad en rango, dignidad o importancia; condición de estar, ir o venir primero o antes.

precedent   A person or thing that serves as a model; something done or said that may serve as an example or rule to authorize or justify a subsequent act of the same kind.
precedente   Persona o cosa que sirve como modelo; algo hecho o dicho anteriormente y que puede servir como ejemplo o norma para autorizar o justificar un acto subsiguiente del mismo tipo.

pre-existing condition   A physical condition of an insured person that existed before the issuance of the insurance policy.

afección preexistente   Afección física de una persona asegurada que ya existía antes de la emisión de la póliza de seguro.

premium   The consideration paid for a contract of insurance; the periodic (monthly, quarterly, or annual) payment of a specific sum of money to an insurance company that in return agrees to provide certain benefits.
prima   Pago por un contrato de seguro; pago periódico (mensual, trimestral o anual) de una suma específica de dinero a una compañía aseguradora, la cual, a cambio, acepta proporcionar ciertos beneficios.

preponderance   A superiority or excess in number or quantity; majority.
preponderancia   Superioridad o mayor número o cantidad; mayoría.

preponderance of the evidence   Evidence that is of greater weight or more convincing than the evidence offered in opposition to it; evidence that, as a whole, shows that the fact sought to be proven is more probable than not.
preponderancia de evidencia   Evidencia que tiene mayor peso o que es más convincente que la evidencia con la que se confronta; evidencia que, en conjunto, muestra que el hecho que se pretende probar es más posible que imposible.

prerequisite   Something that is necessary to achieve a result or to carry out a function.
requisito previo   Algo que es necesario para obtener un resultado o para desempeñar una función.

present illness   The chief complaint, written in chronologic sequence with dates of onset.
enfermedad actual   Problema principal, descrito en secuencia cronológica con las fechas de cada acceso.

preservatives   Substances added to a specimen to prevent deterioration of cells or chemicals.
preservativos   Sustancias añadidas a un espécimen para prevenir el deterioro de células o sustancias químicas.

pressboard   A strong, highly glazed composition board resembling vulcanized fiber; heavy card stock.
cartón prensado   Cartón de composición resistente y muy satinado que se parece a la fibra vulcanizada; cartulina de gran resistencia.

primary diagnosis   The condition or chief complaint for which a patient is treated in outpatient medical care (e.g., the physician's office or a clinic).
diagnóstico primario   Afección o problema principal por el cual se trata a un paciente con atención médica externa (en un consultorio médico o una clínica).

principal   A capital sum of money due as a debt or used as a fund, for which interest is either charged or paid.

551

principal   Capital o suma de dinero que se debe como deuda o que se usa como fondo, por el cual se cargan o se cobran intereses.

principal diagnosis   A condition, established after study, that is chiefly responsible for the admission of a patient to the hospital. It is used in coding inpatient hospital insurance claims.
diagnóstico principal   Enfermedad o lesión que, tras su estudio, se determina que es la causa principal por la que un paciente ingresa en el hospital. Es usado en la codificación de reclamaciones de seguros de pacientes hospitalizados.

privately owned laboratories (POLs)   Laboratories owned by a private individual or corporation, such as a freestanding laboratory or the laboratory inside a physician's office.
laboratorios privados (POLs)   Laboratorios cuyo propietario es un individuo o una corporación privada, como el laboratorio dentro de un consultorio médico o un laboratorio independiente.

processing   The way an individual internalizes new information and makes it his or her own.
procesar   Forma en la que un individuo interioriza y asimila la información nueva.

procrastination   Intentionally putting off doing something that should be done.
procrastinación   Dejar a un lado o retrasar, de manera intencional, algo que debe hacerse.

professional behaviors   Actions that identify the medical assistant as a member of a healthcare profession, including dependability, respectful patient care, initiative, positive attitude, and teamwork.
comportamientos profesionales   Características que identifican al asistente médico como profesional de la atención sanitaria, incluyendo confiabilidad, trato respetuoso a los pacientes, iniciativa, actitud positiva y disposición para trabajar en equipo.

professional courtesy   The reduction or omission of a fee for professional associates.
cortesía profesional   Reducción o supresión de un cargo para los asociados profesionales.

professionalism   Characterizing or conforming to the technical or ethical standards of a profession; exhibiting a courteous, conscientious, and generally businesslike manner in the workplace.
profesionalismo   Actitud que se caracteriza por cumplir o actuar de acuerdo con los estándares técnicos y éticos de una profesión; dar muestras de cortesía, meticulosidad y, en general, mostrar un comportamiento adecuado en el lugar de trabajo.

proficiency   Competency as a result of training or practice.

pericia   Estado de competencia en algo, que se alcanza por medio de entrenamiento o práctica.

profit sharing   An offer of part of the company's profits to employees or other designated individuals or groups.
participación en los beneficios   Oferta de parte de los beneficios de la compañía a los empleados u otros individuos o grupos designados.

progress notes   Notes entered in a patient's chart to track the individual's progress and condition.
notas del progreso   Notas escritas en historial médico del paciente para seguir el progreso y estado del mismo.

prokaryote   A unicellular organism that lacks a membrane-bound nucleus.
procaryota   Organismo unicelular cuyo núcleo no está unido por una membrana.

prolactin (PRL)   A hormone secreted by the anterior pituitary gland that stimulates the development of the mammary gland.
prolactina (PRL)   Hormona que segrega la glándula pituitaria anterior y que estimula el desarrollo de la glándula mamaria.

proofread   To read text and mark corrections.
corregir pruebas   Leer un texto y marcar correcciones.

prosthesis   An artificial replacement for a body part.
prótesis   Pieza artificial para reemplazar una parte del cuerpo.

proteins   Organic compounds in plants and animals that contain the major elements carbon, hydrogen, oxygen, and nitrogen and the amino acids essential to maintain life.
proteínas   Compuestos orgánicos que existen en plantas y animales y que contienen los elementos principales: carbón, hidrógeno, oxígeno y nitrógeno y los aminoácidos esenciales para el mantenimiento de la vida.

provider   An individual or company that provides medical care and services to patients or the public.
proveedor   Individuo o compañía que proporciona atenciones y servicios médicos pacientes o al público.

provisional diagnosis   A temporary diagnosis made before all test results have been received.
diagnóstico provisional   Diagnóstico temporal llevado a cabo antes de recibir todos los resultados de las pruebas.

proxemics   The study of the nature, degree, and effect of the spatial separation individuals naturally maintain.
proxemia   Estudio de la naturaleza, grado y efecto de la separación espacial que los individuos mantienen de forma natural.

552

prudent   Marked by wisdom or judiciousness; shrewd in the management of practical affairs.
prudente   Caracterizado por poseer sabiduría o sensatez; hábil en el manejo de los asuntos prácticos.

psoriasis   A usually chronic, recurrent skin disease marked by bright red patches covered with silvery scales.
psoriasis   Enfermedad recurrente de la piel, por lo general crónica, caracterizada por manchas de color rojo brillante cubiertas por escamas plateadas.

psychosocial   Pertaining to a combination of psychological and social factors.
psicosocial   Perteneciente o relativo a una combinación de factores psicológicos y sociales.

public domain   The realm embracing property rights that belong to the community at large, are unprotected by copyright or patent, and are subject to appropriation by anyone.
dominio público   Campo que abarca los derechos de propiedad que pertenecen a la comunidad en general, que no están protegidos por leyes de derechos de autor ni por patentes y están sujetos a apropiación por parte de cualquiera.

pulmonary consolidation   In pneumonia, the process by which the lungs become solidified as they fill with exudates.
solidificación pulmonar   Proceso por el cual los pulmones se vuelven rígidos a medida que se llenan con exudados en los casos de pulmonía.

pulse deficit   A condition in which the radial pulse is less than the apical pulse. It may indicate a peripheral vascular abnormality.
déficit del pulso   Cuando el pulso radial es menor que el apical. Puede indicar una anomalía vascular periférica.

pulse pressure   The difference between the systolic and the diastolic blood pressures (less than 30 points or more than 50 points is considered normal).
presión del pulso   Diferencia entre las presiones sanguíneas sistólica y diastólica (menos de 30 puntos o más de 50 puede considerarse normal).

pure culture   A bacterial or fungal culture that contains a single organism.
cultivo puro   Cultivo de bacterias u hongos que contiene un solo organismo.

putrefaction   The decomposition of organic matter, which produces a foul smell.
putrefacción   Descomposición de materia orgánica que da como resultado un olor fétido.

pyemia   The presence of pus-forming organisms in the blood.

piemia   Presencia en la sangre de organismos formadores de pus.

quackery   The pretense of curing disease.
curanderismo   Práctica del que finge curar enfermedades.

quality control   An aggregate of activities designed to ensure adequate quality, especially in manufactured products or in the service industries.
control de calidad   Conjunto de actividades destinadas a garantizar la calidad adecuada, en especial en productos manufacturados o en las industrias de servicios.

queries   Requests for information from a database.
consultas   Peticions de información de una base de datos.

rad   The conventional unit of absorbed radiation dose.
rad   Unidad convencional de dosis de radiación absorbido.

radiograph   An x-ray image.
radiografía   Imagen obtenida con el uso de rayos-x.

radiographer   A person qualified to perform radiographic examinations.
técnico de radiología   Persona cualificada para realizar exámenes radiológicos.

radiography   Making diagnostic images using x-rays.
radiografía   Proceso de diagnosticar imágenes usando rayos x.

radiologist   A physician who specializes in medical imaging and/or therapeutic applications of radiation.
médico radiólogo   Médico especialista en formación de imágenes o en aplicaciones terapéuticas de la radiación.

radiolucent   Referring to a substance that is easily penetrated by x-rays; these substances appear dark on radiographs.
transparente a la radiación   Término que se aplica a una substancia que puede ser penetrada con facilidad por los rayos x; estas substancias aparecen oscuras en las radiografías.

radiopaque   Referring to a substance that can be easily seen on an x-ray image (i.e., is is not easily penetrated by x-rays); these substances appear light on radiographs.
opaco a la radiación   Sustancia que puede visualizarse con facilidad en la imagen de rayos x. Término que se aplica a una substancia que no puede ser penetrada con facilidad por los rayos x; estas substancias aparecen claras en las radiografías.

rales   Abnormal or crackling breath sounds during inspiration.
estertores   Sonidos respiratorios o crujidos anómalos durante la inspiración.

553

ramifications   Consequences produced by a cause or following from a set of conditions.
ramificaciones   Consecuencias producidas por una causa o que siguen a una serie de estados.

rapport   A relationship of harmony and accord between the patient and the healthcare professional.
concordia   Relación de armonía y acuerdo entre el paciente y el profesional de la atención sanitaria.

Raynaud's phenomenon   Intermittent attacks of ischemia in the extremities that result in cyanosis, numbness, tingling, and pain.
fenómeno de Raynaud   Ataques intermitentes de isquemia en las extremidades, resultando en cianosis, entumecimiento, picazón y dolor.

RBRVS (resource-based relative value system)   A fee schedule designed to provide national uniform payment of Medicare benefits after adjustment to reflect the differences in practice costs across geographic areas.
RBRVS (sistema de valor relativo basado en recursos)   Escala de cargos diseñada para proporcionar un pago de beneficios de Medicare uniforme a nivel nacional después de haber sido ajustado para reflejar las diferencias en los costos prácticos a través de áreas geográficas.

ream   A quantity of paper consisting of 20 quires or variously 480, 500, or 516 sheets.
resma   Una cantidad de papel que consiste de 20 manos o que varía entre 480, 500 o 516 hojas.

reasonable doubt   Doubt based on reason and arising from evidence or lack of evidence; not doubt that is imagined or conjured up, but doubt that would cause reasonable persons to hesitate before acting in a manner important to themselves.
duda razonable   Duda basada en la razón o que surge de evidencia o falta de evidencia; no es una duda imaginaria ni inventada, sino una duda que puede hacer que una persona razonable vacile antes de dar un paso importante.

receipts   Amounts paid on patients' accounts.
recibos   Sumas pagadas en las cuentas de los pacientes.

recipient   The receiver of something.
receptor   El que recibe un artículo u objeto.

rectify   To correct by removing errors.
rectificar   Corregir eliminando errores.

reduction   The return of a structure to its correct anatomic position, as in the reduction of a fracture.
reducción   Regreso a la posición anatómica correcta, como en el caso de reducción de una fractura.

referral (reference) laboratory   A private or hospital-based laboratory that performs a wide variety of tests, many of them specialized. Physicians often send specimens collected in the office to referral laboratories for testing.
laboratorio de referencia   Laboratorio privado o de un hospital que realiza una amplia gama de análisis, muchos de ellos especializados. Con frecuencia los médicos envían especímenes recogidos en la consulta a estos laboratorios para ser analizados.

reflection   The process of considering new information and internalizing it to create new ways of examining information.
reflexión   Proceso de estudiar información nueva e interiorizarla para crear formas nuevas de examinar información.

refractile   Capable of causing light rays to bend, thus altering or distorting an image.
refractante   Capaz de provocar la refracción de la luz, desviación alterando o distorcionando una imagen.

registered dietitian (RD)   A professionally certified person with a bachelor's degree in food and nutrition who is concerned with the maintenance and promotion of health and the treatment of diseases through proper diet.
dietista registrado (RD)   Profesional certificado persona con titulación universitaria en alimentos y nutrición y que se preocupa del mantenimiento y-la promoción de la salud y el tratamiento de las enfermedades a través de la dieta adecuado.

relapse   The recurrence of disease symptoms after apparent recovery.
recaída   Recurrencia de los síntomas de una enfermedad tras una aparente recuperación.

relevant   Having a significant and demonstrable bearing on the matter at hand.
pertinente   Que tiene una relación importante y demostrable con el asunto que se está tratando.

rem   The dose of ionizing radiation equivalent to 1 roentgen of x-ray exposure.
rem   La dosis de radiación ionizante equivalente a un roentgen de exposición a rayos x.

remission   A decrease in the severity of a disease or symptoms; the partial or complete disappearance of the clinical and subjective characteristics of a chronic or malignant disease.
remisión   Disminución de la gravedad de una enfermedad o sus síntomas; desaparición parcial o total de las características clínicas y subjetivas de una enfermedad crónica o maligna.

remittent fever   A fever in which a patient's temperature fluctuates greatly but never falls to the normal level.

554

fiebre remitente   Fiebre en la cual la temperatura fluctúa mucho pero nunca baja al nivel normal.

renal threshold   The level above which a substance cannot be reabsorbed by the renal tubules and therefore is excreted in the urine.
umbral renal   Nivel por encima del cual una sustancia no puede ser reabsorbida por los túbulos renales y por lo tanto es excretada en la orina.

reparations   The act of making amends, offering atonement, or giving satisfaction for a wrong or injury.
reparaciones   Acción de enmendar u ofrecer compensaciones por un error o un daño.

reprimands   Criticisms for a fault; a severe or formal reproof.
reprimendas   Críticas por una falta; reprobación severa o formal.

reproach   An expression of rebuke or disapproval; a cause or occasion for blame, discredit, or disgrace.
reproche   Expresión de crítica o desaprobación; causa o motivo de culpa, descrédito u oprobio.

requisites   Things considered essential or necessary.
requisitos   Cosas que se consideran esenciales o necesarias.

resolution   The ability of the eye to distinguish two objects that are very close together; the sharpness of an image.
resolución   Capacidad del ojo para distinguir dos objetos que están muy cerca uno del otro; nitidez de una imagen.

retention   Keeping something in possession or use; to keep someone's pay or service.
retención   El hecho de mantener en posesión o en uso; mantener a alguien a su servicio o como empleado.

retention schedule   A method or plan for retaining or keeping track of medical records and their movement from active to inactive to closed filing.
plan de retención   Método o plan para retener o guardar expedientes médicos, y el paso de los mismos del estado de expediente activo a pasivo y a cerrado.

retribution   The giving or receiving of reward or punishment; something given or exacted in recompense.
retribución   Acto de dar o recibir una recompensa o castigo; algo que se da o se cobra como recompensa.

rhinitis   Inflammation of the mucous membranes of the nose.
rinitis   Inflamación de las membranas mucosas de la nariz.

rhonchi   Abnormal rumbling sounds during expiration that indicate airway obstruction caused by thick secretions or spasms; a continuous, dry rattling in the throat or bronchial tube resulting from partial obstruction.

ronquido   Ruido sordo y anómalo durante la expiración que indica obstrucción de las vías respiratorias debido a secreciones espesas o a espasmos; ruido seco y continuo en la garganta o en el tubo bronquial debido a una obstrucción parcial.

rider   A special provision or group of provisions added to an insurance policy to expand or limit the benefits otherwise payable. A rider may increase or decrease benefits, waive a condition or coverage, or in any other way amend the original contract.
cláusula adicional   Provisión o conjunto de provisiones especiales añadidas a una póliza de seguro para ampliar o limitar los beneficios que de otro modo se pueden pagar. Puede aumentar o disminuir beneficios, anular una condición o cobertura o puede enmendar el contrato original de otra manera.

robotics   Technology dealing with the design, construction, and operation of robots in automation.
robótica   Tecnología de la automatización que se ocupa del diseño, construcción y operación de robots.

rods   Structures in the retina of the eye that form the light-sensitive elements.
bastoncillos   Estructuras que están en la retina del ojo y constituyen los elementos sensibles a la luz.

Roentgen (R)   The conventional unit of radiation exposure.
Roentgen (R)   Unidad convencional de exposición a radiación.

router   A device used to connect any number of LANs that communicate with other routers and determine the best route between any two hosts.
direccionador   Dispositivo usado para conectar cualquier cantidad de LAN que se comunican con otros direccionadores para determinar la mejor ruta entre dos computadoras conectadas a una red.

sagittal plane   The plane that divides the body into right and left halves.
plano sagital   Plano que divide el cuerpo en la mitad derecha y la mitad izquierda.

salutation   Words or gestures that express greeting, good will, or courtesy.
saludo   Expresión de saludo, buenos deseos o cortesía por medio de palabras o gestos.

sanitization   Reduction of the number of potentially harmful microorganisms to a relatively safe level.
saneamiento   Reducción del número de microorganismos a un nivel relativamente seguro.

sarcasm   A sharp or satiric response or ironic utterance designed to cause pain.
sarcasmo   Respuesta aguda y frecuentemente satírica o declaración irónica destinada a burlarse o a lastimar.

555

scanner   A device that reads text or illustrations on a printed page and translates the information into a form the computer can understand.
escáner   Dispositivo que lee texto o ilustraciones de una página impresa y traduce esa información a un formato comprensible para la computadora.

sclera   The white part of the eye that encloses the eyeball.
esclerótica   Parte blanca del ojo que encierra el globo ocular.

scleroderma   An autoimmune disorder that affects the blood vessels and connective tissue, causing fibrous degeneration of the major organs.
esclerodema   Trastorno autoinmune que afecta a los vasos sanguíneos y los tejidos conectivos provocando degeneración en las fibras de los órganos principales.

sclerotherapy   The injection of sclerosing (hardening) solutions to treat hemorrhoids, varicose veins, or esophageal varices.
escleroterapia   Inyección de soluciones de esclerosis (endorecedores) para tratar hemorroides, venas varicosas o varices esofágicas.

scoliosis   An abnormal lateral curvature of the spine.
escoliosis   Curvatura lateral anómala de la columna.

scored tablet   A drug tablet manufactured with an indentation that allows the tablet to be broken or cut into equal parts.
tableta con hendidura   Tableta que se fabrica con una hendidura que permite dividirla o romperla en partes iguales.

screen   Something that shields, protects, or hides; to select or eliminate products or applicants by comparing them with a set of desired criteria.
pantalla   Algo que actúa como escudo, que protege u oculta para permitir un proceso de selección.

search engines   Computer programs that search documents for keywords and return a list of documents containing those words.
buscadores   Programas de computadoras que buscan documentos a partir de palabras clave y proporcionan una lista de los documentos que contienen esas palabras.

seborrhea   An excessive discharge of sebum from the sebaceous glands, forming greasy scales on the skin or cheesy plugs in skin pores.
seborrea   Descarga excesiva de sebo de las glándulas sebáceas, formando escamas de grasa en la piel o tapones con aspecto de queso en los poros de la piel.

secondary hypertension   Elevated blood pressure caused by another medical condition.
hipertensión secundaria   Presión sanguínea elevada causada por otra enfermedad o afección médica.

"see"   In coding manuals, an instruction to the coder to look in another place; found in volumes 2 and 3 of the Alphabetic Index, this instruction must always be followed.
"ver"   Instrucción que se le da a la persona encargada de la codificación para que consulte en otro lugar. Siempre debe seguirse esta instrucción; la expresión se encuentra en el Índice alfabético, tomos 2 y 3.

"see also"   In coding manuals, an instruction to the coder to look elsewhere if the main term or subterm(s) for an entry are not sufficient for coding the information. If a code number follows, "see also" is enclosed in parentheses; if there is no code number, "see also" is preceded by a dash.
"ver también"   Instrucción que se le da a la persona encargada de la codificación para que consulte en algún otro lugar si el término o subtérminos principales para una entrada no son suficientes para codificar la información. Si "ver también" va seguido por un número de código, dicho código va entre paréntesis; si no hay número de código, "ver también" va precedido por un guión.

"see category"   In coding manuals, an instruction to the coder to refer to a specific category (three-digit code); it must always be followed.
"ver categoría"   Instrucción que se le da a la persona encargada de la codificación para que consulte una categoría específica (código de tres dígitos); Siempre debe seguirse.

self-insured plans   Insurance plans funded by organizations with a large enough employee base that they can afford to fund their own insurance program.
planes de autoaseguración   Planes de seguros implementados por organizaciones con un número de empleados lo suficientemente grande como para permitirles financiar su propio programa de seguros.

sequentially   Happening in relation to or by arrangement in a sequence.
secuencial   Aquello que ocurre relativo a una secuencia o que es ordenado en secuencia.

serous   Pertaining to a thin, watery, serumlike drainage.
seroso   Perteneciente o relativo a una materia poco espesa, acuosa, parecida al suero.

serum   The portion of whole blood that remains liquid after the blood has clotted.
suero   La porción de la sangre que queda líquida después de la coagulación.

service benefit plan   A plan that provides benefits in the form of certain surgical and medical services rendered rather than in cash. A service benefit plan is not restricted to a fee schedule.
plan de beneficios de servicio   Plan que proporciona beneficios en forma de ciertos servicios médico-quirúrgicos

en vez de con dinero en metálico. Un plan de servicio de beneficio no está restringido por una escala de cargos.

sheath The covering surrounding the axon of the nerve cell that acts as an electrical insulator to speed conduction of nerve impulses.
película Recubrimiento que rodea los axones de la célula nerviosa y que se comporta como aislante eléctrico para aumentar la velocidad de conducción del impulso nervioso.

shingling A method of filing whereby each new report is laid on top of the previous report, resembling the shingles of a roof.
laminado Método de archivo en el cual cada informe nuevo se coloca encima del informe anterior, del mismo modo que se colocan las tejas en un techo.

Sievert (Sv) The international unit of radiation dose equivalent.
Sievert (Sv) Unidad internacional de dosis equivalentes de radiación.

sinoatrial (SA) node The pacemaker of the heart, located in the right atrium.
nódulo sinoauricular (SA) Marcapasos del corazón que se halla en la aurícula derecha.

sinus arrhythmia An irregular heartbeat that originates in the sinoatrial (pacemaker) node.
arritmia de seno Ritmo cardiaco irregular que tiene su origen en el nódulo sinoauricular (marcapasos).

socioeconomic Relating to a combination of social and economic factors.
socioeconómico Perteneciente o relativo a una combinación de factores sociales y económicos.

sociologic Oriented or directed toward social needs and problems.
sociologico Que se orienta o dirige hacia las necesidades y problemas sociales.

sonography An imaging modality that uses sound waves to produce images of soft tissues; also called *diagnostic ultrasound.*
sonografía Modalidad de formación de imágenes que usa ondas sonoras para producir imágenes de los tejidos blandos; también se conoce como *ultrasonido de diagnóstico.*

sound card A device that allows a computer to output sound through speakers connected to the main circuitry board (motherboard).
tarjeta de sonido Dispositivo que le permite a una computadora emitir sonido a través de altavoces conectados a la tarjeta principal del circuito.

specimen A sample of body fluid, waste product, or tissue that is collected for analysis and diagnosis.

espécimen Muestra de un fluido corporal, residuo o tejido que se usa para análisis y diagnósticos.

spirometer An instrument that measures the volume of inhaled and exhaled air.
espirómetro Instrumento que sirve para medir el volumen del aire inhalado y exhalado.

spores Thick-walled reproductive cells formed within bacteria and capable of withstanding unfavorable environmental conditions; they are very resistant to disinfection measures.
esporas Células reproductoras de paredes gruesas que se forman dentro de las bacterias y son capaces de resistir condiciones ambientales adversas; tipos de bacterias letárgicas de paredes gruesas que son muy resistentes a las medidas de desinfección.

staff privileges Authorization for a healthcare professional to practice within a specific facility.
privilegios del personal Autorización para un profesional de atención sanitaria, para ejercer la práctica dentro de unas instalaciones específicas.

standards Items or indicators used to measure quality or compliance with a statutory or accrediting body's policies and regulations.
estándares Artículos o indicadores usados para medir la calidad o cumplimiento de las pólizas y regulaciones de un cuerpo normativo o acreditativo.

stat A medical term meaning "immediately" or "at this moment"; an order found on a laboratory requisition that indicates that the test must be done immediately (from the Latin word *statin,* meaning "at once").
stat Abreviatura usada en medicina que significa inmediatamente o ahora mismo. Orden encontrada en un pedido de laboratorio que indica que el análisis debe llevarse a cabo inmediatamente (de la palabra latina statin, que significa "ahora"); inmediatamente.

stationers Sellers of writing paper.
dependientes de papelería Vendedores de artículos de papelería.

statute A law enacted by the legislative branch of a government.
estatuto Ley sancionada por la rama legislativa de un gobierno.

stereotactic An x-ray procedure to guide the insertion of a needle into a specific area of the breast.
estereotáctico Procedimiento de rayos x para guiar la inserción de una aguja en zonas específicas del pecho.

stereotype Something conforming to a fixed or general pattern; a standardized mental picture that is held in common by many and represents an oversimplified opinion, prejudiced attitude, or uncritical judgment.

557

estereotipo   Algo que se ajusta a un patrón fijado o general; imagen mental estandarizada que tienen en común muchas personas y que representa opiniones simplificadas, actitudes con prejuicios o razonamientos carentes de sentido crítico.

sterilization   Complete destruction of all forms of microbial life.
esterilización   Destrucción total de toda forma de vida microbiana.

stertorous   Referring to a strenuous respiratory effort marked by a snoring sound.
estertóreo   Esfuerzo respiratorio penoso que tiene el sonido de un ronquido.

stipulate   To specify as a condition or requirement of an agreement or offer; to make an agreement or covenant to do or forbear from doing something.
estipular   Especificar como condición o requisito de un acuerdo u oferta; establecer un acuerdo o prometer hacer, o dejar de hacer, algo.

stock option   An offer of stocks for purchase to a certain individual or to certain groups, such as employees of a for-profit hospital.
opción sobre acciones   Oferta de venta de acciones que se le hace a un ciertos individuos o grupos, como a los empleados de un hospital.

stressors   Stimuli that cause stress.
estresantes   Dícese de los estímulos que causan estrés.

stridor   A shrill, harsh respiratory sound heard during inhalation during laryngeal obstruction.
estridor   Sonido respiratorio estridente que se oye durante la inhalación en los casos de obstrucción laríngea.

stroke   Sudden paralysis and/or loss of consciousness caused by extreme trauma or injury to an artery in the brain.
apoplejía   Súbita pérdida de conocimiento y parálisis causada por una lesión o daño grave de una arteria del cerebro.

stylus   A metal probe inserted into or passed through a catheter, needle, or tube to clear the device or to facilitate its passage into a body orifice.
punzón   Sonda metálica que se inserta o pasa por medio de un catéter, aguja o tubo y que se usa para limpiar o para facilitar el paso a un orificio del cuerpo.

subjective information   Information gained by questioning the patient or taking it from a form.
información subjetiva   Información obtenida haciendo preguntas al paciente o tomándola de un formulario.

subluxation   Incomplete dislocation of a bone from its normal anatomic location.
subluxación   Dislocación incompleta de un hueso desde su posición anatómica normal.

subluxations   Slight misalignments of the vertebrae or partial dislocations.
subluxaciones   Alineamientos ligeramente defectuosos o dislocaciones parciales de las vértebras.

subordinate   Submissive to or controlled by authority; placed in or occupying a lower class, rank, or position.
subordinado   Que está sometido a una autoridad o controlado por ella; que ostenta un cargo u ocupa una clase, rango o puesto inferior.

subpoena   A writ or document commanding a person to appear in court under penalty for failure to appear.
subpoena   Documento escrito ordenando a una persona comparecer en el juzgado bajo penalidad en caso de no comparecencia.

substance number   A number based on the weight of a ream of paper containing 500 sheets.
número de sustancia   Número basado en el peso de una resma de papel de 500 hojas.

subtle   Difficult to understand or perceive; having or marked by keen insight and the ability to penetrate deeply and thoroughly.
sutil   Difícil de comprender o percibir; que tiene perspicacia y la capacidad de penetrar a fondo y en toda su extensión en un asunto.

succinct   Marked by compact, precise expression without wasted words.
sucinto   Caracterizado por una expresión precisa y concisa sin palabras inútiles.

superfluous   Exceeding what is sufficient or necessary.
superfluos   Que exceden aquello que es suficiente o necesario.

suppurative   Forming and/or discharging pus.
supuración   Formación o emisión de pus.

surrogate   A substitute; something put in place of another.
subrogado   Sustituto; puesto en lugar de otro.

switch   In networks, a device that filters information between LAN segments, reduces overall network traffic, and increases the speed and efficiency of bandwidth use.
conmutador   En las redes de comunicación, dispositivo que filtra información entre segmentos de LAN y disminuye el tráfico global de la red, aumentando la velocidad y la eficacia en el uso del ancho de banda.

syncope   Fainting; a brief lapse in consciousness.
síncope   Desmayo; lapso breve en estado de consciencia.

syndrome   A group of signs and symptoms related to a common cause or presenting a clinical picture of a disease or an inherited abnormality.

síndrome   Conjunto de signos y síntomas relacionados con una causa común o que presentan el cuadro clínico de una enfermedad o una anomalía heredada.

synopsis   A condensed statement or outline.
sinopsis   Declaración resumida; resumen.

synovial fluid   Clear fluid found in joint cavities that facilitates smooth movement and nourishes joint structures.
fluido sinovial   Fluido claro que se halla en las cavidades de las articulaciones y que facilita los movimientos suaves y nutre las estructuras articulatorias.

tachycardia   A rapid but regular heart rate; one that exceeds 100 beats per minute.
taquicardia   Ritmo cardiaco rápido pero regular que sobrepasa los 100 latidos por minuto.

tachypnea   Respiration that is rapid and shallow; hyperventilation.
taquipnea   Respiración rápida y profunda; hiperventilación.

tactful   Having a keen sense of what to do or say to maintain good relations with others or avoid offense.
tacto   Tener un sentido de lo que se debe hacer o decir para mantener buenas relaciones con los demás y evitar ofenderlos.

target organ   The organ affected by a particular hormone.
órgano objetivo   Órgano afectado por una hormona específica.

target tissue   A group of cells affected by a particular hormone.
tejido objetivo   Grupo de células afectadas por una hormona específica.

targeted to   Directed toward a specific desire, position, or effect.
dirigido a   Dirigido a un fin o meta específico, usado hacia un fin; dirigido hacia un deseo o un puesto específico.

TCP/IP   Abbreviation for *transmission control protocol/Internet protocol;* a suite of communications protocols used to connect users or hosts to the Internet.
TCP/IP   Abreviatura de *protocolo de control de transmisión/protocolo Internet;* conjunto de protocolos de comunicación que se usa para conectar usuarios o computadoras a Internet.

tedious   Tiresome because of length or dullness.
tedioso   Que cansa porque es demasiado largo o aburrido.

telecommunications   The science and technology of communication by transmission of information from one location to another via telephone, television, telegraph, or satellite.
telecomunicaciones   Ciencia y tecnología de la comunicación basada en la transmisión de información de un lugar a otro por teléfono, televisión, telégrafo o satélite.

telemedicine   The use of telecommunications in the practice of medicine, allowing great distances between healthcare professionals, colleagues, patients, and students.
telemedicina   Uso de las telecomunicaciones en la práctica médica, permitiendo la comunicación entre profesionales de atención sanitaria, colegas, pacientes y estudiantes que se hallan a grandes distancias.

teleradiology   The use of telecommunications devices to enhance and improve the results of radiologic procedures.
telerradiología   Uso de dispositivos de telecomunicación para mejorar y perfeccionar los resultados de procedimientos radiológicos.

tendon   A tough band of connective tissue that connects muscle to bone.
tendón   Banda resistente de tejido conectivo que conecta los músculos con los huesos.

teratogen   Any substance that interferes with normal prenatal development.
teratógeno   Cualquier sustancia que interfiere con el desarrollo prenatal normal.

teratogenic   A substance known to cause birth defects.
teratogénico   Sustancia que se sabe que provoca defectos de nacimiento.

testimony   A solemn declaration usually made orally by a witness under oath in response to interrogation by a lawyer or an authorized public official.
testimonio   Declaración solemne, por lo general oral, hecha por un testigo bajo juramento como respuesta a una pregunta (o preguntas) de un abogado o un funcionario público autorizado.

thanatology   The description or study of the phenomena of death and of psychological methods of coping with death.
tanatología   Descripción o estudio del fenómeno de la muerte y de los métodos psicológicos para hacerle frente.

third-party payer   An entity (usually an insurance company) that makes a payment on an obligation or debt but is not a party to the contract that created the debt.
pagador mediador   Entidad (por lo general una compañía aseguradora) que hace un pago de una obligación o deuda pero que no es parte del contrato que ha creado dicha deuda.

third-party payer   Someone other than the patient, spouse, or parent who is responsible for paying all or part of the patient's medical costs.
pagador mediador   Alguien ajeno al paciente, cónyuge, padre o madre que es responsable del pago de todo o parte de los gastos médicos del paciente o de parte de ellos.

thixotropic gel   A material that appears to be a solid until subjected to a disturbance, such as centrifugation, when it becomes a liquid.
gel tisotrópico   Material que parece ser sólido hasta el momento en que se somete a una alteración como la centrifugación, cuando se convierte en líquido.

thoracic   Pertaining to the region between the neck and low back that contains the 12 thoracic vertebrae.
torácica   Perteneciente o relativo a región de la espalda entre el cuello y la región lumbar inferior en la que hay 12 vértebras torácicas.

thready pulse   A pulse that is scarcely perceptible.
pulso débil   Pulso que es apenas perceptible.

thrombus   A blood clot.
trombo   Cóagulo de sangre.

thyroid-stimulating hormone (TSH)   A hormone secreted by the anterior lobe of the pituitary gland that stimulates the secretion of hormones produced by the thyroid gland.
hormona estimulante de la tiroides (TSH)   Hormona que segrega el lóbulo anterior de la glándula pituitaria y que estimula la secreción de hormonas producidas por la glándula tiroides.

tickler file   A chronologic file used as a reminder that something must be taken care of on a certain date.
archivo cronológico   Archivo que se usa para recordar que algo que debe llevarse a cabo en una fecha determinada.

tinea   A fungal skin disease that results in scaling, itching, and inflammation.
tinea   Enfermedad de la piel causada por hongos y que produce descamación, picazón e inflamación.

tissue culture   The technique or process of keeping tissue alive and growing in a culture medium.
cultivo de tejidos   Técnica o proceso de mantener un tejido vivo y en fase de crecimiento en un medio de cultivo.

toxemia   An abnormal condition of pregnancy characterized by hypertension, edema, and protein in the urine.
toxemia   Característica anómala del embarazo, con presencia de hipertensión, edema y proteínas en la orina.

tracer   A radioactive substance administered to a patient undergoing a nuclear medicine imaging procedure.
trazador   Sustancia radioactiva que se administra al paciente para someterlo a procedimientos de formación de imágenes en medicina nuclear.

tracheostomy   A surgical opening through the neck into the trachea that is made to facilitate breathing.
traqueotomía   Abertura realizada quirúrgicamente en el cuello a la altura de la tráquea para facilitar la respiración.

transaction   An exchange or transfer of goods, services, or funds.
transacción   Intercambio o transferencia de bienes, servicios o fondos.

transcription   A written copy made either in longhand or by machine.
transcripción   Copia escrita de algo, hecha a mano, o con la ayuda de una máquina.

transducer   The part of the sonography machine in contact with the patient that sends high-frequency sound waves and receives the sound echoes that return from the patient's body.
transductor   Parte de una máquina de sonografía que está en contacto con el paciente envía ondas sonoras de alta frecuencia y recibe los ecos de los sonidos que regresan del cuerpo del paciente.

transection   A cross-section; division by cutting across.
sección transversal   División cortando a través.

transient ischemic attack   A condition of temporary neurologic symptoms caused by gradual or partial occlusion of a cerebral blood vessel.
ataque isquémico transitorio   Síntomas neurológicos temporales causados por una oclusión gradual o parcial de un vaso sanguíneo del cerebro.

transillumination   Inspection of a cavity or an organ by passing light through its walls.
diafanoscopia   Inspección de una cavidad u órgano haciendo pasar luz a través de sus paredes.
transport medium   A medium used to keep an organism alive during transport to the laboratory.
medio para transporte   Medio usado para mantener un organismo vivo durante el transporte al laboratorio.

transverse plane   The plane that divides the body into superior and inferior parts.
plano transversal   Plano que divide el cuerpo en parte superior e inferior.

trauma   A physical injury or wound caused by an external force or by violence.
trauma   Lesión física o herida causada por una fuerza externa o violencia.

560

treatises   Systematic expositions or arguments in writing, including methodic discussion of the facts and principles involved and the conclusions reached.
tratados   Exposiciones sistemáticas o argumentos escritos que incluyen una descripción metódica de los hechos y principios involucrados y las conclusiones a las que se ha llegado.

triage   A process of responding to requests for immediate care and treatment after evaluating the urgency of the need and prioritizing the treatment; the sorting and allocation of treatment to patients according to a system of priorities designed to maximize the number of survivors and treat the sickest patients first.
criterio de selección   Responder a peticiones de atención y tratamiento inmediato tras evaluar la urgencia de la necesidad y establecer prioridades de tratamiento. Clasificación y asignación de tratamiento a pacientes según un sistema de prioridades destinado a maximizar el número de sobrevivientes y tratar primero a los pacientes más enfermos.

triglycerides   Fatty acids and glycerols that are bound to proteins and form high- and low-density lipoproteins.
triglicéridos   Ácidos grasos y gliceroles que se unen a las proteínas y forman lipoproteínas de alta y baja densidad.

truss   An elastic, canvas, or metallic device for retaining a reduced hernia within the abdominal cavity.
braguero   Malla elástica o dispositivo metálico para retener una hernia reducida dentro de la cavidad abdominal.

turgor   The resistance of the skin to being grasped between the fingers and released; normal skin tension, which is reduced with dehydration and increased with edema.
turgor   Resistencia de la piel a ser pellizcada; tensión normal de la piel que disminuye con la deshidratación y aumenta con el edema.

type and cross-match   Tests performed to assess the compatibility of blood intended for transfusion with the person's own blood.
prueba de tipo y RH   Análisis que se realizan para evaluar la compatibilidad de la sangre que va a ser usada en una transfusión.

unequal pulses   Pulses in which the beats vary in intensity.
pulso desigual   Pulso en el cual los latidos varían en intensidad.

Uniform Commercial Code   A unified set of rules covering many business transactions; often referred to simply as the UCC, it has been adopted in all 50 states, the District of Columbia, and most U.S. territories.
Código de Comercio Uniforme   Conjunto de normas unificadas que cubren muchas transacciones comerciales; se conoce simplemente como UCC y ha sido adoptado en los 50 estados, el Distrito de Columbia y la mayoría de los territorios estadounidenses.

unique identifiers   Codes used as part of a method of anonymous HIV testing in which the code is used, instead of a name, to protect the patient's confidentiality.
identificadores únicos   Método de prueba de VIH (HIV) anónimo en el cual se usa un código en lugar de nombres, para proteger la confidencialidad del paciente.

unit-dose   A method used by a pharmacy to prepare individual doses of medications.
dosis unitaria   Método usado por la farmacia para preparar dosis individuales de medicamentos.

universal claim form   The form developed by the HCFA (now known as the Centers for Medicare and Medicaid Services [CMS]) and approved by the American Medical Association (AMA) for use in submitting all government-sponsored claims.
formulario de reclamación universal   Formulario desarrollado por la Administración financiera de la atención sanitaria (HCFA, ahora conocida como Centros de servicios de Medicare y Medicaid, o CMS) y aprobado por AMA para usarse al someter todas las reclamaciones subvencionadas por el gobierno.

upper GI series   Fluoroscopic examination of the esophagus, stomach, and duodenum in which orally administered barium sulfate is used a contrast medium.
serie GI superior   Examen fluoroscópico del esófago, estómago y duodeno usando una administración oral de sulfato de bario como medio de contraste.

urea   The major nitrogenous end product of protein metabolism and the chief nitrogenous component of the urine.
urea   Principal producto final nitrogenado del metabolismo de las proteínas y el principal componente nitrogenado de la orina.

urease   An enzyme that catalyzes the hydrolysis of urea to form ammonium carbonate.
ureasa   Enzima que cataliza la hidrólisis de la urea para formar carbonato de amonio.

uremia   A toxic renal condition characterized by an excess of urea, creatinine, and other nitrogenous end products in the blood.
uremia   Enfermedad renal tóxica que se caracteriza por un exceso de urea, creatinina y otros productos finales en la sangre.

urgency   A sudden, compelling desire to urinate and the inability to control the release of urine.
urgencia   Deseo repentino y apremiante de orinar y la incapacidad de controlarlo.

URL   Abbreviation for *uniform resource locator;* the global address of documents or information on the

Internet. The URL provides the IP address and the domain name for the Web page, such as "microsoft.com."
URL Abreviatura de *localizador universal de recursos;* la dirección a nivel mundial, de documentos o de información en Internet. El URL proporciona la dirección IP y el nombre del dominio de una página web, como por ejemplo: "microsoft.com."

urticaria A skin eruption marked by inflamed wheals; hives.
urticaria Erupción cutánea que produce ampollas imflamadas.

"use additional code" In coding manuals, this term appears only in volume 1 of the ICD-9-CM in those subdivisions where the user should add further information by means of an additional code to give a more complete picture of the diagnosis. In some cases, "if desired" follows the term. However, "if desired" is not used for coding in military medical treatment facilities; in these cases, when the term "use additional code . . . if desired" appears, "if desired" is disregarded and the appropriate additional code is assigned.
"usar código adicional" Esta expresión aparece sólo en el tomo 1, en aquellas subdivisiones en las que el usuario debe añadir más información por medio de un código adicional para proporcionar un cuadro más completo del diagnóstico. En algunos casos, se verá "si se desea" tras el término. En la codificación en establecimientos militares de tratamiento médico, no se usará la expresión "si se desea." Por lo tanto, cuando aparezca el término "usar código adicional . . . si se desea," no se tendrá en cuenta "si se desea" y se asignará el código adicional correspondiente.

utilization review The review of individual cases by a committee to make sure that services are medically necessary and to study how providers use medical care resources.
revisión de utilización Revisión de casos individuales por un comité, para asegurarse de que los servicios son médicamente necesarios y estudiar cómo los proveedores usan los recursos de cuidados de salud.

Valsalva's maneuver A maneuver that occurs when a person strains to defecate and urinate, uses the arms and upper trunk muscles to move up in bed, or strains during laughing, coughing, or vomiting. It causes blood to become trapped in the great veins, preventing it from entering the chest and right atrium, which may cause a heart attack and death.
maniobra de Valsalva Ocurre cuando uno hace fuerza para defecar y orinar, usa los brazos y los músculos de la parte superior del tronco para levantarse de la cama, o hace fuerza al reír, toser o vomitar. Causa una retención de sangre en las venas mayores, impidiendole que entre en el pecho y la aurícula derecha y puede provocar un ataque al corazón y la muerte.

vasodilation An increase in the diameter of a blood vessel.
vasodilatación Aumento en el diámetro de un vaso sanguíneo.

vector An organism, such as an insect or a tick, that transmits the causative organisms of disease.
vector Organismos, tales como un insecto o garrapata, que transmite los organismos que provocan enfermedades.

ventricles The two lower chambers of the heart.
ventrículos Las dos cavidades inferiores del corazón.

veracity Devotion to or conformity with the truth.
veracidad Compromiso o conformidad con la verdad.

verdict The finding or decision of a jury on a matter submitted to it in trial.
veredicto Conclusión o decisión de un jurado en un asunto sometido a juicio.

versatile Embracing a variety of subjects, fields or skills; having a wide range of abilities.
versátil Que abarca diferentes sujetos, campos o destrezas; que tiene una amplia gama de destrezas.

vertigo Dizziness; a sensation of faintness or an inability to maintain normal balance.
vertigo Mareo; sensación de desmayo o de incapacidad de mantener el equilibrio normal.

vested Granted or endowed with a particular authority, right, or property; having a special interest in something.
conferirido Concedido o dotado con una autoridad, derecho o propiedad particular; que tiene un interés especial en algo.

viable Capable of living, developing, or germinating under favorable conditions.
viable Capaz de vivir, desarrollarse o germinar bajo condiciones favorables.

virtual reality An artificial environment experienced by a computer user, often by using special gloves, earphones, and goggles to enhance the experience, that feels as if it were a real environment.
realidad virtual Entorno artificial que experimenta el usuario de una computadora, muchas veces usando guantes especiales, audífonos y lentes para mejorar la experiencia, y que parece ser un ambiente real.

virulent Exceedingly pathogenic, noxious, or deadly.
virulento Excesivamente patógeno, nocivo o mortal.

viscosity The quality of being thick and lacking the capability of easy movement.
viscosidad Cualidad de espeso e incapaz de moverse con facilidad.

vocation   The work in which a person is regularly employed.
profesión   Trabajo en el que una persona está empleada regularmente.

volatile   Referring to a flammable substance's capacity to vaporize at a low temperature; easily aroused; tending to erupt in violence.
volátil   Referente a la capacidad de una sustancia flamable para evaporarse a baja temperatura. Que reacciona con facilidad y tiene tendencia a entrar en erupción de forma violenta.

vulva   The external female genitalia, which begins at the mons pubis and terminates at the anus.
vulva   Zona genital exterior femenina que comienza en el monte púbico y termina en el ano.

watermark   A mark in paper resulting from differences in thickness usually produced by pressure from a projecting design in the mold or on a processing roll; it is visible when the paper is held up to the light.
filigrana   Marca en un papel que resulta de diferencias de espesor, por lo general se produce presionando un diseño en relieve en el molde o en un rodillo de procesamiento, y es visible por transparencia.

wet mount   A slide preparation in which a drop of liquid specimen is protected by a coverslip and observed with a microscope.
montaje húmedo   Preparación de una lámina en la que una gota de espécimen líquido por ejemplo, se protege con una cubierta de vidrio y se observa con un microscopio.

wheal   A localized area of edema or a raised lesion.
roncha   Área localizada de un edema o una lesión protuberante.

"with"   In ICD-9-CM coding, the term "with," "with mention of," or "associated with" in a title dictates that both parts of the title must be present in the statement of the diagnosis to assign the particular code.
"con"   En el contexto de la ICD-9-CM, las expresiones "con", "con mención de" y "asociado con" en un título exigen que ambas partes del título estén presentes en la descripción del orden de diagnóstico para asignar el código específico.

workers' compensation   Insurance against liability imposed on certain employers to pay benefits and furnish care to injured employees and to pay benefits to dependents of an employee killed in the course of or in a situation arising out of the worker's employment.
compensación laboral   Seguro contra la responsabilidad impuesta a ciertos patronos para pagar beneficios y proporcionar atenciones a los trabajadores lesionados, y pagar beneficios a las personas que dependan de trabajadores que mueran en el trabajo o a causa de él.

Zip drive   A small, portable disk drive that is used primarily for backing up information and archiving computer files; a 100-megabyte Zip disk holds the equivalent of about 70 floppy disks.
unidad Zip   Unidad de un disco pequeño y portátil que se usa principalmente para hacer copias de seguridad de información y para guardar archivos electrónicos. Un disco Zip de 100 megabytes tiene una capacidad equivalente a la de unos 70 disquetes.

563